Mathematics for technicians

David Smethurst

BSc, MSc, AFIMA
Paddington College, London

Edward Arnold

© David Smethurst 1979

First published 1979
by Edward Arnold (Publishers) Ltd
41 Bedford Square, London WC1B 3DQ

ISBN 0 7131 3415 1

British Library Cataloguing in Publication Data

Smethurst, D.
    Mathematics for level-3 technicians.
    1. Shop mathematics
    I. Title
    510'.2'46   TS1165

    ISBN 0-7131-7415-1

Filmset in 'Monophoto' Times by
Northumberland Press Ltd, Gateshead, Tyne and Wear.
Printed by Richard Clay (The Chaucer Press) Ltd,
Bungay, Suffolk

Contents

Preface

As with earlier books in this series, the aim here is to provide a student text with exercises covering a range of mathematical theory relevant to the needs of engineering, construction, and science technicians.

I have based the content on current level-3 standard units in mathematics issued by the Technician Education Council, and each section of the book relates to a general objective in the mathematics bank of objectives (U78/911) developed by the joint TEC/BEC Committee for Mathematics and Statistics.

As there is no rigid boundary between level-2 and level-3 work, it has occasionally been desirable to repeat or summarise material which appeared in *Mathematics for level-2 technicians*, and I am grateful to my co-author of that book, Clarence Schofield, for agreeing to the use of some of his material in this way.

There are over 200 worked examples together with 300 exercise problems chosen to illustrate practical applications. A further selection of about 100 revision problems is provided at the end of the book. The availability of a scientific calculator has been assumed, and hints on specific uses of calculators appear throughout.

I am most grateful to Bob Davenport of Edward Arnold (Publishers) Ltd for his clear guidance and careful editing. Many thanks also to all my friends, especially Barbara Crook and Ian Foster, who have been so generous with their time and ideas.

The tables of Naperian logarithms on pages 18 and 19 are taken from *Four-figure tables*, by C. Godfrey and A. W. Siddons, by permission of the Cambridge University Press.

David Smethurst

Key to TEC objectives

Key to individual standard units

General objective	TEC units and sections of this book		
	U75/040	U76/353	U77/403
1	C2, C3	A4, A5	C1
2	C4	A4,*	C2, C3
3	C5	A3, B2, C2	C4
4	C6, C8	*	C5
5	D1	*	C6, C7
6	D2	B1,*	C9
7	D3	D4	C9
8	D3	D6	
9	C9	D7	
10	C9	C1, C2,*	
11	D4	C4	
12	D5	C1, C4	
13	D6	C5	
14	B5	C6	
15	A3, B1, B2, C2		
16	E1, E2, E3, E4		

* Additional revision material or objectives not included in bank of objectives

Key to mathematics bank of objectives U78/911

Number		Algebra and graphs		Calculus		Geometry and trigonometry		Probability and statistics	
Section	U78/911	Section	U78/911	Section	U78/911	Section	U78/911	Section	U78/911
A1	AA5	B1	BB9	C1	CA9	D1	DC11	E1	EB12
A2	BE8	B2	BA10, BB10	C2	CA11	D2	DC12	E2	EB13
A3	AB10	B3	BC7	C3	CA12	D3	DC13, DC14	E3	EB14
A4	AC12	B4	BC8	C4	CA13	D4	DD12	E4	EB15
A5	AC13	B5	BD11	C5	CA14	D5	DD13		
		B6	BE11	C6	CB11	D6	DD14		
		B7	BE12	C7	CB12	D7	DD15		
				C8	CB13				
				C9	CD13, CD14				

A   Number

A1 The binary and octal number systems

A1.1 Binary numbers

We are familiar, in mathematics and everyday life, with the use of the decimal or *denary* number system, which has a base or *radix* of ten and ten digits: 0 to 9. Early man probably found it convenient to count using his ten fingers.

In the decimal system, we express large numbers in terms of increasing powers of ten from right to left, so that

$$735 = 700 + 30 + 5$$
$$= (7 \times 10^2) + (3 \times 10^1) + (5 \times 10^0)$$

A number system with a base of ten is not ideally suited for use in connection with modern digital electronic equipment. It is more convenient to produce components (such as diodes, transistors, and bistables) which operate in only two states, for example OFF and ON. The *binary* number system has a base of two and only two digits: 0 and 1. Although binary numbers are laborious to work with in manual calculations, they are widely used in computers and many types of digital equipment.

If we look at the binary equivalents of the decimal numbers 0 to 8, we see that the binary numbers tend to be longer:

Decimal	0	1	2	3	4	5	6	7	8
Binary	0	1	10	11	100	101	110	111	1000

We can see from the above table that the single-digit decimal number 8 requires four binary digits: 1000. Note that the word *bit* is often used for 'binary digit', particularly in computer literature.

To avoid confusion when there is likely to be doubt about which number system is being used, we can include a subscript to show the base of a number. For example, the decimal number one hundred and one can be written 101_{10} so that we are sure it is not the binary equivalent of the decimal number five, which would be written 101_2.

Converting from decimal to binary

A simple method of obtaining the binary equivalent of a decimal number is to divide the decimal number by two repeatedly and make a note of any remainder after each division.

For example, to express 47_{10} in binary form:

$$2)\overline{47} \quad \text{remainder} = 1$$
$$2)\overline{23} \qquad\qquad\quad 1$$
$$2)\overline{11} \qquad\qquad\quad 1$$
$$2)\overline{5} \qquad\qquad\quad\;\; 1$$
$$2)\overline{2} \qquad\qquad\quad\;\; 0$$
$$2)\overline{1} \qquad\qquad\quad\;\; 1$$
$$0$$

The binary number we seek is the list of 1's and 0's in the remainder column *reading from the bottom*; thus

$$47_{10} = 101111_2$$

Note that the division by two will always continue until we reach zero with a remainder of one, as in the above example.

A useful check when converting a decimal number into binary form is to add together all the equivalent decimal values of 1's in the binary number according to their positions. In the above example, in which we obtained the binary number 101111,

$$\begin{array}{cccccc} 1 & 0 & 1 & 1 & 1 & 1 \end{array}$$
$$= \; 2^5 + 0 + 2^3 + 2^2 + 2^1 + 2^0$$
$$= 32 \;\; + 0 + 8 \;\; + 4 \;\; + 2 \;\; + 1$$
$$= 47$$

Note that *even* decimal numbers in binary form will always end in 0, while the binary equivalent of a decimal number which is *odd* will end in 1.

A1.2 Converting from binary to decimal form

To convert a binary number into its equivalent decimal form, we simply add together the values of the 1's present in the number, remembering that each digit from right to left increases in value by a factor of two.

Example 1 Convert the number 110111_2 into decimal form.

$$110111 \;\; = 32 + 16 + 4 + 2 + 1 = 55$$

i.e. $110111_2 = 55_{10}$

Example 2 What is the decimal equivalent of the binary number 1001000?

2

$$1001000 = 64 + 8 = 72$$

i.e. $1001000_2 = 72_{10}$

A1.3 Binary addition
With only two digits in the binary number system, additions of two numbers will involve only the following sums:

$$0 + 0 = 0$$

$$0 + 1 = 1$$

$$1 + 1 = 0 \quad \text{with a carry of 1 into the next column}$$

Electronic circuits can be designed to perform additions at high speeds. Carrying a 1 into the next most significant column occurs whenever the sum of two 1's gives 2, for which there is no binary symbol.

Carrying a 1 representing two in binary addition is equivalent to carrying a 1 which represents ten in the addition of decimal numbers.

Example 1   Add 11011_2 and 10010_2 together.

We perform the addition as follows:

$$
\begin{array}{r}
11011 \\
10010 \\
\hline
101101 \\
\hline
1 \quad\; 1
\end{array} +
$$

Thus $11011_2 + 10010_2 = 101101_2$

(Note that the decimal equivalents of the numbers which we have added together are 27 and 18 respectively; the answer is therefore 45_{10}.)

Whenever two 1's and a carry from a previous column are added, the result is 1 with 1 to carry into the next most significant column.

Example 2   Add the binary numbers 10110 and 1110 together.

$$
\begin{array}{r}
10110 \\
1110 \\
\hline
100100 \\
\hline
1111
\end{array} +
$$

A1.4 The octal system
The octal system has a base of eight and eight digits: 0 to 7. Each digit position in an octal number represents a power of eight; thus

3

$$254_8 = (2 \times 8^2) + (5 \times 8^1) + (4 \times 8^0)$$
$$= (2 \times 64) + (5 \times 8) + (4 \times 1)$$
$$= \quad 128 \quad + \quad 40 \quad + \quad 4$$
$$= \quad 172_{10}$$

The following table shows the decimal integers 0 to 20 and their octal equivalents:

Decimal	0	1	2	3	4	5	6	7	8	9	10
Octal	0	1	2	3	4	5	6	7	10	11	12

Decimal	11	12	13	14	15	16	17	18	19	20
Octal	13	14	15	15	17	20	21	22	23	24

A division method, similar to the one we used for decimal-to-binary conversion (see section A1.1), can be used to obtain the octal equivalents of decimal numbers.

Example 1   Convert 339_{10} into octal form.

$$8\overline{)339} \quad \text{remainder 3}$$
$$8\overline{)42} \qquad\qquad 2$$
$$8\overline{)5} \qquad\qquad 5$$
$$0$$

Reading the remainder column from bottom to top we have 523; thus

$$339_{10} = 523_8$$

(Check: $523_8 = (5 \times 64) + (2 \times 8) + (3 \times 1) = 339_{10}$)

Octal-to-binary conversion

Any octal number may be converted into binary form simply by taking each digit in the octal number and replacing it with the three digits of its binary equivalent. Leading 0's of these groups of three binary digits must be included in all cases except for the most significant (extreme left) digit of the octal number.

The following table gives the binary equivalents of all eight digits in the octal system:

Octal	0	1	2	3	4	5	6	7
Binary	000	001	010	011	100	101	110	111

Example 2   Convert 513_8 into binary form.

$$
\begin{array}{ccc}
5 & 1 & 3 \\
101 & 001 & 011
\end{array}
$$

Thus $513_8 = 101001011_2$

Example 3   What is the binary equivalent of the octal number 274?

$$2 \quad 7 \quad 4$$
$$010 \quad 111 \quad 100$$

Hence $274_8 = 10111100_2$

Example 4   Express the decimal number 123 as an octal number, and then convert your answer into binary form.

Using the division method,

$$
\begin{array}{ll}
8\overline{)123} & \text{remainder } 3 \\
8\overline{)15} & 7 \\
8\overline{)1} & 1 \\
0 &
\end{array}
$$

Reading the remainder column from the bottom we have 173;

$\therefore$ $123_{10} = 173_8$

Converting each digit of this octal number into binary form,

$$1 \quad 7 \quad 3$$
$$001 \quad 111 \quad 011$$

Hence $123_{10} = 173_8 = 1111011_2$

Binary-to-octal conversion
When converting from binary into octal form, the number is divided into groups of three binary digits, starting from the right. Each of these three-digit binary numbers is converted into its decimal equivalent to give the octal number required.

Example 5   Convert the binary number 110011101010 into octal form.

Grouping the binary digits into threes,

110   011   101   010

Replacing each group with its decimal equivalent,

6   3   5   2

$\therefore$ $110011101010_2 = 6352_8$

Example 6   What are the octal and decimal equivalents of the number 10110111_2?

Grouping the binary digits from the right,

    10   110   111

Writing the decimal equivalent of each group,

    2   6   7

$\therefore$ $10110111_2 = 267_8$

Converting this octal number into decimal form gives

$$267_8 = (2 \times 8^2) + (6 \times 8^1) + (7 \times 8^0)$$
$$= \quad 128 \; + \; 48 \; + \; 7$$
$$= \quad 183$$

i.e. $10110111_2 = 267_8 = 183_{10}$

Negative and fractional numbers can be represented in both binary and octal systems, but methods of doing this are beyond the scope of this book.

A1.5 Subtraction of binary and octal numbers

Binary

Subtraction of binary numbers can be carried out directly by following the familiar methods used for the subtraction of decimal numbers. However, for reasons which we shall look at later, direct subtraction is not used in digital calculating equipment (see section A1.7). When performing subtractions in this way we must, as in decimal subtraction, *borrow* from the digit in the next most significant column whenever it is necessary to subtract a number from a smaller number. Instead of borrowing a *ten*, as we do in decimal arithmetic, we borrow a *two*.

Example 1   Subtract the binary number 1001 from 11001.

```
  11001 _
   1001
 ───────
  10000
```

(Checking this answer: 10000 + 1001 = 11001)

Example 2   Evaluate $10101_2 - 1110_2$.

```
  10101 _
   1010
 ───────
   1011
```

(Check: 1011 + 1010 = 10101)

Note that in example 1 we do not have to borrow to complete the subtraction. In example 2 we borrow twice.

Octal

When we borrow to perform a subtraction of two octal numbers, it is obviously an *eight* that we borrow.

Example 3   Find $267_8 - 123_8$ as an octal number.

$$\begin{array}{r} 267 \\ 123 \\ \hline 144 \end{array} -$$

The answer is 144_8.

Example 4   Subtract 375_8 from 526_8.

$$\begin{array}{r} 526 \\ 375 \\ \hline 131 \end{array} -$$

i.e. $526_8 - 375_8 = 131_8$

A1.6   Finding the complement of a number

The *complement* of a number is often used in computers to represent the negative of a number (e.g. during subtraction – see section A1.7). A general rule for *complementing* a number is to subtract each digit in turn from *one less* than the base of the number, and then add one to the result.

Binary

The base of the binary system is, of course, two; so the number from which to subtract each digit of any binary number we wish to complement is one. Since the only digits present in a binary number are 0 and 1, and $1 - 0 = 1$ while $1 - 1 = 0$, the first part of the complementing process for a binary number has the effect of replacing all the 0's in the number with 1's, and all the 1's with 0's. The number 110101 becomes 1010 (note that it is not necessary to write down leading 0's, although this number would be 001010 in an electronic register). The result of this first step for a binary number is known as the 1's *complement*.

To find the 2's complement, for later use in subtraction, we add one to the 1's complement. The 2's complement of 110101 is therefore 1011 (i.e. 1010 + 1).

Example 1   What is the 2's complement of 1001_2?

The original binary number = 1001

The 1's complement   = 110

The 2's complement   = 111

Example 2   Find the 2's complement of 1100010_2.

The 1's complement = 11101

The 2's complement = 11110

Octal

The general rule for complementing can be applied to octal numbers.

Example 3   Find the complement of the number 254_8.

The 7's complement = 523   (subtracting all digits in 254 from 7)

The 8's complement = 524   (adding 1 to 523)

i.e. the complement of $254_8 = 524_8$.

A1.7 Subtraction using a complement

Using the direct method described in section A1.5 to subtract two binary numbers has two disadvantages when designing electronic equipment capable of performing arithmetic operations. Firstly, the concept of borrowing a 2 cannot easily be implemented, since the number two has no meaning in a two-state system. Secondly, it is expensive to produce four different electronic circuits for addition, subtraction, multiplication, and division. In practice, all four of these arithmetic operations can be carried out as a form of addition. We shall see how subtractions can be performed as additions with the aid of the complement.

The subtraction of a number '*B*' from a number '*A*' is carried out by adding the complement of *B* to *A* and ignoring any carry beyond the most significant digit.

Example 1   Subtract the binary number 1001 from 1110 using a complement.

The 1's complement of 1001 = 110   (i.e. all 0's become 1's and 1's become 0's)

The 2's complement of 1001 = 111   (adding 1 to 110)

Adding the 2's complement of 1001 to 1110 gives

$111 + 1110 = \boxed{1}0101$ (the carry $\boxed{1}$ is not part of the answer)

Ignoring the carry gives

$1110 - 1001 = 101$

8

The above answer can be checked either by direct subtraction without using a complement or by showing that $1001 + 101 = 1110$.

Example 2   Evaluate $423_8 - 167_8$ using a complement.

The 7's complement of $167 = 610$ (i.e. subtracting each digit in 167 from 7)

The 8's complement of $167 = 611$ (i.e. $610 + 1$)

To perform the subtraction we add 423_8 and the complement of 167_8 together:

$$423_8 + 611_8 = 1234_8$$

Thus, after removing the carry,

$$423_8 - 167_8 = 234_8$$

Note that if a number being subtracted has fewer digits than the number we are subtracting from, we must make it the same length before complementing.

Example 3   Express the result of the subtraction $11001_2 - 110_2$ as a binary number.

We write 110 as 00110.

The 1's complement $= 11001$

The 2's complement $= 11010$

Now $11001 + 11010 = 110011$

$\therefore$ $11001_2 - 110_2 = 10011_2$

Example 4   Subtract 25_8 from 167_8 using a complement.

The 7's complement of $025 = 752$

The 8's complement of $025 = 753$

Adding the complement to 167 gives

$$753 + 167 = 1142$$

$\therefore$ $167_8 - 25_8 = 142_8$

Exercise A1
1   Explain the difference between the two numbers 1101_{10} and 1101_2.
2   Convert the following decimal numbers into binary form: (a) 7, (b) 11, (c) 22, (d) 39, (e) 56, (f) 64.
3   Write down the decimal equivalents of the following binary numbers: (a) 101, (b) 1101, (c) 11101, (d) 1001110, (e) 101010, (f) 10010101.

4 Add the following pairs of binary numbers together: (a) $101 + 10$, (b) $1101 + 110$, (c) $110001 + 10110$, (d) $10110 + 1010$, (e) $111101 + 110111$, (f) $110111 + 10110$.

5 Express the following decimal numbers in octal form: (a) 6, (b) 11, (c) 29, (d) 51, (e) 85, (f) 133, (g) 511.

6 Write down the binary equivalents of the following octal numbers: (a) 62, (b) 53, (c) 514, (d) 227, (e) 361, (f) 4013.

7 Convert each of the following binary numbers into both octal and decimal forms: (a) 1011, (b) 11010, (c) 11101, (d) 1101110, (e) 10110101.

8 Perform each of the following subtractions directly, without using a complement: (a) $110_2 - 10_2$, (b) $1110_2 - 1010_2$, (c) $10110_2 - 1100_2$, (d) $111010_2 - 11101_2$, (e) $753_8 - 122_8$, (f) $421_8 - 370_8$, (g) $343_8 - 167_8$.

9 Find the complements of the following numbers [2's complements in (a) to (c) and 8's complements in (d) to (f)]: (a) 110_2, (b) 11101_2, (c) 11011_2, (d) 652_8, (e) 101_8, (f) 772_8.

10 Perform the following subtractions using a complement method: (a) $1110_2 - 1011_2$, (b) $11011_2 - 10010_2$, (c) $11101_2 - 1011_2$, (d) $625_8 - 174_8$, (e) $543_8 - 165_8$, (f) $446_8 - 63_8$.

11 Repeat the subtractions in question 8 using a complement.

A2 Binary codes

A2.1 The need for binary codes

We are by now familiar with the binary system of numbers, which has a base of 2 and uses the digits 0 and 1 (see section A1.1). The decimal numbers from 0 to 9 can be expressed as binary numbers of four digits:

Decimal N_{10}	0	1	2	3	4	5	6	7	8	9
Binary N_2	0000	0001	0010	0011	0100	0101	0110	0111	1000	1001

Note that the word 'bit' is often used for 'binary digit'.

Converting from decimal to binary form becomes a lengthy process for large decimal numbers, and the binary numbers become larger, e.g. $975_{10} = 1111001111_2$. Binary-to-decimal conversion is also complicated for large values, and often inconvenient for automatic digital equipment.

We shall now look at some alternative binary codes which have practical advantages in digital systems. Apart from simplifying conversions, the use of these codes can make the transmission of data more reliable and may facilitate arithmetic in computers and calculators.

A2.2 Binary-coded-decimal (BCD) systems

The 8421-BCD code

In the most common of the number-coding systems, the individual digits of a decimal number are replaced with their usual four-bit binary equivalents. Thus, to convert 52_{10} into 8421-BCD, the decimal digit 5 is replaced with 0101 and the 2 is replaced with 0010, giving 01010010. The same method is used in the following examples:

Decimal	8421-BCD
7	0111
38	00111000
96	10010110
415	010000010101

This system of coding provides some of the advantages of the binary system without some of the disadvantages. Electronic circuits can be designed to carry out arithmetic operations with numbers in 8421-BCD code.

The excess-3 code

Excess-3 BCD numbers are obtained by adding 3 (binary 0011) to the four-bit numbers representing each decimal digit in the 8421-BCD-coded version of a decimal number. For example, the decimal number 24 in 8421-BCD code is 00100100. Adding 0011 to each group of four bits gives the excess-3 code for 24 which is 01010111 (since $0010 + 0011 = 0101$ and $0100 + 0011 = 0111$).

Other examples of numbers expressed in the excess-3 code are shown below:

Decimal	8421-BCD	Excess-3 BCD
5	0101	1000
36	00110110	01101001
109	000100001001	010000111100

The advantage of using the excess-3 system is that it makes arithmetic involving a complement easier. An ordinary binary number 1010 can be subtracted from 1100 by adding the 2's complement (see section A1.6) of 1010 (i.e. 0110) and ignoring any carry beyond the fourth digit. Thus $1100 - 1010 = 1100 + 0110 = 10$. (We have in fact subtracted ten from twelve to give two in binary form.) Subtraction is less straightforward when using the 8421-BCD system, but numbers expressed in the excess-3 code are *self-complementing*.

We need not discuss the arithmetic of coded numbers in detail, but as an illustration consider the decimal number three, for which the excess-3 code is 0110. The 1's complement of 0110 is 1001, and this is the excess-3 BCD code for 6, which in turn is the 9's complement of 3 (since $3 + 6 = 9$). The 10's complement of 3 is therefore $1001 + 1 = 1010$ (i.e. the 9's complement plus one). The use of the 10's complement in digital equipment is beyond the scope of this book, but the fact that it is so easy to find for a number in excess-3 BCD code explains the usefulness of the code.

Example Express the decimal number 238 in 8421-BCD code and in excess-3 BCD code.

The four-bit code for 2 is 0010, while 3 and 8 in binary form are 0011 and 1000 respectively. Thus the 8421-BCD code for 238 is 001000111000. Adding 3 (binary 0011) to the four-bit code for each of the digits in 238 gives the excess-3 BCD code as follows:

$$0010 + 0011 = 0101$$

$$0011 + 0011 = 0110$$

$$1000 + 0011 = 1011$$

Thus the excess-3 BCD code for 238 is 010101101011.

Gray codes
The significant feature of a Gray code (or *cyclic code*) is that moving from one decimal number to an adjacent number involves changing only *one* binary digit in a Gray code. The decimal numbers 0 to 9 are shown in an example of a Gray code below:

Decimal	Binary	Gray
0	0000	0000
1	0001	0001
2	0010	0011
3	0011	0010
4	0100	0110
5	0101	0111
6	0110	0101
7	0111	0100
8	1000	1100
9	1001	1101

Compare the transition from 7 to 8 in the binary system (0111 to 1000), in which all four bits are changed, with the Gray code where 0100 becomes 1100. As with all adjacent numbers in the Gray code, only one digit is changed (the 0 on the left has become a 1).

Gray codes are often used when movements in mechanical systems (e.g. rotating shafts) are measured digitally. Many analogue-to-digital convertors use a Gray code to minimise switching as movement occurs. A disadvantage of the Gray codes is that relatively complicated electronic logic circuits are required for arithmetic.

A2.3 Error-detecting codes
Whenever the transmission of coded information occurs (for example in a computer time-sharing system using telephone lines), an error in a single digit may have serious consequences. The accuracy of the data received can be ensured by using an *error-detecting code* for the transmission. An example of such a code is the five-bit code formed by add-

ing a *parity bit* to the standard 8421-BCD code (see section A2.2) as
shown in the following table:

Decimal	8421-BCD	Parity bit	Error-detecting code
0	0000	1	00001
1	0001	0	00010
2	0010	0	00100
3	0011	1	00111
4	0100	0	01000
5	0101	1	01011
6	0110	1	01101
7	0111	0	01110
8	1000	0	10000
9	1001	1	10011

In this error-detecting code the value of the parity bit is such that the
number of '1' bits in each five-bit number is *odd* (we say this code uses
an *odd-parity check*). For example there is a single 1 in 00010 and there
are three 1's in 00111. An error in any digit will always lead to an even
number of 1's in the number, and it is a simple matter to count the 1's
electronically and to test for an even number.

Another error-detecting code which also has the advantage of simplifying arithmetic operations is the *biquinary* code shown below:

Decimal	Biquinary code
0	0100001
1	0100010
2	0100100
3	0101000
4	0110000
5	1000001
6	1000010
7	1000100
8	1001000
9	1010000

In this seven-bit code, each number contains two and only two 1's, so
an error in any digit will lead to three 1's or to a single 1. A simple
count will detect such an error.

The ISO code

Punched paper tape is used in computer systems and some numerically
controlled machine-tools, although faster methods of entering coded
information and programs may soon replace it. One of the codes for
eight-track paper tape is the International Organisation for
Standardisation (ISO) code. Figure A2.1 shows a typical length of
punched paper tape and illustrates the way some of the numbers and
letters appear in ISO code. Note that the smaller holes between

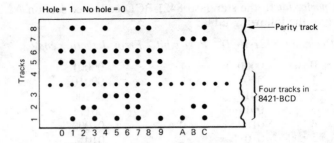

Fig. A2.1 ISO code on 8-track paper tape

tracks 3 and 4 are not part of the coded information but are used to guide the tape through a suitable reader.

Numbers are coded in 8421-BCD form in tracks 1, 2, 3, and 4 and are identified as numbers by two further holes in tracks 5 and 6. Characters from the alphabet have a hole in track 7. Track 8 is a parity bit. The ISO code uses an even-parity check, which means that the total number of holes (including the parity hole if there is one) is always even for a correctly coded character.

Exercise A2

1 Explain why it is often more convenient to use a BCD number system rather than a purely binary system in digital equipment.

2 Describe the way decimal numbers are coded to become 8421-BCD numbers. Convert 9, 15, and 628 into 8421-BCD code.

3 State one advantage of using the excess-3 BCD code. Show how the decimal number 27 becomes 01011010 in the excess-3 BCD system.

4 Write down the following decimal numbers in 8421-BCD code and in excess-3 BCD code: (a) 26, (b) 504, (c) 3178.

5 Describe the significant feature and identify one disadvantage of a Gray code. Explain how the following table could be part of a Gray-code system:

$N_{decimal}$	6	7	8
N_{code}	1000	1100	0100

6 Describe two types of error-detecting code. A five-bit even-parity checking code is to be produced from the following table:

Decimal	8421 BCD	Parity bit
0	0000	
1	0001	
2	0010	
3	0011	?
4	0100	
5	0101	

What values will the six parity bits take?

7 Explain how the following sample of a code could be used in error detection:

Decimal	Error-detecting code
2	01101
3	01110
4	11100
5	11001

A3 Exponentials and natural logarithms

A3.1 The exponential function
The function e^x is known as the *exponential function*. It can also be written as $\exp x$. The constant e (approximately 2.7183) is the base of natural or Naperian logarithms and is also used frequently in engineering and science in connection with the natural laws of growth and decay.

Graphs of the functions $y = e^x$ and $y = e^{-x}$ are shown in fig. B2.1, and we see from these curves that $e^x > 0$ for all values of x. Some values of e^x and e^{-x} are given in the following table.

x	0	1	2	3	4	5
e^x	1.0000	2.7183	7.3891	20.086	54.598	148.41
e^{-x}	1.0000	0.3679	0.1353	0.0498	0.0183	0.0067

A3.2 Evaluating exponential functions
We can use a calculator or tables to evaluate expressions such as $a\,e^{bx}$ or $a(1 - e^{-bx})$. Most scientific calculators have an 'e^x' key with which all practical values of e^x and e^{-x} can easily be found. Many books of tables cover the range from $x = 0$ to $x = 7$, and most tables include details of a method by which exponentials beyond this range may be evaluated.

Example 1 Evaluate $5.4e^{2.1x}$ correct to four decimal places when $x = 0.8$.

Substituting $x = 0.8$, the index becomes $2.1 \times 0.8 = 1.68$.
Using a calculator we enter 1.68 and press the 'e^x' key to display 5.365 56. From four-figure tables of e^x we obtain the value

$$e^{1.68} = 5.3656$$

$\therefore \quad 5.4e^{1.68} = 5.4 \times 5.3656 = 28.9740$ correct to four decimal places

Example 2 Find the value of $0.83e^{-2.75}$ correct to three significant figures.

Using a calculator we enter 2.75 and then, after changing the sign with the '+/−' key, we press the 'e^x' key to display 0.063 93.

Using four-figure tables of e^{-x} we obtain the value e$^{-2.75}$ = 0.0639.

$\therefore$ 0.83e$^{-2.75}$ = 0.83 × 0.0639 = 0.0531 correct to three significant figures

Example 3 Evaluate 3.8(1 − 4e$^{-1.5}$) correct to four decimal places.

The way in which an expression of this type is evaluated using a calculator will depend upon the type of machine you are using. A calculator with parenthesis keys, which operates algebraically and will compute 'sums of products' directly, can be used as follows to evaluate the expression from left to right.

Step	*Display*
i) Enter 3.8	3.8
ii) Press the '×' key	3.8
iii) Press the '(' key	3.8
iv) Enter 1	1
v) Press the '−' key	1
vi) Enter 4	4
vii) Press the '×' key	4
viii) Enter 1.5	1.5
ix) Press the '+/−' key	−1.5
x) Press the 'e^x' key	0.223 130
xi) Press the ')' key	0.107 479
xii) Press the '=' key	0.408 422

$\therefore$ 3.8(1 − 4e$^{-1.5}$) = 0.4084 correct to four decimal places

With a less advanced scientific calculator, it is necessary to plan the sequence of operations carefully to obtain the correct answer. If a memory is available, we can evaluate 4 e$^{-1.5}$ and store it. Next we enter 1 and subtract the number in the memory (which should be 0.892 521) to give 0.107 479. Finally, multiplying by 3.8 gives the answer 0.408 422.

A3.3 Natural logarithms
We define the logarithm of a number a to a base b as follows:

if $a = b^x$ then $x = \log_b a$

Thus, if $25 = e^x$ then $x = \log_e 25$

Logarithms with base e are called natural or Naperian logarithms and are used in many areas of engineering and science. It is preferable to write $\ln x$ rather than $\log_e x$. Most calculators have a key marked 'ln' or 'ln x' which gives the value of the natural logarithm of the number displayed when the key is pressed. We shall use $\ln x$ for $\log_e x$ and $\log x$ for $\log_{10} x$ from now on.

16

A3.4 Natural logarithms from tables and calculators

We can see from the curve $y = \ln x$ in fig. A3.1 that $\ln 1 = 0$ and that the natural logarithm of any number between 0 and 1 is negative. Since the curve is not defined for negative values of x, we say that there are no *real* logarithms of negative numbers. These logarithms can be defined as complex numbers, but this is beyond the scope of this book.

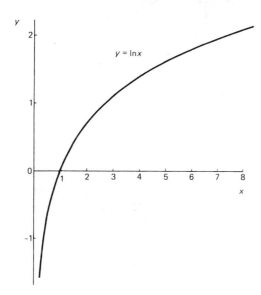

Fig. A3.1 The curve $y = \ln x$

A scientific calculator will give $\ln x$ for any positive value of x within the range of the machine. Most calculators indicate an error if we attempt to find the logarithm of a negative number.

Table A3.1 on pages 18 and 19 gives values of $\ln x$ for values of x between 1 and 10. Logarithms of numbers in this range are simply read from the table.

Example 1 Find $\ln 4.862$ correct to four decimal places, using tables or a calculator

Looking down the column on the left of the table of natural logarithms, we find $\ln 4.80 = 1.5686$. Moving horizontally along this line to the column headed '6', we see that $\ln 4.86 = 1.5810$. To this we add 0.0004, since the number 4 appears in the difference column headed '2'; thus $\ln 4.862 = 1.5810 + 0.0004 = 1.5814$

Using a calculator to evaluate $\ln 4.862$, we enter the number 4.862 and press the '$\ln x$' key to display 1.581 449 9, or 1.5814 correct to four decimal places.

17

N	0	1	2	3	4	5	6	7	8	9	1 2 3	4 5 6	7 8 9
1·0	0·0000	0100	0198	0296	0392	0488	0583	0677	0770	0862	10 19 29	38 48 57	67 76 86
1·1	0·0953	1044	1133	1222	1310	1398	1484	1570	1655	1740	9 17 26	35 44 52	61 70 78
1·2	0·1823	1906	1989	2070	2151	2231	2311	2390	2469	2546	8 16 24	32 40 48	56 64 72
1·3	0·2624	2700	2776	2852	2927	3001	3075	3148	3221	3293	7 15 22	30 37 44	52 59 67
1·4	0·3365	3436	3507	3577	3646	3716	3784	3853	3920	3988	7 14 21	28 35 41	48 55 62
1·5	0·4055	4121	4187	4253	4318	4383	4447	4511	4574	4637	6 13 19	26 32 39	45 52 58
1·6	0·4700	4762	4824	4886	4947	5008	5068	5128	5188	5247	6 12 18	24 30 36	42 48 55
1·7	0·5306	5365	5423	5481	5539	5596	5653	5710	5766	5822	6 11 17	23 29 34	40 46 51
1·8	0·5878	5933	5988	6043	6098	6152	6206	6259	6313	6366	5 11 16	22 27 32	38 43 49
1·9	0·6419	6471	6523	6575	6627	6678	6729	6780	6831	6881	5 10 15	20 26 31	36 41 46
2·0	0·6931	6981	7031	7080	7129	7178	7227	7275	7324	7372	5 10 15	20 24 29	34 39 44
2·1	0·7419	7467	7514	7561	7608	7655	7701	7747	7793	7839	5 9 14	19 23 28	33 37 42
2·2	0·7885	7930	7975	8020	8065	8109	8154	8198	8242	8286	4 9 13	18 22 27	31 36 40
2·3	0·8329	8372	8416	8459	8502	8544	8587	8629	8671	8713	4 9 13	17 21 26	30 34 38
2·4	0·8755	8796	8838	8879	8920	8961	9002	9042	9083	9123	4 8 12	16 20 24	29 33 37
2·5	0·9163	9203	9243	9282	9322	9361	9400	9439	9478	9517	4 8 12	16 20 24	27 31 35
2·6	0·9555	9594	9632	9670	9708	9746	9783	9821	9858	9895	4 8 11	15 19 23	26 30 34
2·7	0·9933	9969	0006	0043	0080	0116	0152	0188	0225	0260	4 7 11	15 18 22	25 29 33
2·8	1·0296	0332	0367	0403	0438	0473	0508	0543	0578	0613	4 7 11	14 18 21	25 28 32
2·9	1·0647	0682	0716	0750	0784	0818	0852	0886	0919	0953	3 7 10	14 17 20	24 27 31
3·0	1·0986	1019	1053	1086	1119	1151	1184	1217	1249	1282	3 7 10	13 16 20	23 26 30
3·1	1·1314	1346	1378	1410	1442	1474	1506	1537	1569	1600	3 6 10	13 16 19	22 25 29
3·2	1·1632	1663	1694	1725	1756	1787	1817	1848	1878	1909	3 6 9	12 15 18	21 25 28
3·3	1·1939	1969	2000	2030	2060	2090	2119	2149	2179	2208	3 6 9	12 15 18	21 24 27
3·4	1·2238	2267	2296	2326	2355	2384	2413	2442	2470	2499	3 6 9	12 15 17	20 23 26
3·5	1·2528	2556	2585	2613	2641	2669	2698	2726	2754	2782	3 6 8	11 14 17	20 22 25
3·6	1·2809	2837	2865	2892	2920	2947	2975	3002	3029	3056	3 5 8	11 14 16	19 22 25
3·7	1·3083	3110	3137	3164	3191	3218	3244	3271	3297	3324	3 5 8	11 13 16	19 21 24
3·8	1·3350	3376	3403	3429	3455	3481	3507	3533	3558	3584	3 5 8	10 13 16	18 21 23
3·9	1·3610	3635	3661	3686	3712	3737	3762	3788	3813	3838	3 5 8	10 13 15	18 20 23
4·0	1·3863	3888	3913	3938	3962	3987	4012	4036	4061	4085	2 5 7	10 12 15	17 20 22
4·1	1·4110	4134	4159	4183	4207	4231	4255	4279	4303	4327	2 5 7	10 12 14	17 19 22
4·2	1·4351	4375	4398	4422	4446	4469	4493	4516	4540	4563	2 5 7	9 12 14	16 19 21
4·3	1·4586	4609	4633	4656	4679	4702	4725	4748	4770	4793	2 5 7	9 12 14	16 18 21
4·4	1·4816	4839	4861	4884	4907	4929	4951	4974	4996	5019	2 5 7	9 11 14	16 18 20
4·5	1·5041	5063	5085	5107	5129	5151	5173	5195	5217	5239	2 4 7	9 11 13	15 18 20
4·6	1·5261	5282	5304	5326	5347	5369	5390	5412	5433	5454	2 4 6	9 11 13	15 17 19
4·7	1·5476	5497	5518	5539	5560	5581	5602	5623	5644	5665	2 4 6	8 11 13	15 17 19
4·8	1·5686	5707	5728	5748	5769	5790	5810	5831	5851	5872	2 4 6	8 10 12	14 16 19
4·9	1·5892	5913	5933	5953	5974	5994	6014	6034	6054	6074	2 4 6	8 10 12	14 16 18
5·0	1·6094	6114	6134	6154	6174	6194	6214	6233	6253	6273	2 4 6	8 10 12	14 16 18
5·1	1·6292	6312	6332	6351	6371	6390	6409	6429	6448	6467	2 4 6	8 10 12	14 16 18
5·2	1·6487	6506	6525	6544	6563	6582	6601	6620	6639	6658	2 4 6	8 10 11	13 15 17
5·3	1·6677	6696	6715	6734	6752	6771	6790	6808	6827	6845	2 4 6	7 9 11	13 15 17
5·4	1·6864	6882	6901	6919	6938	6956	6974	6993	7011	7029	2 4 5	7 9 11	13 15 16

$\ln 10^x$

x	1	2	3	4	5	6
$\ln 10^x$	2.3026	4.6052	6.9078	9.2103	11.5129	13.8155

Table A3.1 Natural or Naperian logarithms – $\ln N$

18

N	0	1	2	3	4	5	6	7	8	9	1 2 3	4 5 6	7 8 9
5·5	1·7047	7066	7084	7102	7120	7138	7156	7174	7192	7210	2 4 5	7 9 11	13 14 16
5·6	1·7228	7246	7263	7281	7299	7317	7334	7352	7370	7387	2 4 5	7 9 11	12 14 16
5·7	1·7405	7422	7440	7457	7475	7492	7509	7527	7544	7561	2 3 5	7 9 10	12 14 16
5·8	1·7579	7596	7613	7630	7647	7664	7681	7699	7716	7733	2 3 5	7 9 10	12 14 15
5·9	1·7750	7766	7783	7800	7817	7834	7851	7867	7884	7901	2 3 5	7 8 10	12 13 15
6·0	1·7918	7934	7951	7967	7984	8001	8017	8034	8050	8066	2 3 5	7 8 10	12 13 15
6·1	1·8083	8099	8116	8132	8148	8165	8181	8197	8213	8229	2 3 5	6 8 10	11 13 15
6·2	1·8245	8262	8278	8294	8310	8326	8342	8358	8374	8390	2 3 5	6 8 10	11 13 14
6·3	1·8405	8421	8437	8453	8469	8485	8500	8516	8532	8547	2 3 5	6 8 9	11 13 14
6·4	1·8563	8579	8594	8610	8625	8641	8656	8672	8687	8703	2 3 5	6 8 9	11 12 14
6·5	1·8718	8733	8749	8764	8779	8795	8810	8825	8840	8856	2 3 5	6 8 9	11 12 14
6·6	1·8871	8886	8901	8916	8931	8946	8961	8976	8991	9006	2 3 5	6 8 9	11 12 14
6·7	1·9021	9036	9051	9066	9081	9095	9110	9125	9140	9155	1 3 4	6 7 9	10 12 13
6·8	1·9169	9184	9199	9213	9228	9242	9257	9272	9286	9301	1 3 4	6 7 9	10 12 13
6·9	1·9315	9330	9344	9359	9373	9387	9402	9416	9430	9445	1 3 4	6 7 9	10 12 13
7·0	1·9459	9473	9488	9502	9516	9530	9544	9559	9573	9587	1 3 4	6 7 9	10 11 13
7·1	1·9601	9615	9629	9643	9657	9671	9685	9699	9713	9727	1 3 4	6 7 8	10 11 13
7·2	1·9741	9755	9769	9782	9796	9810	9824	9838	9851	9865	1 3 4	6 7 8	10 11 12
7·3	1·9879	9892	9906	9920	9933	9947	9961	9974	9988	0001	1 3 4	5 7 8	10 11 12
7·4	2·0015	0028	0042	0055	0069	0082	0096	0109	0122	0136	1 3 4	5 7 8	9 11 12
7·5	2·0149	0162	0176	0189	0202	0215	0229	0242	0255	0268	1 3 4	5 7 8	9 11 12
7·6	2·0281	0295	0308	0321	0334	0347	0360	0373	0386	0399	1 3 4	5 7 8	9 10 12
7·7	2·0412	0425	0438	0451	0464	0477	0490	0503	0516	0528	1 3 4	5 6 8	9 10 12
7·8	2·0541	0554	0567	0580	0592	0605	0618	0631	0643	0656	1 3 4	5 6 8	9 10 12
7·9	2·0669	0681	0694	0707	0719	0732	0744	0757	0769	0782	1 3 4	5 6 8	9 10 11
8·0	2·0794	0807	0819	0832	0844	0857	0869	0882	0894	0906	1 3 4	5 6 8	9 10 11
8·1	2·0919	0931	0943	0956	0968	0980	0992	1005	1017	1029	1 2 4	5 6 7	9 10 11
8·2	2·1041	1054	1066	1078	1090	1102	1114	1126	1138	1150	1 2 4	5 6 7	9 10 11
8·3	2·1163	1175	1187	1199	1211	1223	1235	1247	1258	1270	1 2 4	5 6 7	8 10 11
8·4	2·1282	1294	1306	1318	1330	1342	1353	1365	1377	1389	1 2 4	5 6 7	8 10 11
8·5	2·1401	1412	1424	1436	1448	1459	1471	1483	1494	1506	1 2 4	5 6 7	8 9 11
8·6	2·1518	1529	1541	1552	1564	1576	1587	1599	1610	1622	1 2 3	5 6 7	8 9 10
8·7	2·1633	1645	1656	1668	1679	1691	1702	1713	1725	1736	1 2 3	5 6 7	8 9 10
8·8	2·1748	1759	1770	1782	1793	1804	1815	1827	1838	1849	1 2 3	5 6 7	8 9 10
8·9	2·1861	1872	1883	1894	1905	1917	1928	1939	1950	1961	1 2 3	4 6 7	8 9 10
9·0	2·1972	1983	1994	2006	2017	2028	2039	2050	2061	2072	1 2 3	4 6 7	8 9 10
9·1	2·2083	2094	2105	2116	2127	2138	2148	2159	2170	2181	1 2 3	4 5 7	8 9 10
9·2	2·2192	2203	2214	2225	2235	2246	2257	2268	2279	2289	1 2 3	4 5 6	8 9 10
9·3	2·2300	2311	2322	2332	2343	2354	2364	2375	2386	2396	1 2 3	4 5 6	7 9 10
9·4	2·2407	2418	2428	2439	2450	2460	2471	2481	2492	2502	1 2 3	4 5 6	7 8 10
9·5	2·2513	2523	2534	2544	2555	2565	2576	2586	2597	2607	1 2 3	4 5 6	7 8 9
9·6	2·2618	2628	2638	2649	2659	2670	2680	2690	2701	2711	1 2 3	4 5 6	7 8 9
9·7	2·2721	2732	2742	2752	2762	2773	2783	2793	2803	2814	1 2 3	4 5 6	7 8 9
9·8	2·2824	2834	2844	2854	2865	2875	2885	2895	2905	2915	1 2 3	4 5 6	7 8 9
9·9	2·2925	2935	2946	2956	2966	2976	2986	2996	3006	3016	1 2 3	4 5 6	7 8 9

ı 10^{-x}

10^{-x}	$\dfrac{1}{3.6974}$	$\dfrac{2}{5.3948}$	$\dfrac{3}{7.0922}$	$\dfrac{4}{10.7897}$	$\dfrac{5}{12.4871}$	$\dfrac{6}{14.1845}$

At the foot of the table of natural logarithms on pages 18 and 19, the values of $\ln 10^n$ and $\ln 10^{-n}$ are shown. These values allow logarithms of numbers outside the range of the table to be found (i.e. positive numbers greater than 10 or less than 1).

Example 2   Evaluate $\ln 225.4$ correct to five significant figures.

$$\ln 225.4 = \ln(2.254 \times 100) = \ln(2.254 \times 10^2)$$

From the rule of logarithms which states that

$$\log_a MN = \log_a M + \log_a N$$
$$\ln(2.254 \times 10^2) = \ln 2.254 + \ln 10^2$$

Reading directly from the table of logarithms,

$$\ln 2.254 = 0.8127$$

and, from the foot of the table,

$$\ln 10^2 = 4.6052$$

thus $\ln 225.4 = 0.8127 + 4.6052 = 5.4179$

Using a calculator gives $\ln 225.4 = 5.417\,877$, or 5.4179 correct to five significant figures.

Example 3   Find $\ln 0.007\,83$ correct to four decimal places.

$$\ln 0.007\,83 = \ln(7.83 \times 10^{-3})$$
$$= \ln 7.83 + \ln 10^{-3}$$

From the natural-logarithms table,

$$\ln 7.83 = 2.0580 \quad \text{and} \quad \ln 10^{-3} = \overline{7}.0922$$

Now $\overline{7}.0922 = -7 + 0.0922$
$$= -6.9078$$

$\therefore$ $\ln 0.007\,83 = 2.0580 + (-6.9078)$
$$= -4.8498$$

Using a calculator we simply enter the number $0.007\,83$ and press the '$\ln x$' key to display $-4.849\,79$, or -4.8498 correct to four decimal places.

A3.5 The relationship between common and natural logarithms

If we know $\log N$ and we wish to find $\ln N$, let $\ln N = x$ so that $N = e^x$
Now, taking common logarithms of both sides gives

$$\log N = \log e^x = x \log e = \ln N \times \log e$$

$\therefore$ $\ln N = \dfrac{\log N}{\log e} = \dfrac{\log N}{\log 2.7183} = \dfrac{\log N}{0.4343} = 2.3026 \log N$

i.e. to find the natural logarithm of a number we can simply multiply the common logarithm of the number by 2.3026. To find the common logarithm we can multiply the natural logarithm of the number by 0.4343.

Example   If $\log x = 1.8734$ and $\ln y = 2.2241$, find $\ln x$ and $\log y$.

$\ln x = 2.3026 \log x = 2.3026 \times 1.8734 = 4.3137$

$\log y = 0.4343 \ln y = 0.4343 \times 2.2241 = 0.9659$

A3.6 Equations involving exponentials and natural logarithms

Because laws of natural growth and decay involve exponential functions, it is often necessary to solve equations which include such functions or their corresponding logarithms. In this section we look at methods of solving such equations. For further practical examples turn to section B2. Graphical treatment of growth and decay problems is also included in section B2.

Example 1   Solve the equation $9 = 12e^{-3t}$ to find t.

Dividing both sides of the equation by 12 gives

$0.75 = e^{-3t}$

The definition of a logarithm tells us that if $N = e^x$ then $\ln N = x$,

$\therefore$ $\ln 0.75 = -3t$

or $t = -\frac{1}{3}\ln 0.75 = -\frac{1}{3}(-0.2887) = 0.0959$

$\therefore$ $t = 0.096$

Example 2   If $\theta = 126(1 - e^{-x/4})$, find x when $\theta = 85$.

$85 = 126(1 - e^{-x/4})$

$\therefore$ $e^{-x/4} = 1 - \dfrac{85}{126} = 0.3254$

From the definition of a logarithm,

$-x/4 = \ln 0.3254 = -1.1227$

$\therefore$ $x = 4.491$

Example 3   Solve the equation $t/4.85 = \ln(6.31/x)$ to find x when $t = 11.2$

Substituting for t, the l.h.s. of the equation becomes

$\dfrac{11.2}{4.85} = 2.3093$

$$\therefore \quad \ln(6.31/x) = 2.3093$$

Using the definition of a logarithm,

$$\frac{6.31}{x} = e^{2.3093} = 10.067$$

$$\therefore \quad x = \frac{6.31}{10.067} = 0.627$$

Exercise A3

1 Evaluate the following, using a calculator or tables, correct to four significant figures: (a) $1.1e^{3.7}$, (b) $5.4e^{-1.53}$, (c) $6.71e^{1/2.76}$, (d) $22.1e^{-(1/13-1/17)}$, (e) $4(1 - e^{-2.5})$, (f) $(1 - 3.2e^{-11/4})/16$.

2 Use tables or a calculator to find the following natural logarithms correct to four decimal places: (a) $\ln 3.182$, (b) $\ln 8.049$, (c) $\ln 2.623$, (d) $\ln 2.787$, (e) $\ln 84.75$, (f) $\ln 118.2$, (g) $\ln 0.0674$, (h) $\ln 0.0039$, (i) $\ln(1.224 \times 10^5)$, (j) $\ln(7.785 \times 10^{-4})$.

3 Solve the following equations to find the value of the unknown variable correct to four significant figures: (a) $4.7 = 8e^{-2.4x}$, (b) $e^{16/u}/1.51 = 19.75$, (c) $\ln|(i2.6)| = -1.61$, (d) $1.71 = 31.5 \ln[(2 - \theta)/4.6$

A4 Complex numbers

A4.1 Defining a complex number

If we try to solve the equation $x^2 + 9 = 0$, we arrive at the solution $x = \pm\sqrt{-9}$. There is, however, no *real* number p such that $p^2 = -9$. Similarly, attempts to solve the quadratic equation $x^2 + 2x + 3 = 0$ using the formula method lead to the roots $x = -1 \pm (\sqrt{-8}/2)$. Here again, the square root of a negative number cannot be expressed as a real number. Problems such as these led sixteenth-century mathematicians to define an operator $j = \sqrt{-1}$. Sometimes i is used instead of but this can lead to confusion with the symbol for current in electrical work, and should be avoided.

Having defined $j = \sqrt{-1}$ we can express the solutions of the above equations in terms of j as follows:

$$x^2 + 9 = 0$$

$$\therefore \quad x = \pm\sqrt{-9} = \pm\sqrt{-1 \times 9} = \pm\sqrt{-1} \times \sqrt{9}$$

But $j = \sqrt{-1}$

$$\therefore \quad x = \pm j3$$

In the same way, the roots of the quadratic equation $x^2 + 2x + 3 =$ can be defined as

22

$$x = -1 \pm (\sqrt{-8}/2)$$

or $\quad x = -1 \pm j\sqrt{8}/2 = -1 \pm j\sqrt{2}$

Because numbers such as j3 are not real numbers, they were given the unfortunate name of *imaginary numbers*. Any number $a + jb$ consisting of a real part a and an imaginary part jb (such as $-1 + j\sqrt{2}$ above) we call a *complex number*. Thus j, j2, j6.5, and j0.7 are all examples of purely imaginary numbers; while $2 + j3$, $-1 - j4$, and $0.8 + j$ are all complex numbers.

Complex numbers are useful in many branches of mathematics, particularly in connection with electrical (alternating-current) theory.

Having said that $j = \sqrt{-1}$, it follows that $j^2 = -1$ and we can replace j^2 wherever it appears with -1. We also note that $j^3 = -j$, and $j^4 = +1$.

Example Express the roots of the quadratic equation $4x^2 - 3x + 2 = 0$ as complex numbers in the form $a + jb$.

Using the formula method of solution,

$$x = \frac{3 \pm \sqrt{9 - 32}}{8} = \frac{3 \pm \sqrt{-23}}{8}$$

$$= \frac{3 \pm j\sqrt{23}}{8} = \frac{3 \pm j4.796}{8}$$

The roots of the quadratic equation are $0.375 + j0.599$ and $0.375 - j0.599$. (Note that a curve representing the equation $y = 4x^2 - 3x + 2$ would not cross the x-axis.)

A4.2 The Argand diagram

Complex numbers can be shown on a diagram called an *Argand diagram*, after its originator. We draw a real axis horizontally and an imaginary axis vertically. Figure A4.1 shows the complex number $3 + j5$ as a vector $\overline{OQ}$ on an Argand diagram. (Students unfamiliar with vectors should note that a vector quantity is one which has both magnitude and direction.) The line OQ is drawn by measuring three units along the real axis and then five units vertically from P to Q.

Any lines drawn along the horizontal axis of an Argand diagram represent real numbers; so vector $\overline{OP}$ denotes the real number $+3$. Similarly, imaginary numbers are drawn along the vertical axis. Vector $\overline{OR}$ therefore represents the imaginary number j5. Students familiar with vector addition will see that $\overline{OQ} = \overline{OR} + \overline{OP}$.

All complex numbers with positive or negative real and imaginary parts can be represented on the Argand diagram. In fig. A4.2 we have the four complex numbers $2 + j6$, $-4 + j3$, $-5 - j7$, and $6 - j4$ drawn in the first, second, third, and fourth quadrants respectively.

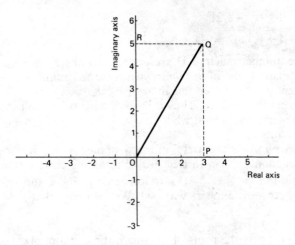

Fig. A4.1 The complex number $3 + j5$ on an Argand diagram

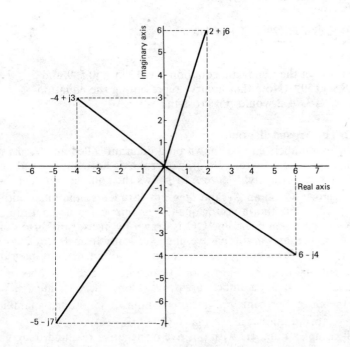

Fig. A4.2 Argand diagram showing the complex numbers $2 + j6$, $-4 + j3$, $-5 - j7$, and $6 - j4$

24

A4.3 Addition and subtraction of complex numbers

To add two complex numbers $a + jb$ and $c + jd$ together, we add their real parts together and then add their imaginary parts together, giving

$$(a + jb) + (c + jd) = (a + c) + j(b + d)$$

The result of the addition is also a complex number and will always be so unless the imaginary parts of the two complex numbers have the same value but opposite signs (e.g. $(6 + j7) + (5 - j7) = 11$, a real number).

Example 1 Find the sum of the complex numbers $2 + j7$ and $5 - j3$.

$$(2 + j7) + (5 - j3) = (2 + 5) + j(7 - 3)$$
$$= 7 + j4$$

The rule of addition may be shown on the Argand diagram. Figure A4.3 shows the complex numbers $a + jb$ and $c + jd$ together with their sum $(a + c) + j(b + d)$ as represented by the vectors $\overline{OL}$, $\overline{ON}$, and $\overline{OM}$ respectively.

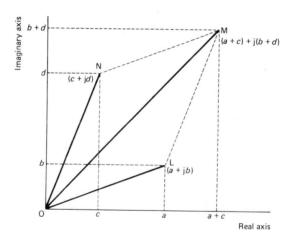

Fig. A4.3 Addition of complex numbers on an Argand diagram

The addition can be carried out graphically as a vector addition by drawing the two vectors $\overline{OL}$ (representing $a + jb$) and $\overline{ON}$ (representing $c + jd$) and completing the parallelogram OLMN (in the same way that we construct a parallelogram of forces in mechanics or find the resultant current from a phasor diagram in electrical work). The diagonal $\overline{OM}$ of the parallelogram is the vector representing the sum of the two original complex numbers.

25

Example 2 Show the addition of the complex numbers $8 + j2$ and $3 + j5$ on an Argand diagram.

The two complex numbers are shown represented by vectors $\overline{OS}$ and $\overline{OU}$ on the Argand diagram in fig. A4.4. From parallelogram OSTU we see that $\overline{OS} + \overline{OU} = \overline{OT}$ or that $(8 + j2) + (3 + j5) = 11 + j7$.

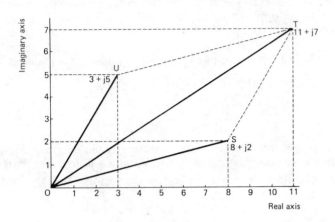

Fig. A4.4 Addition of $8 + j2$ and $3 + j5$

To subtract one complex number from another, we subtract their real parts and subtract their imaginary parts. Thus

$$(a + jb) - (c + jd) = (a - c) + j(b - d)$$

Example 3 Subtract $6 - j5$ from $9 + j2$ and express the answer in the form $a + jb$. Show your answer on an Argand diagram.

$$(9 + j2) - (6 - j5) = (9 - 6) + j(2 - (-5))$$
$$= 3 + j7$$

On the Argand diagram in fig. A4.5, we show the above subtraction by drawing the parallelogram OVWX. Vector $\overline{OV}$ represents the complex number $9 + j2$ and $\overline{OX}$ is $-(6 - j5)$ or $-6 + j5$. The diagonal $\overline{OW}$ shows the result of the subtraction, which is $3 + j7$.

A4.4 Multiplication of complex numbers
To multiply two complex numbers together, we write down all four products of the real and imaginary parts of the numbers. (This process is similar to the way in which we multiply the factors of a quadratic equation together.) We then simplify the result, remembering to replace j^2 with -1. Thus

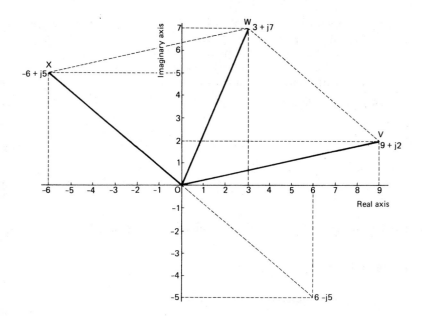

Fig. A4.5 Subtraction of $6 - j5$ from $9 + j2$

$$(a + jb)(c + jd) = ac + jad + jbc + j^2bd$$
$$= ac + j(ad + bc) + (-1)bd$$
$$= (ac - bd) + j(ad + bc)$$

Example 1 Express $(3 + j6)(4 + j5)$ in the form $a + jb$.

$$(3 + j6)(4 + j5) = 12 + j15 + j24 - 30$$
$$= -18 + j39$$

Example 2 Evaluate $j(2 - j8)(5 + j12)$.

$$j(2 - j8)(5 + j12) = j(10 + j24 - j40 + 96)$$
$$= j(106 - j16)$$
$$= 16 + j106$$

A4.5 Division of complex numbers

The process of dividing two complex numbers which are both expressed in the form $a + jb$ is simplified by the introduction of the *conjugate* of a complex number. For any complex number $a + jb$, the conjugate is $a - jb$. We simply change the sign of the imaginary part of the complex

27

number to obtain its conjugate. The conjugate of $3 + j5$ is therefore $3 - j5$. (Note that the conjugate of a number is always the reflection of the number in the real axis of an Argand diagram.)

The reason for using the conjugate here is that any complex number multiplied by its conjugate becomes a real number. Thus

$$(3 + j5)(3 - j5) = 9 - j15 + j15 + 25$$
$$= 9 + 25$$
$$= 34$$

In general,

$$(a + jb)(a - jb) = a^2 + b^2$$

To divide two complex numbers, we first multiply both the numerator and the denominator by the conjugate of the denominator.

Example 1   Express $\dfrac{(3 + j2)}{(5 + j4)}$ in the form $a + jb$.

Multiplying the numerator and the denominator by the conjugate of $5 + j4$ gives

$$\frac{(3 + j2)(5 - j4)}{(5 + j4)(5 - j4)} = \frac{15 - j12 + j10 + 8}{25 + 16}$$

$$= \frac{23 - j2}{41} = 0.561 - j0.049$$

Example 2   Divide $(-8 + j5)$ by $(6 - j3)$.

$$\frac{(-8 + j5)}{(6 - j3)} = \frac{(-8 + j5)(6 + j3)}{(6 - j3)(6 + j3)}$$

$$= \frac{-48 - j24 + j30 - 15}{36 + 9}$$

$$= \frac{-63 + j6}{45} = -1.40 + j0.13$$

Exercise A4

1   State whether the solutions of the following equations are real, imaginary, or complex numbers:

(a) $t^2 + 5 = 0$ (b) $x^2 - 6 = 2$ (c) $4 - r^2 = 1$
(d) $2x^2 + x - 4 = 0$ (e) $x^2 + 3x + 5 = 0$

2   If the roots of the quadratic equation $x^2 + 3x + k = 0$ are real, what is the largest value which the constant k can have?

3 Show the complex numbers $3 + j7$, $-4 - j9$, $-5 + j8$, and $2 - j5$ on the same Argand diagram.

4 Add together the following pairs of complex numbers and express your answers in the form $a + jb$:

(a) $(2 + j6) + (5 + j9)$ (b) $(2 - j5) + (4 + j12)$
(c) $(4 + j9) + (-2 - j9)$ (d) $(-3 - j7) + (-8 + j13)$
(e) $(15 + j8) + (-15 - j3)$ (f) $(-8 + j5) + (13 - j6)$
(g) $(2.75 - j1.83) + (4.01 + j7.22)$

5 Show each of the complex-number additions in question 4 on a separate Argand diagram.

6 Carry out the following subtractions:

(a) $(5 + j9) - (2 + j4)$ (b) $(7 + j3) - (4 - j8)$
(c) $(-5 - j6) - (6 + j2)$ (d) $(11 + j7) - (3 + j5) - (-4 + j2)$
(e) $(13 - j3) - (-5 + j)$ (f) $(4.73 - j2.11) - (9.05 - j3.37)$

7 Show each of the complex-number subtractions in question 6 on a separate Argand diagram.

8 Multiply the following complex numbers together:

(a) $(2 + j7)(5 + j3)$ (b) $(3 - j4)(6 + j9)$
(c) $(-2 - j11)(3 + j5)$ (d) $(8 - j)(-2 - j6)$
(e) $(4 - j8)(4 + j8)$ (f) $(2.62 + j8.15)(1.90 - j3.32)$

9 Find the real and imaginary parts of the following:

(a) $\dfrac{(6 + j4)}{(2 + j3)}$ (b) $\dfrac{(11 - j5)}{(3 + j7)}$ (c) $\dfrac{(8 + j2)}{(5 - j)}$ (d) $\dfrac{108}{(2 - j3)}$

10 If $Z = R + j\omega L + 1/j\omega C$, express Z in the form $a + jb$ when $R = 20$, $L = 10$, $C = 0.05$, and $\omega = 2$.

A5 Complex numbers in polar form

A5.1 Rectangular and polar representation

We have seen in section A4 that complex numbers may be expressed as $a + jb$, where a and b are the real and imaginary rectangular co-ordinates of the number when it is shown on an Argand diagram. The complex number $5 + j7$ is shown in fig. A5.1 as a vector $\overline{OQ}$. We can express the same complex number in *polar form* by defining r, the length of line OQ, and θ, the angle which OQ makes with the positive real axis.

By applying the theorem of Pythagoras to triangle OPQ,

$$r^2 = 5^2 + 7^2$$

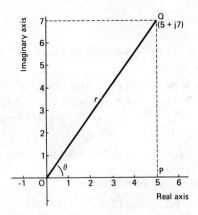

Fig. A5.1 The complex number $5 + j7$ on an Argand diagram

$$\therefore \quad r = \sqrt{74} = 8.60$$

The angle θ can be found as follows:

$$\tan \theta = 7/5 = 1.4$$

$$\therefore \quad \theta = \arctan(1.4) = 54.46° = 0.951 \text{ rad}$$

We express a complex number in polar form as $r\,\underline{/\theta}$, and it follows from the above example that r is always $\sqrt{(a^2 + b^2)}$. The angle θ can be found using trigonometry and a sketch.

For complex numbers in the first and second quadrants, angle θ will be less than 180° measured *anticlockwise* from the positive real axis of the Argand diagram. When the number is in the third quadrant or the fourth, it is sometimes preferable to express θ as an angle between 0° and −180° measured *clockwise* from the positive real axis (i.e. $3.5\,\underline{/-67°}$ rather than $3.5\,\underline{/293°}$).

Example 1 Express the complex numbers $3 + j2$, $-3 + j2$, $-3 - j2$, and $3 - j2$ in polar form.

Figure A5.2 shows a sketch of the four numbers on an Argand diagram. For each of the four complex numbers, $r = \sqrt{(3^2 + 2^2)} = 3.61$.

$3 + j2$:
From triangle OPQ,

$$\angle QOP = \arctan(2/3) = 33.69° = 0.588 \text{ rad}$$

We therefore express $3 + j2$ in polar form as $3.61\,\underline{/33.69°}$ or $3.61\,\underline{/0.588 \text{ rad}}$.

30

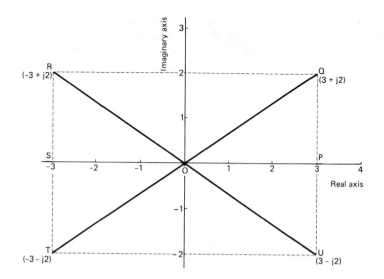

Fig. A5.2

$-3 + j2$:
From triangle ORS,

$\quad \angle \text{ROS} = \arctan (2/3) = 33.69°$ or 0.588 rad

$\therefore \quad \angle \text{ROP} = 180° - 33.69° = 146.31°$

$\quad\quad\quad\quad = \pi - 0.588 \,\text{rad} = 2.554 \,\text{rad}$

The complex number $-3 + j2$ in polar form is therefore $3.61 \,\underline{/146.31°}$
or $3.61 \,\underline{/2.554 \,\text{rad.}}$

$-3 - j2$:
From triangle OST,

$\quad \angle \text{TOS} = \arctan(2/3) = 33.69°$ or $0.588 \,\text{rad}$

$\therefore \quad \angle \text{TOP} = 180° - 33.69° = 146.31°$

$\quad\quad\quad\quad = \pi - 0.588 \,\text{rad} = 2.554 \,\text{rad}$

The complex number $-3 - j2$ in polar form is therefore

$\quad 3.61 \,\underline{/213.69°} = 3.61 \,\underline{/-146.31°} \quad$ or $\quad 3.61 \,\underline{/-2.554 \,\text{rad.}}$

$3 - j2$:
From triangle OUP,

$\quad \angle \text{POU} = \arctan(2/3) = 33.69°$ or $0.588 \,\text{rad}$

The complex number $3 - j2$ in polar form is therefore

$\quad 3.61 \,\underline{/326.61°} = 3.61 \,\underline{/-33.69°} \quad$ or $\quad 3.61 \,\underline{/-0.588 \,\text{rad}}$

31

To convert from polar form to $a + jb$ form, we again refer to the complex number $r\underline{/\theta}$ in fig. A5.1. From triangle OPQ,

$$OP = r \cos \theta$$
$$PQ = r \sin \theta$$

These lengths give the real and imaginary parts of the complex number.

It is usually worthwhile drawing a sketch when carrying out these conversions. Some scientific calculators will carry out these conversions from rectangular to polar form and vice versa, using stored programs.

Example 2 Convert $7.8\underline{/59°}$ into $a + jb$ form.

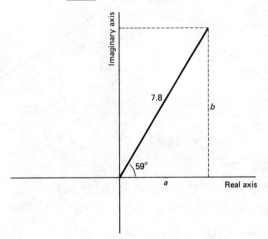

Fig. A5.3

Figure A5.3 shows a sketch of the complex number $7.8\underline{/59°}$ on an Argand diagram. From the sketch,

$$a = 7.8 \cos 59° = 7.8 \times 0.515 = 4.02$$
$$b = 7.8 \sin 59° = 7.8 \times 0.857 = 6.68$$

Both the real and the imaginary parts are positive; the complex number $7.8\underline{/59°}$ can therefore be expressed as $4.02 + j6.68$.

Example 3 Express $12.5\underline{/-2.7\,\text{rad}}$ in $a + jb$ form.

$$2.7\,\text{rad} = 154.7°$$

The complex number $12.5\underline{/-154.7°}$ is shown in fig. A5.4. From the sketch,

$$a = 12.5 \cos(180° - 154.7°)$$
$$= 12.5 \cos 25.3°$$
$$= 11.3$$

32

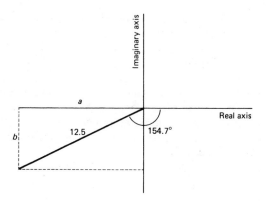

Fig. A5.4

and $b = 12.5 \sin 25.3°$
    $= 5.34$

Both the real and the imaginary parts are negative; the complex number $12.5 \underline{/-2.7 \, \text{rad}}$ can therefore be expressed as $-11.3 - j5.34$.

A5.2 The modulus and argument of a complex number

If a complex number $a + jb$ (see fig. A5.5) is expressed in polar form as $r \underline{/\theta}$, we have seen in the previous section that

$$r = \sqrt{(a^2 + b^2)} \quad \text{and} \quad \theta = \arctan(b/a)$$

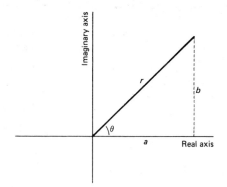

Fig. A5.5

For any complex number $r \underline{/\theta}$, r is known as the *modulus* and may also be written as $\text{mod} \, z$ or $|z|$. The angle θ is known as the *argument* of the complex number, sometimes written $\arg z$. The steps involved in finding the modulus and argument of a complex number $a + jb$ have been covered in section A5.1.

33

If we consider as an example the complex number $z = 5 + j7$ shown in fig. A5.1, we have seen that $|z| = r = 8.60$ and $\arg z = \theta = 54.46°$ or 0.951 rad.

It is clear that a complex number with the same modulus as the number in fig. A5.1 but having an argument $0.951 + 2\pi$ would look exactly the same in the diagram. The same is true of the complex numbers $8.60\underline{/0.951 + 4\pi}$, $8.60\underline{/0.951 + 6\pi}$, and $8.60\underline{/0.951 + 8\pi}$. In some cases it is necessary to use the more complete polar form $r\underline{/\theta + 2k\pi}$, where $k = 0, 1, 2, ...$, etc. When we write $r\underline{/\theta}$ without the $2k\pi$, we are using the *principal* value.

Referring again to fig. A5.5, we have seen that $a = r\cos\theta$ and $b = r\sin\theta$, and so

$$a + jb = r\cos\theta + jr\sin\theta$$

$$= r(\cos\theta + j\sin\theta)$$

This is another way of expressing the same complex number. It will be useful when we come to multiply complex numbers together in polar form, and also when we determine the square roots of complex numbers.

Note that $r\underline{/\theta}$ can also be expressed as $r\,e^{j\theta}$, although the origin and uses of this expression are beyond our present needs.

A5.3 Multiplication and division in polar form

Multiplication

The method of multiplying complex numbers expressed as $a + jb$ has been discussed in section A4.4. We shall now see that multiplication is simpler when the complex numbers are in polar form.

To multiply $r_1\underline{/\theta_1}$ by $r_2\underline{/\theta_2}$,

$$r_1\underline{/\theta_1} \times r_2\underline{/\theta_2} = r_1(\cos\theta_1 + j\sin\theta_1) \times r_2(\cos\theta_2 + j\sin\theta_2)$$

Multiplying the expressions on the r.h.s. together gives

$$r_1 r_2(\cos\theta_1\cos\theta_2 + j\cos\theta_1\sin\theta_2 + j\sin\theta_1\cos\theta_2 - \sin\theta_1\sin\theta_2)$$

Now it can be shown (see section D6.1) that

$$\cos(A + B) = \cos A\cos B - \sin A\sin B$$

and $\sin(A + B) = \sin A\cos B + \sin B\cos A$

$$\therefore\quad r_1\underline{/\theta_1} \times r_2\underline{/\theta_2} = r_1 r_2[\cos(\theta_1 + \theta_2) + j\sin(\theta_1 + \theta_2)]$$

We can write this result as

$$r_1\underline{/\theta_1} \times r_2\underline{/\theta_2} = r_1 r_2\underline{/\theta_1 + \theta_2}$$

Thus, to multiply two complex numbers together, we simply find the product of their moduli $(r_1 r_2)$ and the sum of their arguments $(\theta_1 + \theta_2)$.

Example 1 Multiply $8.5\,\underline{/33.8°}$ by $2.6\,\underline{/81.4°}$.

$$r_1\,\underline{/\theta_1} \times r_2\,\underline{/\theta_2} = r_1 r_2\,\underline{/\theta_1 + \theta_2}$$

$$\therefore \quad 8.5\,\underline{/33.8°} \times 2.6\,\underline{/81.4°} = (8.5 \times 2.6)\,\underline{/33.8° + 81.4°}$$
$$= 22.1\,\underline{/115.2°}$$

Example 2 Express $2.5\,\underline{/0.68\,\text{rad}} \times 4.6\,\underline{/-2.21\,\text{rad}}$ as $r\,\underline{/\theta}$.

$$2.5\,\underline{/0.68} \times 4.6\,\underline{/-2.21} = (2.5 \times 4.6)\,\underline{/0.68 + (-2.21)}$$
$$= 11.5\,\underline{/-1.53\,\text{rad}}$$

Division

$$\frac{r_1\,\underline{/\theta_1}}{r_2\,\underline{/\theta_2}} = \frac{r_1(\cos\theta_1 + j\sin\theta_1)}{r_2(\cos\theta_2 + j\sin\theta_2)}$$

Multiplying both the numerator and the denominator by $r_2(\cos\theta_2 - j\sin\theta_2)$ (the conjugate of the denominator – see section A4.5) gives

$$\frac{r_1(\cos\theta_1 + j\sin\theta_1)r_2(\cos\theta_2 - j\sin\theta_2)}{r_2(\cos\theta_2 + j\sin\theta_2)r_2(\cos\theta_2 - j\sin\theta_2)}$$

$$= \frac{r_1 r_2(\cos\theta_1\cos\theta_2 - j\cos\theta_1\sin\theta_2 + j\sin\theta_1\cos\theta_2 + \sin\theta_1\sin\theta_2)}{(r_2)^2(\cos^2\theta_2 + \sin^2\theta_2)}$$

Now, it can be shown that

$$\cos(A - B) = \cos A \cos B + \sin A \sin B$$

and $\quad \sin(A - B) = \sin A \cos B - \cos A \sin B$

(see section D6.1 for the origin of these identities)

$$\therefore \quad \frac{r_1\,\underline{/\theta_1}}{r_2\,\underline{/\theta_2}} = \frac{r_1}{r_2}[\cos(\theta_1 - \theta_2) + j\sin(\theta_1 - \theta_2)]$$

or $\quad \dfrac{r_1\,\underline{/\theta_1}}{r_2\,\underline{/\theta_2}} = \dfrac{r_1}{r_2}\,\underline{/\theta_1 - \theta_2}$

Thus, to divide two complex numbers, we divide their moduli and subtract their arguments.

Example 3 Divide $14\,\underline{/60°}$ by $8\,\underline{/25°}$.

$$\frac{r_1\,\underline{/\theta_1}}{r_2\,\underline{/\theta_2}} = \frac{r_1}{r_2}\,\underline{/\theta_1 - \theta_2}$$

$$\therefore \quad \frac{14\,\underline{/60°}}{8\,\underline{/25°}} = (14/8)\,\underline{/60° - 25°}$$

$$= 1.75\,\underline{/35°}$$

Example 4   Express $(9.5\,\underline{/1.6\,\text{rad}})/(2.4\,\underline{/-0.75\,\text{rad}})$ as $r\,\underline{/\theta}$.

$$(9.5\,\underline{/1.6}\,)/(2.4\,\underline{/-0.75}\,) = (9.5/2.4)\,\underline{/1.6-(-0.75)}$$
$$= 3.96\,\underline{/2.35\,\text{rad}}$$

A5.4 The square roots of a complex number

In section A5.3 we showed that

$$r_1(\cos\theta_1 + j\sin\theta_1) \times r_2(\cos\theta_2 + j\sin\theta_2)$$
$$= r_1 r_2[\cos(\theta_1+\theta_2)+j\sin(\theta_1+\theta_2)]$$

Making $r_1 = r_2 = r$ and $\theta_1 = \theta_2 = \theta$, the equation becomes

$$[r(\cos\theta+j\sin\theta)]^2 = r^2(\cos 2\theta + j\sin 2\theta)$$

Again multiplying both sides by $r(\cos\theta + j\sin\theta)$ gives

$$[r(\cos\theta+j\sin\theta)]^3 = r^3(\cos 3\theta + j\sin 3\theta)$$

In general form,

$$[r(\cos\theta+j\sin\theta)]^n = r^n(\cos n\theta + j\sin n\theta)$$

The above equation may be written more simply as

$$(r\underline{/\theta})^n = r^n\underline{/n\theta}$$

and is known as *De Moivre's theorem*. It is true for all values of n.

Example 1   Express $(1.3\,\underline{/28°})^2$ in the form $a+jb$.

From De Moivre's theorem,

$$(1.3\,\underline{/28°})^2 = (1.3)^2\underline{/2 \times 28°}$$
$$= 1.69\,\underline{/56°}$$
$$= 0.945 + j1.40$$

De Moivre's theorem can also be used to find roots of complex numbers by making n a fraction. In doing this it is necessary to work with the complex numbers in their full form (i.e. $r\,\underline{/\theta + 2k\pi}$ – see section A5.2).

Applying the theorem to find square roots,

$$(r\,\underline{/\theta + 2k\pi})^{1/2} = r^{1/2}\underline{/\tfrac{1}{2}(\theta + 2k\pi)} = r^{1/2}\underline{/(\theta/2) + k\pi}$$

It would appear from this that there is an infinite number of square roots, since we could substitute $k = 0, 1, 2, \ldots$, etc. However, we find that there are only two different square roots and that further values simply repeat these two alternately. Putting $k = 0$ gives the first (principal) square root:

36

$$r^{1/2}\,\underline{/\theta/2}$$

With $k = 1$, the second square root is

$$r^{1/2}\,\underline{/(\theta/2) + \pi}$$

Note that with $k = 2$ a root $r^{1/2}\,\underline{/(\theta/2) + 2\pi}$ is obtained. This is not a new square root, however; since it coincides with the principal root on the Argand diagram, it is the same complex number.

Example 2 Find the square roots of the complex number $4.8\,\underline{/86°}$.

From De Moivre's theorem,

$$(4.8\,\underline{/86° + 2k\pi})^{1/2} = 4.8^{1/2}\,\underline{/\tfrac{1}{2}(86° + 2k\pi)}$$
$$= 2.19\,\underline{/43° + k\pi}$$

With $k = 0$ the principal square root is $2.19\,\underline{/43°}$, and with $k = 1$ the second square root is $2.19\,\underline{/43° + \pi} = 2.19\,\underline{/223°}$ or $2.19\,\underline{/-137°}$.

The square roots in the above example are shown on the Argand diagram in fig. A5.6, together with the original complex number $4.8\,\underline{/86°}$.

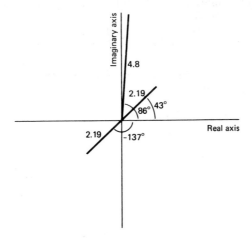

Fig. A5.6 The complex number $4\,\underline{/86°}$ and its square roots

We note that the square roots of a complex number are separated by an angle of 180°, so they form a straight line. You may like to show that there are three different values of $(r\,\underline{/\theta})^{1/3}$ which are separated by angles of 120°.

37

Exercise A5

1 Express the following complex numbers as $r\underline{/\theta}$, with θ measured in degrees: (a) $8 + j5$, (b) $5.1 + j2.7$, (c) $-6 + j11$, (d) $-2.7 - j3.5$, (e) $13.4 - j7.9$.

2 Convert the following numbers into polar form $r\underline{/\theta}$, giving θ in radians in the range $-\pi \leqslant \theta \leqslant \pi$: (a) $-6 + j3$. (b) $-23.6 - j19.4$, (c) $1.6 - j2.2$, (d) $j3$, (e) $-j5$.

3 Express the following complex numbers as $a + jb$: (a) $7.2\underline{/51°}$, (b) $0.26\underline{/113°}$, (c) $16.8\underline{/0.85\,\mathrm{rad}}$, (d) $5.20\underline{/-129°}$, (e) $3.75\underline{/5.8\,\mathrm{rad}}$.

4 Express the following products as $r\underline{/\theta}$: (a) $6\underline{/15°} \times 5\underline{/38°}$, (b) $1.8\underline{/28°} \times 0.85\underline{/-36°}$, (c) $15\underline{/(\pi/4)} \times 11\underline{/(\pi/6)}$, (d) $6.15\underline{/0.18\,\mathrm{rad}} \times 3.96\underline{/1.11\,\mathrm{rad}}$.

5 Evaluate the following and give your answers in polar form:

(a) $\dfrac{8\underline{/68°}}{3\underline{/25°}}$ (b) $\dfrac{3.98\underline{/118°}}{2.26\underline{/77°}}$ (c) $\dfrac{15\underline{/(\pi/2)}}{6\underline{/(-\pi/4)}}$ (d) $\dfrac{88.6\underline{/-22.5°}}{113.4\underline{/-80.8°}}$

6 A capacitor C of 300×10^{-6} farads is connected in series with a coil, which has resistance $R = 8$ ohms and inductance $L = 0.05$ henrys, across a supply of voltage $V = 250$ volts and frequency 50 hertz. The impedance of the circuit is given by $Z = R + j\omega L - (j/\omega C)$, where $\omega = 50 \times 2\pi\,\mathrm{rad/s}$. Express Z and the current I in polar form if $V = IZ$.

7 Express the square roots of the following complex numbers as $r\underline{/\theta}$, with values of θ measured in degrees between $-\pi$ and $+\pi$: (a) $16\underline{/82°}$, (b) $5.7\underline{/162°}$, (c) $13.6\underline{/-27.6°}$, (d) $19 + j11.5$, (e) $7.73[\cos(5\pi/6) + j\sin(5\pi/6)]$.

8 The transfer function of a servomechanism is given by $G = 1/(1 + j\omega T)$. Determine the modulus and argument of G when $\omega = 2.5$ and $T = 0.10$.

B   Algebra and graphs

B1 Laws of the form $y = ax^n$

B1.1 Using logarithms to reduce $y = ax^n$ to straight-line form

Plotting values of y against corresponding values of x from an equation of the form $y = mx + c$ gives a straight-line graph with gradient m and intercept c. If we plot y against x for an equation $y = ax^n$ (for example $y = 5x^{1.6}$) we produce a curve, which may not be as useful to us as a straight line.

We can reduce $y = ax^n$ to straight-line form by taking logarithms of both sides of the equation:

$$\log y = \log(ax^n)$$
$$= \log x^n + \log a$$
$$= n \log x + \log a$$

Comparing this equation with $y = mx + c$ we observe that plotting values of $\log y$ against $\log x$ will yield a straight-line graph with gradient n and intercept $\log a$.

Example 1 Reduce the equation $y = 1.4x^{2.2}$ to straight-line form and draw a suitable graph for values of x between $x = 1$ and $x = 15$.

Taking logarithms of both sides,

$$\log y = 2.2 \log x + \log 1.4$$

We complete the following table for the required range of x values:

x	1	3	5	7	9	11	13	15
$\log x$	0.00	0.48	0.70	0.85	0.95	1.04	1.11	1.18
$\log y$	0.15	1.20	1.69	2.01	2.25	2.44	2.60	2.74

Plotting a graph of $\log x$ against $\log y$ gives the straight line in fig. B1.1.

Graphs relating the logarithms of two variables can be useful in deciding whether experimental data is related by an equation of the form $y = ax^n$. If plotting $\log x$ against $\log y$ gives a perfectly straight line, allowing for experimental errors, we can deduce that the relationship is as we predicted. If some points do not lie exactly on a line formed by the majority of points on the graph, it may be due to experimental er-

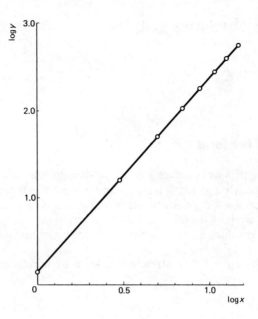

Fig. B1.1 The graph of $\log y = 2.2 \log x + \log 1.4$

rors rather than any inconsistency in the relationship between x and y which we assumed. In such cases the experiment can be repeated to check the data.

Example 2 Measurements of the torque required to rotate drills with different diameters (at a constant feed rate) produced the following table of values:

Torque T (N m)	2.47	4.80	8.59	12.3	17.6	22.7
Diameter D (mm)	10.0	15.0	20.0	25.0	30.0	35.0

Draw a graph of $\log D$ against $\log T$ to show that, within the limits of experimental accuracy, the experimental results suggest that $T = aD^n$, where a and n are constants.

If $T = aD^n$, a graph of $\log D$ against $\log T$ will be a straight line. Taking logarithms of the values given for T and D,

$\log T$	0.393	0.681	0.934	1.10	1.25	1.36
$\log D$	1.00	1.18	1.30	1.40	1.48	1.54

The graph of $\log T$ against $\log D$ is shown in fig. B1.2. Although all the points do not lie on a straight line, the line drawn on the graph is sufficiently close to all the points to conclude that, within the limits of the experiment, the results show that $T = aD^n$.

40

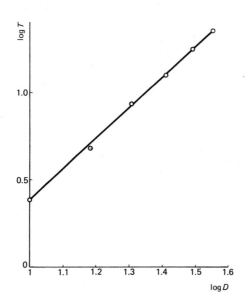

Fig. B1.2 The graph of $\log T = n \log D + \log a$

B1.2 Finding *a* and *n* from graphs of $y = ax^n$ in logarithmic form

A graph of $\log x$ against $\log y$ when $y = ax^n$ will, as we have seen, be a straight line. To find values of the constants *a* and *n* from such a graph requires an understanding of the basic equation of a straight line ($y = mx + c$) and of how this relates to the equation $\log y = n \log x + \log a$.

In cases when the axes of the graph intersect at the origin, $\log a$ will be the intercept on the $\log y$ axis and *n* will be the slope of the line.

Example 1   Draw a straight-line graph from the following table of values to show that $s = at^n$, where *a* and *n* are constants. Use your graph to find the values of *a* and *n*.

t	0.50	1.00	1.50	2.00	2.50	3.00
s	2.47	7.50	14.4	22.7	32.5	43.5

If $s = at^n$, a graph of $\log t$ against $\log s$ will be a straight line. Taking logarithms of the values in the table:

$\log t$	−0.301	0.000	0.176	0.301	0.398	0.477
$\log s$	0.393	0.875	1.16	1.36	1.51	1.64

These values are shown plotted on the graph in fig. B1.3. Since the line joining the points is straight, our graph confirms that *s* and *t* are related by an equation of the form $s = at^n$.

41

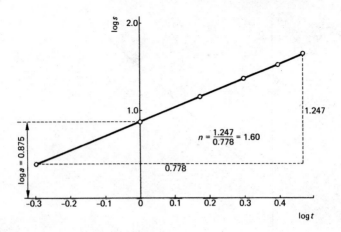

Fig. B1.3 The graph of $\log s = n \log t + \log a$

The axes of the graph intersect at the origin, and so the intercept on the $\log s$ axis gives the value of $\log a$ directly. From the graph,

$$\log a = 0.875$$
$$\therefore \quad a = 7.50$$

Using the triangle marked on the graph,

$$\text{slope of the line} = \frac{1.247}{0.778} = 1.60$$
$$\therefore \quad n = 1.60$$

The values of s and t are therefore related by the equation $s = 7.50t^{1.60}$.

When the $\log x$ and $\log y$ axes on a straight-line graph of $\log y = n \log x + \log a$ do not intersect at the origin, the intercept on the $\log y$ axis will not be $\log a$. To determine values of a and n in such cases we take two points from the graph and use them to form a pair of simultaneous equations which we can solve.

Example 2 Draw a graph of $\log v$ against $\log u$ using values from the following table. Show that $u = av^n$ and find constants a and n from the graph.

v	1000	1250	1500	1750	2000	2250
u	57.72	60.36	62.60	64.56	66.31	67.89

Values of $\log v$ and $\log u$ corresponding to those of v and u in the table are as follows:

42

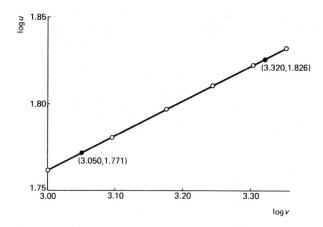

Fig. B1.4 The graph of $\log u = n \log v + \log a$

$\log v$	3.000	3.097	3.176	3.243	3.301	3.352
$\log u$	1.761	1.781	1.797	1.810	1.822	1.832

The graph of $\log v$ against $\log u$ is shown in fig. B1.4.

Taking logarithms of both sides of the equation $u = av^n$ gives

$$\log u = n \log v + \log a$$

Substituting values of u and v from two points $(3.050, 1.771)$ and $(3.320, 1.826)$ which lie on the line gives the equations

$$1.771 = n \times 3.050 + \log a \tag{i}$$

$$1.826 = n \times 3.320 + \log a \tag{ii}$$

Subtracting equation (i) from equation (ii),

$$0.055 = 0.27n$$

$$\therefore \qquad n = 0.20$$

Substituting $n = 0.20$ in equation (i) gives

$$1.771 = 0.61 + \log a$$

or $\quad \log a = 1.161$

$$\therefore \qquad a = 14.5$$

Variables u and v are therefore related by the equation $u = 14.5v^{0.20}$.

B1.3 Using logarithmic graph paper

In section B1.2 we saw that, to draw a straight-line graph on ordinary graph paper from a relationship of the form $y = ax^n$, we take logarithms of both sides to give $\log y = n \log x + \log a$. A graph of $\log x$

43

against log y will then be a straight line which we can use to determine the values of a and n. Graph paper with *logarithmic scales* is available to save time and avoid the repeated use of tables or a calculator. Log–log graph paper has logarithmic horizontal and vertical scales so that points may be marked on a graph directly.

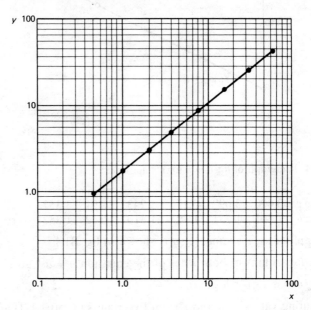

Fig. B1.5 The graph of $y = 1.7x^{0.8}$ on log–log graph paper

Figure B1.5 shows a graph of $y = 1.7x^{0.8}$ drawn using the values below:

x	0.500	1.00	2.00	4.00	8.00	16.0	32.0	64.0
y	0.976	1.70	2.96	5.15	8.97	15.6	27.2	47.4

The graph is drawn on *three-cycle* × *three-cycle log–log* graph paper. The cycles on both the x-axis and the y-axis are 0.1 to 1.0, 1.0 to 10, and 10 to 100.

Note that the three cycles each cover equal distances along the axis, even though each cycle represents a range which is ten times that of the previous cycle. These lengths are equal because

$$(\log 100 - \log 10) = (\log 10 - \log 1) = (\log 1 - \log 0.1) = 1$$

If a fourth cycle was added to extend the axes, it would cover values between 100 and 1000.

Graphs drawn on log–log graph paper can be used to determine constants a and n for relationships of the form $y = ax^n$. We can choose two

44

points from the graph and solve the resulting pair of simultaneous equations as we did in section B1.2.

Example 1 In an experiment to examine insulation properties, values of breakdown voltage V were measured for a range of material thicknesses. Draw a graph on log–log graph paper to show that the following results indicate that $V = kt^n$. Use the graph to evaluate k and n.

Breakdown voltage V (kV)	153	282	387	479	563	641
Insulator thickness t (mm)	2.00	5.00	8.00	11.0	14.0	17.0

Figure B1.6 shows the values of V and t plotted directly on to two-cycle × one-cycle log–log graph paper. The fact that the points form a straight line shows that $\log V = n \log t + \log k$, so that $V = kt^n$.

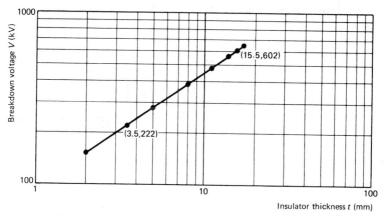

Fig. B1.6 The graph of $V = kt^n$ on log–log graph paper

Consider two points, $(3.5, 222)$ and $(15.5, 602)$, on the line in fig. B1.6. Substituting the values of V and t at the two selected points,

$$\log 222 = n \log 3.5 + \log k$$

or $\quad 2.35 = 0.544n + \log k \qquad\qquad\qquad$ (i)

and $\log 602 = n \log 15.5 + \log k$

or $\quad 2.78 = 1.19n + \log k \qquad\qquad\qquad$ (ii)

Subtracting equation (i) from equation (ii),

$$0.43 = 0.646n$$

$\therefore \qquad n = 0.666$

45

Substituting this value for n in equation (i),

$$\log k = 2.35 - (0.544 \times 0.666)$$

$$= 1.98$$

$$\therefore \quad k = 95.5$$

The equation relating V and t is therefore $V = 96t^{0.67}$.

Intermediate values

Graphs on log–log paper, as well as being easy to draw, have the advantage that intermediate values can be taken directly from a graph without the use of antilogarithms.

Values of t and z from the following table are shown on a graph (drawn using three-cycle × two-cycle log–log graph paper) in fig. B1.7:

t	1.50	3.00	6.00	12.0	24.0
z	17.55	70.20	280.8	1123	4493

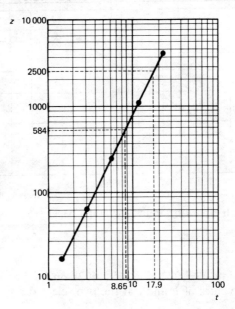

Fig. B1.7 The graph of $z = at^b$ on log–log graph paper

The straightness of the line confirms the relationship $z = at^b$. If we wish to determine the value of z when $t = 8.65$ we simply follow the line marked at 8.65 on the t-axis up to the curve (see fig. B1.7) and then across horizontally to the z-axis. Thus, when $t = 8.65$, $z = 584$. Similarly, to obtain the value of t when $z = 2500$, the process is reversed and we see that $t = 17.9$

46

Exercise B1

1 Complete the following table of values for the equation $y = 6.5x^{1.3}$ and use the table to draw a graph of $\log x$ against $\log y$.

x	0.75	7.50	75.0	750	7500
y					
$\log x$					
$\log y$					

2 By plotting a graph of $\log s$ against $\log r$ with axes which intersect at the origin, show that the following results define a relationship $r = as^b$. At what value does the line cross the $\log r$ axis?

s	5.00	15.0	35.0	75.0	155	315
r	396	1.2×10^4	1.65×10^5	1.75×10^6	1.67×10^7	1.50×10^8

3 The current flowing in an electronic circuit was measured for a range of applied voltages. One of the currents was misread.

Voltage V (V)	2.00	8.00	14.0	20.0	26.0	32.0
Current I (mA)	18.03	47.49	70.41	90.37	118.6	125.6

Draw a straight-line graph of $\log V$ against $\log I$ to show that $I = aV^n$ for this circuit. What should the incorrect current reading be?

4 If $y = ax^n$, use the following table to draw a straight-line graph and use it to find values for the constants a and n:

x	1.75	3.50	7.00	14.0	28.0
y	3.26	16.1	79.1	389	1920

5 Use three-cycle × three-cycle log–log graph paper to show that the following values for z and t are related by an equation of the form $z = at^b$, where a and b are constants:

t	5.00	15.0	35.0	75.0	155	315
z	40.52	169.0	508.5	1369	3519	8847

From the graph, determine the value of z when $t = 105$.

6 A volume of 300 litres of a gas with initial pressure 1 bar is compressed during an experiment, until the volume is reduced to 100 litres. Use the volume and pressure readings below to plot $\log V$ against $\log(1/P)$ on log–log graph paper. Use the graph to show that $1/P = CV^{1.4}$, where C is a constant.

V (litres)	300	275	250	225	200	175	150	125	100
P (bars)	1.00	1.13	1.29	1.48	1.77	2.13	2.64	3.41	4.65

7 The following results were obtained during tests on a milling machine:

Cutting speed S (m/min)	0.10	0.15	0.20	0.25	0.30
Tool life T (min)		4250	280	42	9.5	2.6

Draw a graph of S against T on log–log graph paper to show that $S = aT^n$. Evaluate constants a and n using the graph. What would be the optimum cutting speed for a tool life of 2 hours?

B2 Exponential growth and decay

Students unfamiliar with the use of tables or a calculator to evaluate exponential functions of the form $a\,e^{bx}$ should read section A3.1 before starting this chapter.

B2.1 The functions $a\,e^{bx}$, $a\,e^{-bx}$, and $a(1-e^{-bx})$
The function e^x is unique in the way its value remains unchanged when differentiated with respect to x [i.e. $\mathrm{d}(e^x)/\mathrm{d}x = e^x$, see section C2.1]. This means that the slope or gradient of the curve $y = e^x$ for any value of x is equal to the value of e^x at that point. As x increases, the value of e^x and the rate of change of e^x increase together.

The curves $y = e^x$, $y = e^{-x}$, and $y = 1 - e^{-x}$ are shown in fig. B2.1. They are important in many areas of technological work because they define mathematically the natural laws of growth and decay.

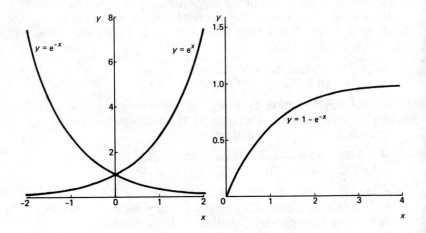

Fig. B2.1 The curves $y = e^x$, $y = e^{-x}$, and $y = 1 - e^{-x}$

A graph drawn from any equation of the form $y = a\,e^{bx}$, $y = a\,e^{-bx}$, or $y = a(1 - e^{-bx})$, where a and b are constants, will have the same basic shape as the corresponding curve in fig. B2.1.

Example 1 Using the same axes, draw the curves $y = 250\,e^{0.3x}$ and $y = 0.8\,e^{2x}$ for a range of points between $x = 0$ and $x = 3$.

We complete a table of values, using a calculator or tables to evaluate the exponential functions:

x	0.00	0.50	1.00	1.50	2.00	2.50	3.00
$250\,e^{0.3x}$	250	290	337	392	456	529	615
$2\,e^{2x}$	2.00	5.44	14.8	40.2	109	297	807

The curves are shown in fig. B2.2

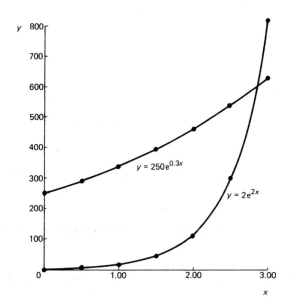

Fig. B2.2 The graphs of $y = 250\,e^{0.3x}$ and $y = 2\,e^{2x}$

Example 2 Draw the curves $y = 1.5\,e^{-1.8x}$ and $y = 1.1(1 - e^{-2.3x})$ with the same axes over a range of values between $x = 0$ and $x = 1$. Use your graph to solve the simultaneous equations.

First we complete a table of values:

x	0.00	0.20	0.40	0.60	0.80	1.00
$1.5\,e^{-1.8x}$	1.50	1.05	0.730	0.509	0.355	0.248
$1.1(1 - e^{-2.3x})$	0.00	0.406	0.662	0.823	0.925	0.990

The curves drawn using values from this table are shown in fig. B2.3.

The solution of the simultaneous equations is given by locating the point where the curves cross. Referring to fig. B2.3, we see that they cross at the point $(0.43, 0.69)$. The solution of the equations is therefore $x = 0.43$, $y = 0.69$.

49

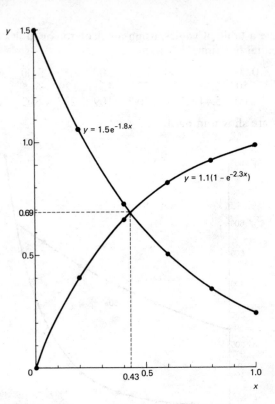

Fig. B2.3

The graph shows two curves: $y = 1.5e^{-1.8x}$ (decay) and $y = 1.1(1 - e^{-2.3x})$ (growth), intersecting near $x = 0.43$, $y = 0.69$.

B2.2 Practical examples of growth and decay
In this section we shall deal graphically and algebraically with practical examples of exponential growth and decay taken from various branches of engineering and science.

Exponential growth defined by $y = a\,e^{bx}$ and $y = a(1 - e^{-bx})$
a) The electrical resistance R of some materials increases as the temperature θ increases according to a law of the form $R = a\,e^{b\theta}$.
b) Bacterial growth is exponential under certain conditions, so that N, the number of bacteria at time t, is given by a natural-growth law of the form $N = a\,e^{bt}$.
c) Materials which increase in length with increasing temperature will do so such that length l at temperature θ is given by $l = a\,e^{b\theta}$.
d) The tension on the tight side of a belt drive is related to ϕ, the angle of lap, by an equation of the form $F = a\,e^{b\phi}$.
e) The current i in an inductive circuit grows with increasing time t to a value given by $i = a(1 - e^{-bt/L})$, where L is the inductance.
f) The instantaneous potential difference v across a capacitor at time t, as it is charged, is given by $v = a(1 - e^{-bt/C})$, where C is the capacitance.

50

Example 1   An aluminium-alloy bush in a jet engine has length $l_0 = 53.30$ mm at $0\,°C$. Find the increase in the length of the bush when the temperature is raised to $290\,°C$, if the length l at temperature θ is given by $l = l_0\,e^{\alpha\theta}$, where α is the coefficient of linear expansion for the alloy and is $21 \times 10^{-6}/°C$.

Substituting the given values into the natural-growth law,

$$l = l_0\,e^{\alpha\theta}$$

$$= 53.30\,e^{(21 \times 10^{-6} \times 290)}$$

$$= 53.63\text{ mm}$$

i.e. the bush will increase in length by 0.33 mm.

Example 2   A coil having a resistance $R = 15$ ohms and an inductance $L = 2.5$ henrys is connected to a 12 volt d.c. supply. The current i in the coil t seconds after connection is given by the equation

$$i = \frac{V}{R}(1 - e^{-Rt/L})$$

Draw a graph showing the increase in current during the first 0.8 seconds. Use the graph to show that the current will reach 50% of its final value when $t = 0.693L/R$.

Substituting the given values into the formula defining the exponential growth of current in the coil,

$$i = \frac{12}{15}(1 - e^{-15t/2.5}) = 0.8(1 - e^{-6t})$$

We construct a table of values of i for a range $t = 0$ s to $t = 0.8$ s (note that the time intervals chosen here are shorter during the initial period when current changes are most rapid):

t	0.00	0.05	0.10	0.15	0.20	0.30	0.50	0.80
i	0.00	0.207	0.361	0.475	0.559	0.668	0.760	0.793

Figure B2.4 shows the graph of current against time drawn from the table of values.

It is clear that the graph is tending towards a final value of 0.800 A, since i approaches the value $V/R = 12/15 = 0.800$ as t becomes very large. A line drawn from the vertical axis at $i = 0.40$ A across to the curve and down to the horizontal axis at $t = 0.116$ s shows that the current in the coil will reach 50% of its final value when $t = 0.693L/R$, since

$$\frac{0.693L}{R} = \frac{0.693 \times 2.5}{15} = 0.116$$

51

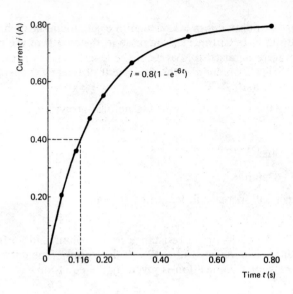

Fig. B2.4 The growth of current in a coil

The result can be checked by substituting $i = 0.40$ A into the equation

$$i = \frac{V}{R}(1 - e^{-Rt/L})$$

giving

$$i = \frac{12}{15}(1 - e^{-15t/2.5})$$

$$\therefore \quad e^{-15t/2.5} = 1 - \frac{15 \times 0.40}{12} = 0.50$$

$$\therefore \quad \frac{-15t}{2.5} = \ln 0.50 = -0.693$$

or $\qquad t = 0.116$ s

Exponential decay defined by $y = a\,e^{-bx}$
a) When a body cools, the temperature difference $\Delta\theta$ between the body and its surroundings at a time t is given by an equation of the form $\Delta\theta = a\,e^{-bt}$.
b) The voltage across a capacitor as it discharges will decay with time according to a law of the form $v = a\,e^{-bt}$.
c) Atmospheric pressure P decays as height h above the ground increases according to an equation $P = a\,e^{-bh}$.

52

d) **The** atomic decay of an initial quantity of a radioactive substance is exponential. The number of radioactive atoms remaining at a time t is given by an equation $N = a\,\mathrm{e}^{-bt}$.

e) When the current i in an inductive circuit is decreasing, we can calculate the value of i at a time t using an equation $i = a\,\mathrm{e}^{-bt}$.

Note that, in each of the examples of exponential growth and decay described, the constants a and b will be specific to the mechanical, electrical, chemical, or other type of process involved.

Example 3   Newton's law of cooling states that $\Delta\theta$, the temperature difference between a body and its surroundings, at a time t is given by $\Delta\theta = \Delta\theta_0\,\mathrm{e}^{-kt}$, where k is a constant and $\Delta\theta_0$ is the temperature of the body relative to its surroundings when $t = 0$. Find the reduction in temperature which takes place between $t = 100\,\mathrm{s}$ and $t = 250\,\mathrm{s}$ when a body cools from $\Delta\theta_0 = 59.0\,°\mathrm{C}$ if $k = 8.0 \times 10^{-4}$.

At $t = 100\,\mathrm{s}$, $\Delta\theta = 59.0\,\mathrm{e}^{-(8.0 \times 10^{-4} \times 100)}$

$\qquad\qquad\qquad = 54.5\,°\mathrm{C}$

At $t = 250\,\mathrm{s}$, $\Delta\theta = 59.0\,\mathrm{e}^{-(8.0 \times 10^{-4} \times 250)}$

$\qquad\qquad\qquad = 48.3\,°\mathrm{C}$

There is therefore a temperature drop of $6.2\,°\mathrm{C}$ during the period between $100\,\mathrm{s}$ and $250\,\mathrm{s}$ after the start of cooling.

Example 4   A coil with inductance L and resistance R is connected as shown in fig. B2.5. The switch is moved from A to B so that the current i falls according to the equation $i = I\,\mathrm{e}^{-Rt/L}$, where $I = V/R = 0.273\,\mathrm{A}$ (the original current in the coil with the switch at A). Draw a graph of i against t and estimate the rate of change of current when $t = 0.15\,\mathrm{s}$.

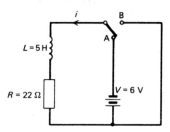

Fig. B2.5

A table of values for i and t is shown below:

t	0.00	0.05	0.10	0.15	0.20	0.25	0.30
i	0.273	0.219	0.176	0.141	0.113	0.091	0.073

The graph of i against t drawn from these points is shown in fig. B2.6.

53

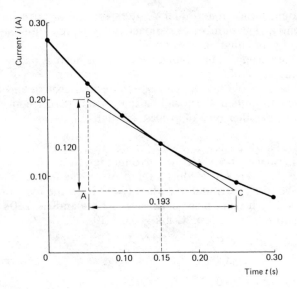

Fig. B2.6

Drawing a triangle ABC, where BC is the tangent to the curve at $t = 0.15\,\text{s}$, we find the slope of the line as follows:

$$\text{slope of BC} = -(\text{AB/AC}) = -(0.120/0.193) = -0.62$$

At $t = 0.15\,\text{s}$ the current is therefore decreasing at the rate of $0.62\,\text{A/s}$.

We can check this answer using differential calculus, since the rate of change of current with time is given by $\text{d}i/\text{d}t$.

Now $\quad i = I\,\text{e}^{-Rt/L}$

$$\therefore \quad \frac{\text{d}i}{\text{d}t} = \frac{-RI}{L}\,\text{e}^{-Rt/L} \quad \text{(see section C3)}$$

When $t = 0.15\,\text{s}$,

$$\frac{\text{d}i}{\text{d}t} = \frac{-22 \times 0.273}{5}\,\text{e}^{-(22 \times 0.15/5)} = -0.62\,\text{A/s}$$

This confirms our value from the graph.

B2.3 Using log–linear graph paper
In section B1.3 we used log–log graph paper (graph paper on which both horizontal and vertical scales are logarithmic) to save time when plotting graphs from equations of the form $y = ax^n$. Log–linear graph

54

paper, on which only one scale is logarithmic, can be used with the same advantage to draw graphs of $y = a\,e^{bx}$ and other exponential equations.

Taking logarithms of both sides of the equation $y = a\,e^{bx}$ gives

$$\log y = bx \log e + \log a$$

Now log e is a constant (i.e. log 2.7183 = 0.4343), so plotting x against log y will give a straight line with slope $b \log e$.

Figure B2.7 shows the graph of $y = 2.4\,e^{0.41x}$ drawn on log–linear graph paper using values from the following table:

x	0.00	1.50	3.00	4.50	6.00	7.50
y	2.40	4.44	8.21	15.2	28.1	52.0

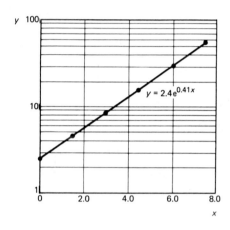

Fig. B2.7 The graph of $y = 2.4\,e^{0.41x}$ on log–linear graph paper

The advantages of using straight-line graphs in experimental work have been outlined in previous sections. A straight-line graph drawn using data thought to relate to a function of the form $y = a\,e^{bx}$ or $y = a(1 - e^{-bx})$ can be used to find the values of a and b.

Example 1 A drive belt makes contact with a pulley over an angle $\phi = 3.6\,\text{rad}$. The tension on the tight side of the belt is given by $F = F_0\,e^{\mu\phi}$, where F_0 is the tension on the slack side of the belt and μ is the coefficient of friction. Draw a graph using log–linear graph paper to show how F may be increased as μ increases from 0.20 to 0.45 with $F_0 = 120\,\text{newtons}$ and a constant. What value of μ does the graph indicate would be necessary for a belt tension $F = 450\,\text{N}$ under these conditions?

55

Substituting known values into the formula $F = F_0\,e^{\mu\phi}$ over the range of values specified for the coefficient of friction gives the following table of values:

μ	0.20	0.25	0.30	0.35	0.40	0.45
F (N)	246.1	295.1	353.4	423.1	506.5	606.4

The values from this table are plotted on log–linear graph paper in fig. B2.8.

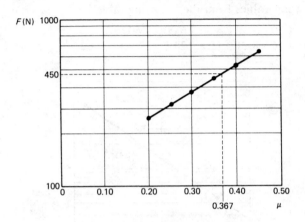

Fig. B2.8 The graph of $F = 120\,e^{3.6\mu}$ on log–linear graph paper

From the graph, the coefficient of friction corresponding to $F = 450\,\text{N}$ is $\mu = 0.367$. Note that this value can be confirmed as follows.

When $F = 450\,\text{N}$, $\quad 450 = 120\,e^{3.6\mu}$

Taking logarithms of both sides,

$$\log 450 = 3.6\mu \log e + \log 120$$
$$\therefore \quad 2.653 = 1.563\mu + 2.079$$
$$\therefore \quad \mu = 0.367$$

Example 2 During an experiment in which a capacitor C was discharged from an initial voltage E through a resistor $R = 330\,\text{k}\Omega$, measurements of voltage v against time t were as follows:

t (s)	5.00	10.0	15.0	20.0	25.0	30.0
v (V)	8.51	4.93	2.70	1.66	0.901	0.515

The voltage v at a time t is given by the equation $v = E\,e^{-t/RC}$. Draw a graph of v against t on log–linear graph paper and use it to find the values of E and C.

56

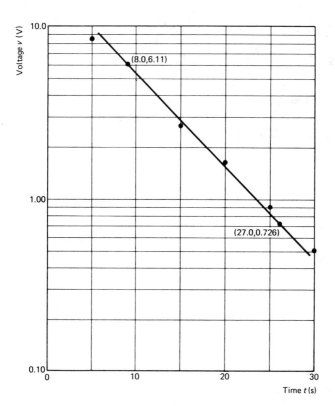

Fig. B2.9 The discharge of a capacitor shown on log–linear graph paper

Drawing the best line through the points on log–linear graph paper gives the graph in fig. B2.9.

Taking two points, (8.0, 6.11) and (27.0, 0.726), which lie on the line, we substitute these values of v and t into the logarithmic form of the equation $v = E\,e^{-t/CR}$:

$$\log v = \frac{-t}{CR} \log e + \log E$$

At $(8.0, 6.11)$,

$$\log 6.11 = \frac{-8}{CR} \log e + \log E$$

which, since $R = 3.30 \times 10^5\,\Omega$, gives

$$0.786 = \frac{-1.05 \times 10^{-5}}{C} + \log E \tag{i}$$

At (27, 0.726),

$$\log 0.726 = \frac{-27}{CR} \log e + \log E$$

or $\quad -0.139 = \dfrac{-3.55 \times 10^{-5}}{C} + \log E \qquad\qquad$ (ii)

Subtracting (ii) from (i),

$$0.925 = \frac{2.5 \times 10^{-5}}{C}$$

$\therefore \qquad C = 2.7 \times 10^{-5}$

Substituting this value for C in (i),

$$0.786 = \frac{-1.05 \times 10^{-5}}{2.70 \times 10^{-5}} + \log E$$

$\therefore \qquad E = 14.96$

i.e. the capacitor value is $27\,\mu\text{F}$ and the initial voltage was $15\,\text{V}$.

Exercise B2

1 Plot the graph of s against t using the following table of values from an equation $s = a\,e^{bt}$. Draw a tangent to the curve at $t = 1.15$ and measure its slope. Show that the slope of the curve is equal to $0.45s$ at that point.

t	0.00	0.25	0.50	0.75	1.00	1.25	1.50	1.75
s	58.0	64.9	72.6	81.3	91.0	102	114	127

2 Use values from the following table to draw the curves $y = a\,e^{bx}$ and $z = c\,e^{-dx}$ with the same axes. At what point do the curves cross?

x	1.00	1.40	1.80	2.20	2.60	3.00
y	4.45	6.13	8.44	11.6	16.0	22.1
z	15.1	9.32	5.77	3.57	2.21	1.37

3 In an experiment to study the growth of bacteria, measurements of the number of bacteria N over a range of time t were made. A straight-line graph of $\log N$ against t had a slope of 3.51×10^{-3} and crossed the $\log N$ axis at $(0, 2.11)$. If $N = N_0\,e^{kt}$, find values for N_0 and k.

4 Plot values of $\log y$ against x from the following table of results. Show that $y = a\,e^{bx}$ and use your graph to find a and b.

x	2.50	3.50	4.50	5.50	6.50	7.50
y	21.5	87.3	354	1440	5820	23 600

5 The resistance of a coil of copper wire at $0\,°C$ is $R_0 = 470\,\Omega$. As the temperature θ increases, resistance R is given by $R = R_0\,e^{\alpha\theta}$, where $\alpha = 0.0043/°C$ (the temperature coefficient of resistance of copper). Find the temperature at which the resistance will be $485\,\Omega$ and the resistance of the coil when $\theta = 15.5\,°C$.

6 Plot the following points on log–linear graph paper to show that $y = a\,e^{bx}$. Find the values of a and b using the graph.

x	0.10	0.20	0.40	0.80	1.60
y	1.49	1.93	3.25	9.21	73.7

7 The following measurements of voltage v in a capacitive circuit were recorded during an experiment:

Time t (s)	15.0	20.0	25.0	35.0	45.0	60.0
Voltage v (V)	2.88	2.66	2.07	1.62	1.11	0.713

It is known that $v = V\,e^{-t/CR}$, where $R = 300\,k\Omega$. Plot values of v against t on log–linear graph paper and draw the best straight line through these points. Obtain values of V (in volts) and C (in microfarads) using your graph.

B3 Matrices and determinants

B3.1 Matrix notation

A *matrix* is a two-dimensional array which can be used to depict information of many kinds. The following matrix A is a 3×2 matrix (we say 'three *by* two') since it has three *rows* and two *columns*:

$$A = \begin{pmatrix} a_{11} & a_{12} \\ a_{21} & a_{22} \\ a_{31} & a_{32} \end{pmatrix}$$

We shall use curved brackets on all our matrices.

In matrix A we have six *elements* labelled a_{mn}, where subscript m denotes the row and n denotes the column in which the element is located. Thus, a_{31} lies in row three and in column one. The elements can have numerical values, as in the 2×2 matrix B and the 2×1 matrix C which follow:

$$B = \begin{pmatrix} 1 & 0 \\ 3 & 4 \end{pmatrix} \quad \text{and} \quad C = \begin{pmatrix} 2 \\ 5 \end{pmatrix}$$

The matrix itself does not have a value, being simply an arrangement of elements in rows and columns. (Note that a matrix with a single column is called a *column vector*, while a single-row matrix is known as a *row vector*.

Consider two football teams A and B, both having played eight games. Team A has won three, drawn four, and lost one game; while team B has lost all eight games. We can show the performance of the two teams in the form of a matrix, as follows:

	Won	Drawn	Lost
Team A	3	4	1
Team B	0	0	8

Each row of the matrix refers to a particular team, while the columns give information about wins, draws, and losses. For example, we can quickly determine that there has been a total of four draws by adding the elements in column two. Referring to the written summary of the performance of the two teams, we can see that numerical information expressed in the form of a matrix is much more accessible than when it is contained in descriptive sentences containing a series of numbers.

Example During one year of a course at a college, a student studies five units in different subjects. For each unit there are four tests which account for different percentages of the overall assessment. These percentages are as follows: mathematics $20, 25, 20, 35$; physical science $25, 20, 25, 30$; engineering drawing $20, 30, 25, 25$; electronics $20, 20, 30, 30$; and communications $15, 20, 25, 40$. Arrange this information in the form of a 5×4 matrix.

As the dimensions of the matrix have been defined, we shall have one row for each subject studied by the student and one column for each test. The matrix is shown below:

$$\begin{pmatrix} 20 & 25 & 20 & 35 \\ 25 & 20 & 25 & 30 \\ 20 & 30 & 25 & 25 \\ 20 & 20 & 30 & 30 \\ 15 & 20 & 25 & 40 \end{pmatrix}$$

One reason for the growing importance of matrices is that they provide an excellent way of presenting large amounts of data in a form which a computer can manipulate easily and quickly.

B3.2 Addition and subtraction of matrices
In the following sections dealing with matrix arithmetic we shall confine ourselves to examples of 2×2 matrices, although the rules which we use can be extended easily to matrices of any size. Students will find that manipulation of large matrices can be laborious and that some of the methods discussed are suitable for computer application only.

Consider the following two matrices added together:

$$\begin{pmatrix} 2 & 5 \\ 6 & 3 \end{pmatrix} + \begin{pmatrix} 1 & 4 \\ 7 & 8 \end{pmatrix} = \begin{pmatrix} 3 & 9 \\ 13 & 11 \end{pmatrix}$$

It is clear that the addition is carried out by finding the sum of elements in corresponding positions in the two matrices; so that $2 + 1 = 3$, $5 + 4 = 9$, $6 + 7 = 13$, and $3 + 8 = 11$.

In general, to add two matrices A and B where

$$A = \begin{pmatrix} a_{11} & a_{12} \\ a_{21} & a_{22} \end{pmatrix} \quad \text{and} \quad B = \begin{pmatrix} b_{11} & b_{12} \\ b_{21} & b_{22} \end{pmatrix}$$

the sum of these is the 2×2 matrix

$$\begin{pmatrix} a_{11} + b_{11} & a_{12} + b_{12} \\ a_{21} + b_{21} & a_{22} + b_{22} \end{pmatrix}$$

Note that we can only add an $m \times n$ matrix to another $m \times n$ matrix, and that, when we do, the result will also be an $m \times n$ matrix.

Subtraction is carried out similarly by subtracting corresponding elements, and again the two matrices must have the same dimensions.

Example 1   Find $A + B$ and $A - B$ if

$$A = \begin{pmatrix} 7 & 4 \\ 3 & 5 \end{pmatrix} \quad \text{and} \quad B = \begin{pmatrix} 6 & -2 \\ 1 & 8 \end{pmatrix}$$

$$A + B = \begin{pmatrix} 7 & 4 \\ 3 & 5 \end{pmatrix} + \begin{pmatrix} 6 & -2 \\ 1 & 8 \end{pmatrix} = \begin{pmatrix} 13 & 2 \\ 4 & 13 \end{pmatrix}$$

$$A - B = \begin{pmatrix} 7 & 4 \\ 3 & 5 \end{pmatrix} - \begin{pmatrix} 6 & -2 \\ 1 & 8 \end{pmatrix} = \begin{pmatrix} 1 & 6 \\ 2 & -3 \end{pmatrix}$$

Example 2   An airline has two flights to New York on Saturdays. The first, from London, has 24 first-class seats and 372 economy-class seats; the second flight, from Manchester, has 20 first-class and 137 economy-class seats. The same airline also operates two flights to New York on Sundays from the same airports, and the seating on these flights consists of 28 first-class on the London flight and 8 first-class on the Manchester flight, with 376 and 117 economy-class seats from London and Manchester respectively. Show the total weekend capacity of these flights as the sum of two 2×2 matrices, one for each day.

We can represent seating on the Saturday flights as a 2×2 matrix A with rows representing the flights and columns showing first-class and economy-class seating. Thus

$$A = \begin{pmatrix} 24 & 372 \\ 20 & 137 \end{pmatrix}$$

Similarly for the two Sunday flights:

$$B = \begin{pmatrix} 28 & 376 \\ 8 & 117 \end{pmatrix}$$

The total number of seats over the weekend can be shown by adding matrices A and B to give a third 2×2 matrix with rows which give totals for each airport and columns which show total numbers of seats in first-class and economy-class:

$$\begin{pmatrix} 24 & 372 \\ 20 & 137 \end{pmatrix} + \begin{pmatrix} 28 & 376 \\ 8 & 117 \end{pmatrix} = \begin{pmatrix} 52 & 748 \\ 28 & 254 \end{pmatrix}$$

B3.3 Matrix multiplication

Consider the 2×2 matrices A and B:

$$A = \begin{pmatrix} a_{11} & a_{12} \\ a_{21} & a_{22} \end{pmatrix} \quad \text{and} \quad B = \begin{pmatrix} b_{11} & b_{12} \\ b_{21} & b_{22} \end{pmatrix}$$

We multiply them together as follows to give another 2×2 matrix:

$$C = AB = \begin{pmatrix} a_{11} & a_{12} \\ a_{21} & a_{22} \end{pmatrix} \times \begin{pmatrix} b_{11} & b_{12} \\ b_{21} & b_{22} \end{pmatrix}$$

$$= \begin{pmatrix} a_{11}b_{11} + a_{12}b_{21} & a_{11}b_{12} + a_{12}b_{22} \\ a_{21}b_{11} + a_{22}b_{21} & a_{21}b_{12} + a_{22}b_{22} \end{pmatrix}$$

We can see from this result that, to find the element in the first row and first column of matrix C, we multiply elements in the first row of matrix A by elements in the first column of matrix B as shown to give $a_{11}b_{11} + a_{12}b_{21}$. Other elements in matrix C are found by performing similar operations with corresponding rows and columns.

Matrices to be multiplied together need not have the same dimensions, nor do they have to be square matrices. We can multiply any $m \times n$ matrix A by any $n \times p$ matrix B to give the $m \times p$ matrix $C = AB$. It is essential that *the number of columns in* A *is the same as the number of rows in* B.

Example 1 Find AB and AC if

$$A = \begin{pmatrix} 2 & 9 \\ 1 & 4 \end{pmatrix} \quad B = \begin{pmatrix} 8 & 3 \\ 7 & 6 \end{pmatrix} \quad \text{and} \quad C = \begin{pmatrix} 11 \\ -5 \end{pmatrix}$$

$$AB = \begin{pmatrix} 2 & 9 \\ 1 & 4 \end{pmatrix} \begin{pmatrix} 8 & 3 \\ 7 & 6 \end{pmatrix}$$

$$= \begin{pmatrix} (2 \times 8 + 9 \times 7) & (2 \times 3 + 9 \times 6) \\ (1 \times 8 + 4 \times 7) & (1 \times 3 + 4 \times 6) \end{pmatrix} = \begin{pmatrix} 79 & 60 \\ 36 & 27 \end{pmatrix}$$

$$AC = \begin{pmatrix} 2 & 9 \\ 1 & 4 \end{pmatrix} \begin{pmatrix} 11 \\ -5 \end{pmatrix}$$

$$= \begin{pmatrix} (2 \times 11 + 9 \times -5) \\ (1 \times 11 + 4 \times -5) \end{pmatrix} = \begin{pmatrix} -23 \\ -9 \end{pmatrix}$$

Note that it is impossible to perform the multiplication CA, since there is only one column in matrix C but there are two rows in matrix A.

Example 2 Matrix Q is used to show the distribution of carbon and hydrogen atoms in molecules of methane (CH_4) and benzene (C_6H_6). Matrix P contains the relative atomic masses of carbon (12) and hydrogen (1). Show how matrix multiplication can give the relative molecular masses of methane and benzene in a third matrix R.

From the information given,

$$Q = \begin{pmatrix} 1 & 4 \\ 6 & 6 \end{pmatrix} \quad \text{and} \quad P = \begin{pmatrix} 12 \\ 1 \end{pmatrix}$$

Since Q is a 2×2 matrix and P is a 2×1 matrix, we can multiply them together to give $R = QP$ (i.e. the condition that the number of columns in Q = the number of rows in P is satisfied). Thus

$$R = QP = \begin{pmatrix} 1 & 4 \\ 6 & 6 \end{pmatrix} \begin{pmatrix} 12 \\ 1 \end{pmatrix} = \begin{pmatrix} 16 \\ 78 \end{pmatrix}$$

i.e. the relative molecular masses of methane and benzene are 16 and 78 respectively.

Matrix multiplication is, in general, non-commutative

We are familiar with the commutative nature of numerical multiplication whereby the order in which we write the numbers to be multiplied is of no importance (i.e. $3 \times 6 = 6 \times 3$). The multiplication of algebraic expressions is also commutative ($xyz = yxz = zxy$, etc.). Matrix multiplication is not generally commutative, and so we must take care to multiply matrices in the correct order.

Consider the following matrices A and B:

$$A = \begin{pmatrix} 1 & 8 \\ 6 & 2 \end{pmatrix} \quad \text{and} \quad B = \begin{pmatrix} 4 & 7 \\ 5 & 3 \end{pmatrix}$$

We shall find the products AB, where matrix B is *premultiplied* by A, and BA, where matrix A is premultiplied by B.

$$\text{Let} \quad C = AB = \begin{pmatrix} 1 & 8 \\ 6 & 2 \end{pmatrix} \begin{pmatrix} 4 & 7 \\ 5 & 3 \end{pmatrix} = \begin{pmatrix} 44 & 31 \\ 34 & 48 \end{pmatrix}$$

$$\text{and} \quad D = BA = \begin{pmatrix} 4 & 7 \\ 5 & 3 \end{pmatrix} \begin{pmatrix} 1 & 8 \\ 6 & 2 \end{pmatrix} = \begin{pmatrix} 46 & 46 \\ 23 & 46 \end{pmatrix}$$

Matrices C and D are clearly different, demonstrating that, in this case at least, $AB \neq BA$.

The unit matrix

The *unit matrix* is any $n \times n$ square matrix in which all the elements on the *leading diagonal* (i.e. $a_{11}, a_{22}, a_{33}, a_{nn}$) are 1 while all other elements are 0. The 3×3 unit matrix I is shown below:

$$I = \begin{pmatrix} 1 & 0 & 0 \\ 0 & 1 & 0 \\ 0 & 0 & 1 \end{pmatrix}$$

Multiplying any square matrix A by the unit matrix with the same dimensions leaves matrix A unchanged. Thus $AI = IA = A$. For example,

if $\quad A = \begin{pmatrix} 2 & 3 \\ -5 & 6 \end{pmatrix}$

then $\quad AI = \begin{pmatrix} 2 & 3 \\ -5 & 6 \end{pmatrix} \begin{pmatrix} 1 & 0 \\ 0 & 1 \end{pmatrix} = \begin{pmatrix} 2 & 3 \\ -5 & 6 \end{pmatrix} = A$

and $\quad IA = \begin{pmatrix} 1 & 0 \\ 0 & 1 \end{pmatrix} \begin{pmatrix} 2 & 3 \\ -5 & 6 \end{pmatrix} = \begin{pmatrix} 2 & 3 \\ -5 & 6 \end{pmatrix} = A$

Multiplying by the unit matrix is therefore an exception to the rule that matrix multiplication is non-commutative.

B3.4 Determinants

The *determinant D* shown below looks like a matrix with straight lines used instead of brackets:

$$D = \begin{vmatrix} 4 & 6 \\ 2 & 8 \end{vmatrix}$$

However, determinants are not simply arrays of numbers but a way of writing down expressions (often from simultaneous equations). A determinant, unlike a matrix, has a value. In the case of D above,

$$D = \begin{vmatrix} 4 & 6 \\ 2 & 8 \end{vmatrix} = 20$$

We shall see how to carry out this evaluation later.

Determinants are always square (i.e. they have the same number of rows as columns), and, rather than speak of 2×2 or 3×3 determinants, it is usual to refer to second- and third-*order* determinants.

We are often required to use the determinant of a matrix. The determinant of matrix A is expressed as det A or $|A|$. For example,

if $\quad$ matrix $A = \begin{pmatrix} 5 & -7 \\ 3 & 0 \end{pmatrix}$ $\quad$ then $\quad |A| = \begin{vmatrix} 5 & 7 \\ 3 & 0 \end{vmatrix}$

Since all determinants are square, we can define $|A|$ only when matrix A is square.

The evaluation of determinants

As in previous sections, we shall limit ourselves to 2×2 (second-order) determinants. Consider the general determinant G, where

$$G = \begin{vmatrix} a_{11} & a_{12} \\ a_{21} & a_{22} \end{vmatrix}$$

To find the value of G, we multiply the elements on the *principal diagonal* together and subtract from this the product of the remaining two elements. Thus

$$\begin{vmatrix} a_{11} & a_{12} \\ a_{21} & a_{22} \end{vmatrix} = a_{11}a_{22} - a_{12}a_{21}$$

The method outlined here for evaluating a second-order determinant does not define completely the general method for the evaluation of all determinants including those of higher order. To find the value of G above, we have in fact *expanded the determinant about the first row*. Elements a_{22} and a_{21} are known as the *minors* of elements a_{11} and a_{12} respectively. Finding the minor of an element in a higher order determinant can be a lengthy process and need not concern us here.

Returning to the determinant D used earlier,

$$|D| = \begin{vmatrix} 4 & 6 \\ 2 & 8 \end{vmatrix} = (4 \times 8) - (6 \times 2) = 20$$

Example   Find the value of $|P|$, where matrix $P = \begin{pmatrix} -2 & 3 \\ 6 & 11 \end{pmatrix}$.

The determinant of matrix P is evaluated as follows:

$$|P| = \begin{vmatrix} -2 & 3 \\ 6 & 11 \end{vmatrix} = (-2 \times 11) - (3 \times 6) = -40$$

Exercise B3

1   Define the following terms as applied to matrices: (a) element, (b) column vector, (c) unit matrix.

2   A motor manufacturer produces a vehicle which is available in four versions. These vary in the number of doors, seats, and engine cylinders. The saloon has four doors, five seats, and four cylinders. The estate has five doors, five seats, and six cylinders. The sports car has two doors, two seats, and six cylinders. The van has three doors, two seats, and four cylinders. Express this numerical information as a 4×3 matrix.

3 Add the following matrices where possible.

(a) $\begin{pmatrix} 6 & 2 \\ 1 & 4 \end{pmatrix} + \begin{pmatrix} 2 & 5 \\ 7 & 3 \end{pmatrix}$

(b) $\begin{pmatrix} 5 & -4 \\ 2 & 0 \end{pmatrix} + \begin{pmatrix} 1 & -8 \\ -2 & 11 \end{pmatrix}$

(c) $\begin{pmatrix} 2 \\ 3 \\ 4 \end{pmatrix} + \begin{pmatrix} -7 \\ 0 \\ 6 \end{pmatrix}$

(d) $\begin{pmatrix} 5 & -4 \\ 2 & 1 \end{pmatrix} + (6 \quad -5 \quad -4)$

(e) $\begin{pmatrix} 3.2 & 6.1 \\ -8.1 & -2.5 \end{pmatrix} + \begin{pmatrix} 5.9 & -11.3 \\ 7.6 & 6.2 \end{pmatrix}$

(f) $(-9 \quad 6 \quad 11 \quad) + (2 \quad 8 \quad 5)$

(g) $(8 \quad 1 \quad 3) + \begin{pmatrix} 6 \\ 4 \\ 9 \end{pmatrix}$

(h) $\begin{pmatrix} a & 2b \\ c & d \end{pmatrix} + \begin{pmatrix} 2c & 3b \\ -a & -2d \end{pmatrix}$

4 Carry out the following matrix subtractions where possible.

(a) $\begin{pmatrix} 12 & 5 \\ 8 & 6 \end{pmatrix} - \begin{pmatrix} 4 & 3 \\ 7 & 9 \end{pmatrix}$

(b) $\begin{pmatrix} 8.1 & 6.5 \\ 4.3 & 9.9 \end{pmatrix} - \begin{pmatrix} -11.2 & 3.6 \\ 0 & -2.7 \end{pmatrix}$

(c) $(3.6 \quad 2.2) - \begin{pmatrix} 1.5 \\ 4.8 \end{pmatrix}$

(d) $\begin{pmatrix} 1.9 \\ 7.5 \end{pmatrix} - \begin{pmatrix} 6.6 \\ -3.2 \end{pmatrix}$

(e) $\begin{pmatrix} 2x & y \\ 3x & 4y \end{pmatrix} - \begin{pmatrix} 6x & x \\ 3y & 2y \end{pmatrix}$

5 If matrix $A = \begin{pmatrix} 2 & 6 \\ 5 & 9 \end{pmatrix}$ and $B = \begin{pmatrix} 1 & 4 \\ 8 & -7 \end{pmatrix}$, find (a) $A + B$, (b) $A - B$, (c) AB, (d) BA.

6 Multiply the following matrices together where possible.

(a) $\begin{pmatrix} 2 & 1 \\ 3 & 4 \end{pmatrix} \times \begin{pmatrix} 5 & 0 \\ 8 & 6 \end{pmatrix}$

(b) $\begin{pmatrix} 8 & 4 \\ 6 & 5 \end{pmatrix} \times \begin{pmatrix} 2 \\ 1 \end{pmatrix}$

(c) $\begin{pmatrix} 3 & 2 \\ -4 & -1 \end{pmatrix} \times \begin{pmatrix} 6 & 8 \\ 5 & -7 \end{pmatrix}$ (d) $\begin{pmatrix} 3 \\ 5 \end{pmatrix} \times \begin{pmatrix} 6 & 4 \\ 5 & 8 \end{pmatrix}$

(e) $\begin{pmatrix} -8.1 & 5.5 \\ -2.3 & 7.1 \end{pmatrix} \times \begin{pmatrix} -2.6 \\ 8.5 \end{pmatrix}$

(f) $\begin{pmatrix} 7.2 & -4.8 \\ 11.2 & 5.6 \end{pmatrix} \times \begin{pmatrix} 2.6 & -1.4 \\ 0.7 & -6.1 \end{pmatrix}$

(g) $\begin{pmatrix} 1 & 1 \\ 2 & 2 \end{pmatrix} \times \begin{pmatrix} -1 & 1 \\ 1 & -1 \end{pmatrix}$ (h) $\begin{pmatrix} x & 2x \\ x^2 & 3x^2 \end{pmatrix} \times \begin{pmatrix} 4x \\ -x \end{pmatrix}$

7 Show that $AI = IA = A$, where $A = \begin{pmatrix} 6 & 8 \\ 2 & 3 \end{pmatrix}$ and $I = \begin{pmatrix} 1 & 0 \\ 0 & 1 \end{pmatrix}$.

8 Evaluate the following determinants:

(a) $\begin{vmatrix} 1 & 3 \\ 5 & 2 \end{vmatrix}$ (b) $\begin{vmatrix} 2 & 6 \\ -3 & 4 \end{vmatrix}$ (c) $\begin{vmatrix} 8 & -6 \\ -9 & 11 \end{vmatrix}$

(d) $\begin{vmatrix} x & -2x \\ x^2 & 3x^2 \end{vmatrix}$ (e) $\begin{vmatrix} 2.10 & -3.80 \\ 7.20 & 11.50 \end{vmatrix}$,   (f) $\begin{vmatrix} 4 & 0 \\ 3 & 7 \end{vmatrix}$

(g) $\begin{vmatrix} \sin 30° & \cos 30° \\ \sin 60° & \cos 60° \end{vmatrix}$ (h) $\begin{vmatrix} 3.60 & 4.70 \\ -2.20 & 0.00 \end{vmatrix}$

B4 Using matrices and determinants to solve simultaneous equations

B4.1 The inverse of a matrix

The *inverse* of a square matrix A is written A^{-1} and can be used to solve simultaneous equations. We shall now consider the three steps involved in finding the inverse of a matrix and look at a quick way to deal with 2×2 matrices. Before starting, we should note that it is possible to find the inverse of *square matrices only* and, furthermore, the determinant of the matrix must have a *non-zero value* (we say the matrix must be *non-singular*). The reasons for these limitations should become clear as we proceed.

To find A^{-1} when $A = \begin{pmatrix} 3 & 1 \\ 2 & 4 \end{pmatrix}$ we proceed as follows.

Step 1 We replace each element of the matrix with its *cofactor*. In the case of a 2×2 matrix, this is a simple process. We exchange elements diagonally and then change the sign of the element in row 1 column 2 and the element in row 2 column 1. The resulting matrix is the *matrix of cofactors*:

$$\begin{pmatrix} 4 & -2 \\ -1 & 3 \end{pmatrix}$$

(For larger matrices this step can take a long time. A complete analysis of the process is beyond the scope of this book.)

Step 2 We *transpose* the matrix of cofactors. To do this, row 1 becomes column 1 and row 2 becomes column 2. (In a larger $n \times n$ matrix, this exchange of rows and columns continues until row n becomes column n). The resulting matrix is known as the *adjoint* of the original matrix A, or adj A.

$$\therefore \quad \text{adj } A = \begin{pmatrix} 4 & -1 \\ -2 & 3 \end{pmatrix}$$

Note that the transpose of a matrix M can be written M'.

Step 3 To complete the process of finding the inverse of the matrix A, we divide the adjoint by the determinant of the matrix A. Thus

$$A^{-1} = \frac{\text{adj } A}{|A|}$$

where $|A| = \begin{vmatrix} 3 & 1 \\ 2 & 4 \end{vmatrix} = 12 - 2 = 10$

$$\therefore \quad A^{-1} = \frac{1}{10} \begin{pmatrix} 4 & -1 \\ -2 & 3 \end{pmatrix} = \begin{pmatrix} 0.4 & -0.1 \\ -0.2 & 0.3 \end{pmatrix}$$

From the above result we can deduce a quick method by which we can invert any 2×2 matrix. Comparing the matrix A with its adjoint,

$$A = \begin{pmatrix} 3 & 1 \\ 2 & 4 \end{pmatrix} \quad \text{and} \quad \text{adj } A = \begin{pmatrix} 4 & -1 \\ -2 & 3 \end{pmatrix}$$

We can see that the elements 1 and 2 have remained in the same positions but have had their signs changed, while the elements 3 and 4 have changed positions and kept their original signs. The adjoint of any 2×2 matrix can be obtained in this way. Thus

if $M = \begin{pmatrix} a_{11} & a_{12} \\ a_{21} & a_{22} \end{pmatrix}$ then $\text{adj } M = \begin{pmatrix} a_{22} & -a_{12} \\ -a_{21} & a_{11} \end{pmatrix}$

It must be stressed that this short-cut does not provide a general method of finding the inverse of larger matrices, when each of the three steps identified must be carried out in full.

Example 1 Find the inverse of the matrix $Q = \begin{pmatrix} 5 & 4 \\ 6 & 8 \end{pmatrix}$.

$$\text{adj } Q = \begin{pmatrix} 8 & -4 \\ -6 & 5 \end{pmatrix} \quad \text{and} \quad |Q| = \begin{vmatrix} 5 & 4 \\ 6 & 8 \end{vmatrix} = (5 \times 8) - (6 \times 4) = 16$$

$$\therefore \quad Q^{-1} = \frac{\text{adj } Q}{|Q|} = \frac{1}{16} \begin{pmatrix} 8 & -4 \\ -6 & 5 \end{pmatrix} = \begin{pmatrix} 0.50 & -0.25 \\ -0.38 & 0.31 \end{pmatrix}$$

Example 2 If $R = \begin{pmatrix} 2.2 & -1.6 \\ 5.1 & -7.4 \end{pmatrix}$, find R^{-1}.

$$\text{adj } R = \begin{pmatrix} -7.4 & 1.6 \\ -5.1 & 2.2 \end{pmatrix} \quad \text{and} \quad |R| = \begin{vmatrix} 2.2 & -1.6 \\ 5.1 & -7.4 \end{vmatrix} = -8.12$$

$$\therefore \quad R^{-1} = \frac{1}{-8.12} \begin{pmatrix} -7.4 & 1.6 \\ -5.1 & 2.2 \end{pmatrix} = \begin{pmatrix} 0.91 & -0.20 \\ 0.63 & -0.27 \end{pmatrix}$$

When a matrix is multiplied by its inverse, the result is always the unit matrix I. Thus

$$A^{-1}A = AA^{-1} = I$$

For example, if $A = \begin{pmatrix} 6 & -3 \\ 5 & -2 \end{pmatrix}$,

$$\text{adj } A = \begin{pmatrix} -2 & 3 \\ -5 & 6 \end{pmatrix} \quad \text{and} \quad |A| = -12 - (-15) = 3$$

$$\therefore \quad A^{-1} = \begin{pmatrix} -\frac{2}{3} & 1 \\ -\frac{5}{3} & 2 \end{pmatrix}$$

and $\quad A^{-1}A = \begin{pmatrix} -\frac{2}{3} & 1 \\ -\frac{5}{3} & 2 \end{pmatrix} \begin{pmatrix} 6 & -3 \\ 5 & -2 \end{pmatrix} = \begin{pmatrix} 1 & 0 \\ 0 & 1 \end{pmatrix}$

We shall use this property in the next section when we solve simultaneous equations in matrix form.

B4.2 Simultaneous equations in matrix form

The solution of n simultaneous linear equations in n unknowns is an important application of matrices. For example, if we wish to find the values of x and y which satisfy the equations

$$2x + 5y = 4$$
$$x + 3y = 6$$

we can write the equations in matrix form as follows:

$$\begin{pmatrix} 2 & 5 \\ 1 & 3 \end{pmatrix} \begin{pmatrix} x \\ y \end{pmatrix} = \begin{pmatrix} 4 \\ 6 \end{pmatrix}$$

Note that, if the matrices on the l.h.s. are multiplied together, the equations revert to their original form.

The above matrix equation is of the form $AB = C$, and premultiplying both sides by A^{-1} gives $A^{-1}AB = A^{-1}C$. We know that $A^{-1}A = I$ (see section B4.1), where I is the unit matrix. Furthermore, we saw in section B3.3 that $IB = BI = B$. The equation simplifies to $B = A^{-1}C$, or, with the original matrices,

$$\begin{pmatrix} x \\ y \end{pmatrix} = \begin{pmatrix} 2 & 5 \\ 1 & 3 \end{pmatrix}^{-1} \begin{pmatrix} 4 \\ 6 \end{pmatrix}$$

Now $A^{-1} = \dfrac{\text{adj } A}{|A|}$ and, since A is a 2×2 matrix, we can use the simplified method from section B4.1 to find adj A:

$$\begin{pmatrix} x \\ y \end{pmatrix} = \frac{1}{1} \begin{pmatrix} 3 & -5 \\ -1 & 2 \end{pmatrix} \begin{pmatrix} 4 \\ 6 \end{pmatrix} = \begin{pmatrix} -18 \\ 8 \end{pmatrix}$$

i.e. the solution of the simultaneous equations is $x = -18$ and $y = 8$.

Check by substituting these values into both of the original equations:

$$(2 \times -18) + (5 \times 8) = 4$$
$$-18 \quad + (3 \times 8) = 6$$

Example 1   Find the point at which the line $x - 2y = -6$ crosses the line $6x - 4y = 5$.

The simultaneous equations are

$$x - 2y = -6$$
$$6x - 4y = 5$$

In matrix form, these become

$$\begin{pmatrix} 1 & -2 \\ 6 & -4 \end{pmatrix} \begin{pmatrix} x \\ y \end{pmatrix} = \begin{pmatrix} -6 \\ 5 \end{pmatrix}$$

$$\therefore \qquad \begin{pmatrix} x \\ y \end{pmatrix} = \begin{pmatrix} 1 & -2 \\ 6 & -4 \end{pmatrix}^{-1} \begin{pmatrix} -6 \\ 5 \end{pmatrix}$$

and $\qquad \begin{pmatrix} 1 & -2 \\ 6 & -4 \end{pmatrix}^{-1} = \frac{1}{8} \begin{pmatrix} -4 & 2 \\ -6 & 1 \end{pmatrix} = \begin{pmatrix} -\frac{1}{2} & \frac{1}{4} \\ -\frac{3}{4} & \frac{1}{8} \end{pmatrix}$

$$\therefore \quad \begin{pmatrix} x \\ y \end{pmatrix} = \begin{pmatrix} -\frac{1}{2} & \frac{1}{4} \\ -\frac{3}{4} & \frac{1}{8} \end{pmatrix} \begin{pmatrix} -6 \\ 5 \end{pmatrix} = \begin{pmatrix} 4.25 \\ 5.13 \end{pmatrix}$$

i.e. the lines cross at the point (4.25, 5.13).

Example 2 Analysis of the currents in each mesh of an electrical circuit, using Kirchhoff's law, gave the equations

$$1.45I_1 - 1.25I_2 = 12$$
$$1.35I_1 - 2.25I_2 = 6$$

Use a matrix method to find I_1 and I_2.

Expressing the equations in matrix form,

$$\begin{pmatrix} 1.45 & -1.25 \\ 1.35 & -2.25 \end{pmatrix} \begin{pmatrix} I_1 \\ I_2 \end{pmatrix} = \begin{pmatrix} 12 \\ 6 \end{pmatrix}$$

$$\therefore \quad \begin{pmatrix} I_1 \\ I_2 \end{pmatrix} = \begin{pmatrix} 1.45 & -1.25 \\ 1.35 & -2.25 \end{pmatrix}^{-1} \begin{pmatrix} 12 \\ 6 \end{pmatrix}$$

$$= \frac{1}{-1.58} \begin{pmatrix} -2.25 & 1.25 \\ -1.35 & 1.45 \end{pmatrix} \begin{pmatrix} 12 \\ 6 \end{pmatrix}$$

$$= \begin{pmatrix} 1.42 & -0.79 \\ 0.85 & -0.92 \end{pmatrix} \begin{pmatrix} 12 \\ 6 \end{pmatrix} = \begin{pmatrix} 12.3 \\ 4.68 \end{pmatrix}$$

i.e. the currents in the circuit are $I_1 = 12.3$ A and $I_2 = 4.68$ A.

We saw in the previous section that the inverse of a matrix A cannot exist if A is singular (i.e. if $|A| = 0$). Consider the equations

$$3s + 2t = 4$$
$$6s + 4t = 1$$

In matrix form,

$$\begin{pmatrix} 3 & 2 \\ 6 & 4 \end{pmatrix} \begin{pmatrix} s \\ t \end{pmatrix} = \begin{pmatrix} 4 \\ 1 \end{pmatrix}$$

Now $\begin{vmatrix} 3 & 2 \\ 6 & 4 \end{vmatrix} = 0$ and so the inverse does not exist.

Note that the straight lines represented by these equations are parallel and will therefore never cross.

B4.3 Using determinants to solve simultaneous equations

To solve two linear equations in two unknowns using determinants, the following procedure is adopted.

We write down the equations:

$$ax + by = c$$
$$dx + ey = f$$

Form a determinant Δ from the coefficients of x and y on the l.h.s. –

$$\Delta = \begin{vmatrix} a & b \\ d & e \end{vmatrix}$$

Values of x and y can be found using the following determinants derived from Δ:

$$\Delta_x = \begin{vmatrix} c & b \\ f & e \end{vmatrix} \quad \text{and} \quad \Delta_y = \begin{vmatrix} a & c \\ d & f \end{vmatrix}$$

In the determinant Δ_x, elements a and d (the coefficients of x) in Δ have been replaced by c and f. In the second determinant, Δ_y, elements b and e (the coefficients of y) have been replaced by c and f.

The solution is found by evaluating the following ratios of determinants:

$$x = \frac{\Delta_x}{\Delta} \quad \text{and} \quad y = \frac{\Delta_y}{\Delta}$$

These formulae are known as Cramer's rule and can be applied only when Δ is non-zero.

Example 1 Solve the simultaneous equations $5x - y = 7$ and $3x + 4y = 2$ using determinants.

$$5x - y = 7$$
$$3x + 4y = 2$$

From these equations,

$$\Delta = \begin{vmatrix} 5 & -1 \\ 3 & 4 \end{vmatrix} \qquad \Delta_x = \begin{vmatrix} 7 & -1 \\ 2 & 4 \end{vmatrix} \quad \text{and} \quad \Delta_y = \begin{vmatrix} 5 & 7 \\ 3 & 2 \end{vmatrix}$$

Using Cramer's rule,

$$x = \frac{\Delta_x}{\Delta} = \frac{30}{23} = 1.30$$

$$\text{and } y = \frac{\Delta_y}{\Delta} = \frac{-11}{23} = -0.48$$

72

Example 2 The effort E applied to a hydraulic jack is related to the load W by the equation $E = aW + b$. If a load of 42 N can be raised by an effort of 23 N and a load of 37 N requires an effort of 21 N, use Cramer's rule to find a and b.

Substituting the values given into the equation,

$$23 = 42a + b$$
$$21 = 37a + b$$

$$\therefore \quad \Delta = \begin{vmatrix} 42 & 1 \\ 37 & 1 \end{vmatrix} \quad \text{and} \quad \Delta_a = \begin{vmatrix} 23 & 1 \\ 21 & 1 \end{vmatrix} \quad \Delta_b = \begin{vmatrix} 42 & 23 \\ 37 & 21 \end{vmatrix}$$

From Cramer's rule,

$$a = \frac{\Delta_a}{\Delta} = \frac{2}{5} = 0.4$$

$$b = \frac{\Delta_b}{\Delta} = \frac{31}{5} = 6.2$$

While Cramer's rule provides a useful method of solving small numbers of simultaneous equations, the number of calculations involved increases rapidly as the number of equations increases. For example, it would take over 18 years for a computer capable of performing 100 000 multiplications per second to solve sixteen equations in sixteen unknowns using this determinant method!

Exercise B4

1 Find the inverse, where possible, of each of the following matrices:

(a) $\begin{pmatrix} 2 & 5 \\ 3 & 8 \end{pmatrix}$ (b) $\begin{pmatrix} 7 & -2 \\ -9 & 3 \end{pmatrix}$ (c) $\begin{pmatrix} -4 & 0 \\ -8 & 1 \end{pmatrix}$

(d) $\begin{pmatrix} 1.7 & 3.5 \\ 2.3 & 4.8 \end{pmatrix}$ (e) $\begin{pmatrix} 4 & 3 & 5 \\ 6 & 2 & 7 \end{pmatrix}$ (f) $\begin{pmatrix} x & x \\ -3x & -2x \end{pmatrix}$

(g) $\begin{pmatrix} -2.3 & 1.4 \\ -3.2 & 4.6 \end{pmatrix}$ (h) $\begin{pmatrix} 16 & 6 \\ -8 & -3 \end{pmatrix}$

2 The masses m_1 and m_2 in fig. B4.1 are supported by springs with stiffnesses k_1 and k_2. We can relate the accelerations of the masses to their displacements y_1 and y_2 with the equations

$$a_1 = -4y_1 + 3(y_2 - y_1)$$
$$a_2 = -3(y_2 - y_1)$$

Express these equations in matrix form as $a = Ay$, and find A^{-1}.

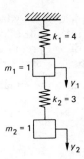

Fig. B4.1

3 Use a matrix method to solve the following pairs of simultaneous equations where possible:

(a) $6x - 7y = -2$
    $4x - 3y = 7$

(b) $3r + 5s = 18$
    $2r - 3s = 43$

(c) $4.2x + 5.1y = 1.7$
    $2.8x + 3.5y = 7.5$

(d) $3.5u - 1.4v = 6.7$
    $2.8v - 7.0u = -18.1$

4 Solve the following simultaneous equations, using a matrix method to find the currents I_1 and I_2 in the circuit in fig. B4.2:

$$8I_1 - 15I_2 = 0$$
$$5(I_1 + I_2) + 8I_1 = 12$$

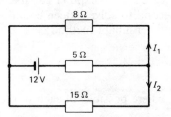

Fig. B4.2

5 A force F pulls a load of 115 N up a ramp inclined at 20° to the horizontal against a frictional force. The rope pulling the load is inclined at an angle of 10° to the ramp. Resolving forces parallel and perpendicular to the ramp gave the following equations:

$$F \cos 10° = 0.42R + 115 \cos 70°$$
$$F \cos 80° = 115 \cos 20° - R$$

Simplify the equations and solve them to find the force F and the reaction R.

6 Solve the following pairs of simultaneous equations, where possible, using determinants:

(a) $3x - 5y = 4$
    $2x + 8y = 1$

(b) $1.27s + 3.63t = 2.81$
    $4.72s - 1.44t = -5.23$

(c) $11.2x - 4.2y = -15.7$ (d) $r \cos 60° - t \sin 40° = 1.85$
     $23.1y - 61.6x = 114.3$ $r \sin 80° + t \cos 20° = 2.27$

7 Two points, $(1.2, 7.6)$ and $(2.7, 12.1)$, lie on a straight line $y = mx + c$. Form a pair of simultaneous equations and find m and c using determinants.

8 For what value of k will the determinant $\begin{vmatrix} -4.3 & 1.8 \\ 6.4 & 2+k \end{vmatrix}$ be zero?

B5 The binomial theorem

B5.1 The expansion of $(a+x)^n$ when n is a positive integer

If we carry out the expansion of $(a + x)^n$ for whole-number values of n between 0 and 5, we obtain the following results:

$$(a + x)^0 = 1$$
$$(a + x)^1 = a + x$$
$$(a + x)^2 = a^2 + 2ax + x^2$$
$$(a + x)^3 = a^3 + 3a^2x + 3ax^2 + x^3$$
$$(a + x)^4 = a^4 + 4a^3x + 6a^2x^2 + 4ax^3 + x^4$$
$$(a + x)^5 = a^5 + 5a^4x + 10a^3x^2 + 10a^2x^3 + 5ax^4 + x^5$$

Looking closely at the coefficients of x in these expansions, we see a pattern with which we could predict the form of other expansions of $(a + x)^n$. For example, it is clear that the expansion of $(a + x)^7$ will start with a^7 and end with x^7. There will be eight terms, since all the above expansions of $(a + x)^n$ have $n + 1$ terms. Predicting the coefficients in terms other than the first and last is not so easy.

Let us consider $(a + x)^4$ to discover the general form of the expansions:

$$(a + x)^4 = a^4 + 4a^3x + 6a^2x^2 + 4ax^3 + x^4$$

We can write this as

$$(a + x)^4 = a^4 + 4a^{4-1}x + \frac{4(4 - 1)}{2 \times 1}a^{4-2}x^2$$

$$+ \frac{4(4 - 1)(4 - 2)}{3 \times 2 \times 1}a^{4-3}x^3 + x^4$$

If we treat the other expansions of $(a + x)^n$ in the same way, we find that they all conform to this pattern. The general expansion may be written in the form of the *binomial theorem* as follows:

$$(a + x)^n = a^n + na^{n-1}x + \frac{n(n-1)}{2!}a^{n-2}x^2$$

$$+ \frac{n(n-1)(n-2)}{3!}a^{n-3}x^3 + \ldots + x^n$$

where 3! is *factorial 3*, a quick way of writing $3 \times 2 \times 1$. (Some calculators have a key marked '$x!$' with which factorials of a defined range of whole numbers can be evaluated; e.g. $69! = 1.711 \times 10^{98}$.)

The expansion of $(a + x)^n$ using the binomial theorem will have $n + 1$ terms for all positive integer values of n. We shall not consider a proof of the theorem.

Example 1   Use the binomial theorem to write down the expansion of $(2 + x)^7$.

The binomial theorem states that, for all positive integer values of n,

$$(a + x)^n = a^n + na^{n-1}x + \frac{n(n-1)}{2!}a^{n-2}x^2$$

$$+ \frac{n(n-1)(n-2)}{3!}a^{n-3}x^3 + \ldots + x^n$$

With $a = 2$ and $n = 7$,

$$(2 + x)^7 = 2^7 + 7(2^6)x + \frac{7(6)}{2!}(2^5)x^2$$

$$+ \frac{7(6)(5)}{3!}(2^4)x^3 + \frac{7(6)(5)(4)}{4!}(2^3)x^4$$

$$+ \frac{7(6)(5)(4)(3)}{5!}(2^2)x^5 + \frac{7(6)(5)(4)(3)(2)}{6!}(2)x^6 + x^7$$

$$= 128 + 448x + 672x^2 + 560x^3 + 280x^4 + 84x^5 + 14x^6 + x^7$$

If we look at the coefficient of x^3 in the binomial expansion of $(a + x)^n$:

$$\frac{n(n-1)(n-2)}{3!}a^{n-3}$$

we see that there are *three* factors involving n (i.e. $n(n-1)(n-2)$), a is raised to the power n minus *three*, and the denominator is factorial *three*. There is a regular form for all the coefficients in the expansion. The term containing x^r will be

$$\frac{n(n-1)(n-2)\ldots(n-(r+1))}{r!}a^{n-r}x^r$$

76

This general term can also be written

$$\frac{n!}{(n-r)!\,r!}a^{n-r}x^r$$

Incidentally, it is interesting to note that $\dfrac{n!}{(n-r)!\,r!}$ is the number of

combinations of n items taken r at a time and can be denoted by $\binom{n}{r}$

or $_nC_r$ (see section E2.1).

Example 2 Write down the term containing x^5 in the binomial expansion of $(3+x)^8$.

The general term containing x^r in the binomial expansion of $(a+x)^n$ is

$$\frac{n!}{(n-r)!\,r!}a^{n-r}x^r$$

With $a=3$, $r=5$, and $n=8$ we have

$$\frac{8!}{(8-5)!\,5!}3^{8-5}x^5 = \frac{8!}{3!\,5!}3^3x^5 = \frac{(8\times7\times6)(27)x^5}{3\times2\times1} = 1512x^5$$

B5.2 The expansion of $(1+x)^n$ for all values of n
In the binomial theorem for the expansion of $(a+x)^n$ discussed in section B5.1 there are $n+1$ terms when n is a positive integer. The expansion of $(1+x)^n$ is obtained by simply substituting $a=1$ in the expansion:

$$(1+x)^n = 1 + nx + \frac{n(n-1)}{2!}x^2 + \frac{n(n-1)(n-2)}{3!}x^3 + \ldots + x^n$$

When n is not a positive integer, the expansion does not terminate after $n+1$ terms but continues indefinitely. We say that the expansion of $(1+x)^n$ under these conditions is an *infinite series*. The terms of this infinite series may be developed from the binomial theorem exactly as before. As an example, if we expand $(1+x)^{-1}$ using the binomial theorem with $n=-1$ we obtain the following infinite series:

$$(1+x)^{-1} = 1 + (-1)x + \frac{(-1)(-2)}{2!}x^2 + \frac{(-1)(-2)(-3)}{3!}x^3 + \ldots$$

$$= 1 - x + x^2 - x^3 + \ldots \text{continuing indefinitely}$$

We can see from the first four terms of this series how it would proceed if further terms were evaluated (e.g. the eleventh term is x^{10}).

If we substitute particular values for x in this infinite series we see that, unless x is numerically less than one, the terms become numerically larger and are alternately positive and negative. The series is said to be *divergent* when x lies outside the range of values between $x = -1$ and $x = 1$. For example, with $x = 2$ the first four terms of the series are

$$1 - 2 + 4 - 8$$

There is clearly no point in adding together these four values, since the fifth term ($+16$) is larger than the sum of all the previous terms.

For all values of x between $x = -1$ and $x = 1$ (we write $-1 < x < 1$ or $|x| < 1$), adding together an increasing number of terms of the series gives a progressively more accurate evaluation of $(1 + x)^{-1}$. We say that the series is *convergent* when $|x| < 1$. For example, when $x = 0.5$ the first four terms can be added together as follows:

$$1 - 0.5 + 0.25 - 0.125 = 0.625$$

Now $(1 + 0.5)^{-1} = 2/3 = 0.667$, and by taking more terms of the series we can obtain a closer approximation to the true value.

To summarise, we write down the binomial theorem for $(1 + x)^n$ when n is not a positive integer as

$$(1 + x)^n = 1 + nx + \frac{n(n - 1)}{2!}x^2 + \dots \quad \text{where} \quad |x| < 1$$

The series will be convergent only when successive terms become numerically smaller, so that the sum of a large number of terms approaches, but does not exceed, a finite value.

Example 1 Write down the binomial expansion of $1/(1 + 3t)^2$ as far as the term in t^3. For what values of t is the series convergent?

From the binomial theorem, the expansion of $(1 + x)^n$ is

$$(1 + x)^n = 1 + nx + \frac{n(n - 1)}{2!}x^2 + \frac{n(n - 1)(n - 2)}{3!}x^3 + \dots$$

Substituting $x = 3t$ and $n = -2$ gives

$$(1 + 3t)^{-2} = 1 + (-2)(3t) + \frac{(-2)(-3)}{2!}(3t)^2 + \frac{(-2)(-3)(-4)}{3!}(3t)^3 + \dots$$

$$= 1 - 6t + 27t^2 - 108t^3 \quad \text{as far as the term in } t^3$$

Now the expansion of $(1 + x)^n$ is convergent if $|x| < 1$, and so the series for $(1 + 3t)^{-2}$ will be convergent if $|3t| < 1$ or $|t| < \frac{1}{3}$. (This means that t must be numerically less than $\frac{1}{3}$.)

Example 2 Use the binomial theorem to write down the first three terms of the expansion $\sqrt{(2 - z)}$ in ascending powers of z. For what values of z is the series convergent?

$$\sqrt{(2-z)} = (2-z)^{1/2} = 2^{1/2}(1-z/2)^{1/2}$$

From the binomial theorem, the first three terms of the expansion of $(1+x)^n$ are

$$1 + nx + \frac{n(n-1)}{2!}x^2$$

Substituting $x = -z/2$ and $n = \tfrac{1}{2}$, these three terms become

$$1 + \tfrac{1}{2}(-z/2) + \frac{\tfrac{1}{2}(-\tfrac{1}{2})}{2 \times 1}(-z/2)^2 = 1 - z/4 - z^2/32$$

$$\therefore \quad \sqrt{(2-z)} = \sqrt{2}(1-z/2)^{1/2}$$

$$= \sqrt{2}(1 - z/4 - z^2/32) \quad \text{ignoring terms after the first three}$$

The expansion is useful only when the series for $(1-z/2)^{1/2}$ is convergent, i.e. when $|z/2| < 1$ or $|z| < 2$.

B5.3 Applying the binomial theorem to small changes
When x is very small, the binomial expansion of $(1+x)^n$ is approximately $1 + nx$ if we ignore all terms involving higher powers of x. Taking a slightly closer approximation by including the next term of the expansion gives

$$(1+x)^n = 1 + nx + \frac{n(n-1)}{2!}x^2 \quad \text{approximately}$$

Such approximations can be useful in calculating the effect on the subject of a formula when one or more of the independent variables is changed slightly.

The volume of a sphere with radius r is $\tfrac{4}{3}\pi r^3$. If the radius of a sphere is increased by $t\%$, we can estimate the change in the volume of the sphere. If V_1 is the original volume and V_2 is the volume after the increase in the radius, then

$$V_1 = \tfrac{4}{3}\pi r^3 \quad \text{and} \quad V_2 = \tfrac{4}{3}\pi\left(r + \frac{rt}{100}\right)^3$$

$$\therefore \quad V_2 = \tfrac{4}{3}\pi r^3(1 + 0.01t)^3$$

But $V_1 = \tfrac{4}{3}\pi r^3$

$$\therefore \quad V_2 = V_1(1 + 0.01t)^3$$

If t is small, an approximate value for $(1 + 0.01t)^3$ is $1 + (3 \times 0.01t)$.

$$\therefore \quad V_2 = V_1(1 + 0.03t)$$

79

For example, if $t = 1$ (i.e. a change in radius of 1%), then

$$V_2 = V_1(1 + 0.03) = V_1(1 + \tfrac{3}{100})$$

Thus a 1% increase in the radius of the sphere will result in an increase in volume of approximately 3%.

Example 1   The force of a jet of water on a flat plate is given by

$$F = 2\rho Av^2$$

where ρ is the density of water, A is the area of the plate, and v is the velocity of the jet. If ρ and A are constants, find the approximate change in F when v is increased by 2.5%.

The original force of the jet is

$$F_1 = 2\rho Av^2$$

After the increase in velocity,

$$F_2 = 2\rho A\left(v + \frac{2.5v}{100}\right)^2 = 2\rho Av^2(1 + 0.025)^2$$

and, since the change in velocity is small (i.e. 0.025 is small compared with 1), we can use the approximation

$$F_2 = F_1(1 + 2 \times 0.025) = F_1(1 + \tfrac{5}{100}) \quad \text{approximately}$$

Hence the force of the jet will increase by approximately 5%.

Example 2   The second moment of area of a rectangular beam section with depth d and width b about its neutral axis is $bd^3/12$. Estimate the change in second moment of area if b is increased by 5% and d is reduced by 3.5%.

The original second moment of area of the beam section is

$$I_1 = bd^3/12$$

Following the changes in b and d,

$$I_2 = \frac{(b + 5b/100)(d - 3.5d/100)^3}{12} = \frac{bd^3(1 + 0.05)(1 - 0.035)^3}{12}$$

The changes in both b and d are small, and so

$$I_2 = I_1(1.05)(1 - 3 \times 0.035) = 0.940I_1 \quad \text{approximately}$$

$$\therefore \quad I_2 = I_1(1 - \tfrac{6}{100})$$

i.e. the second moment of area of the beam section will be reduced by approximately 6%.

80

Example 3 If $W = ka^{1.2}b^{2.5}/c^{0.8}$, use a binomial approximation to find the percentage error in the calculated value of W when errors of $+2.1\%$, -1.6%, and $+0.9\%$ are made in measuring a, b, and c respectively.

Let W' be the calculated value, where

$$W' = \frac{k(a + 2.1a/100)^{1.2}(b - 1.6b/100)^{2.5}}{(c + 0.9c/100)^{0.8}}$$

$$= \frac{ka^{1.2}b^{2.5}(1 + 0.021)^{1.2}(1 - 0.016)^{2.5}}{c^{0.8}(1 + 0.009)^{0.8}}$$

$$= \frac{W(1 + 0.021)^{1.2}(1 - 0.016)^{2.5}}{(1 + 0.009)^{0.8}}$$

The errors in a, b, and c are small and we can make the following approximation:

$$W' = \frac{W(1 + 1.2 \times 0.021)(1 - 2.5 \times 0.016)}{(1 + 0.8 \times 0.009)} = 0.977W$$

Thus the error in the calculated value for W will be approximately -2.3%.

Exercise B5

1 Write down the expansion of $(a + x)^6$.
2 Expand the following using the binomial expansion of $(a + x)^n$:
(a) $(x + 2y)^3$, (b) $(2x - 3y)^4$, (c) $(m + 2/m)^5$.
3 Write down the term containing x^4 in the binomial expansion of $(a + x)^7$.
4 What is the term containing x^3 in the binomial expansion of $(0.8 + x)^{13}$?
5 What is the fourth term in the expansion of $(3/s - s/4)^9$?
6 Expand $(1 + z)^{-2}$ as far as the term in z^4. For what values of z is the series convergent?
7 Use the binomial theorem for $(1 + x)^n$ to write down the first four terms of the following expansions, giving limits for which the expansions are true: (a) $1/(1 + 2x)^3$, (b) $1/\sqrt{(1 - t)}$, (c) $\sqrt[3]{(1 + s/4)}$, (d) $(2 - 3x)^{-5}$, (e) $\sqrt{(4 + z)}$.
8 Find the approximate increase in the volume of a cone, radius r and height h, (where $V = \frac{1}{3}\pi r^2 h$) when the radius is increased by $1\frac{1}{2}\%$.
9 The kinetic energy in a hammer with mass m as it strikes with velocity v is $\frac{1}{2}mv^2$. Determine the approximate change in kinetic energy when the mass of the hammer is increased by 3% and its velocity is reduced by 4%.

10 The torque applied to a drill with diameter D with a feed rate f is given by $T = kf^{0.8}D^{1.8}$. If k is constant and f is increased by 2% while D is reduced by 3%, find the approximate change in torque.

11 The power in an electrical circuit is V^2/R. Find the approximate percentage change in power when the voltage V is reduced by 2.7% at the same time as the resistance R is increased by 3.8%.

12 When a torque T is applied to a shaft with diameter D, the shear stress is given by $\tau = 16T/\pi D^3$. If an error of $+2.5\%$ is made in measuring T, and -1.5% in measuring D, find the approximate error in the value obtained for τ.

B6 Simplifying Boolean expressions

Many students will by now be familiar with the AND, OR, and NOT functions. The logic-gate symbols for these functions together with their corresponding Boolean expressions and truth tables are summarised in fig. B6.1 for revision. (An introduction to this subject is given in *Mathematics for level-2 technicians*, section B10.)

Function	Logic gate symbol	Boolean expression	Truth table
AND	A —— & —— T B ——	$T = A.B$	A B $T=A.B$ 0 0 0 0 1 0 1 0 0 1 1 1
OR	A —— 1 —— T B ——	$T = A+B$	A B $T=A+B$ 0 0 0 0 1 1 1 0 1 1 1 1
NOT	A —— 1 ◦— T	$T = \bar{A}$	A $T=\bar{A}$ 0 1 1 0

Fig. B6.1 Summary of AND, OR, and NOT functions

B6.1 Logic diagrams from Boolean expressions

We shall now consider how AND, OR, and NOT gates can be connected together to give the range of outputs defined by a Boolean expression. (This process is known as *implementation*.) As an example, take the expression $A \cdot B + C \cdot D$. We can use two AND gates and one OR gate to make a logic circuit to implement this expression. One AND gate will have inputs A and B; the other will have inputs C and D. Outputs from these AND gates provide inputs for the OR gate. The output from the OR gate will always be defined by the expression $A \cdot B + C \cdot D$. (Note that all the possible outputs could be shown in a truth table with 16 lines.) The logic diagram is shown in fig. B6.2.

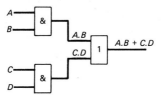

Fig. B6.2

With a little practice, logic diagrams can be drawn from more complicated Boolean expressions.

Example 1   Draw a logic diagram to implement the Boolean expression $(A + B \cdot C) \cdot D$.

Three gates are used as shown in fig. B6.3.

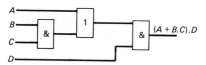

Fig. B6.3

Example 2   Show how five logic gates could be connected together to implement the expression $(A + \bar{B}) \cdot (C + \bar{D})$.

The logic network with two inverters, two OR gates, and one AND gate is shown in fig. B6.4.

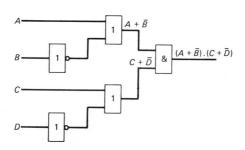

Fig. B6.4

83

Example 3 Draw a logic network, using AND, OR, and NOT gates, which will give the range of outputs defined by the Boolean expression $A \cdot \bar{B} + \bar{C} \cdot \bar{D}$.

The expression is implemented using the network shown in fig. B6.5.

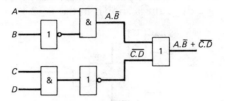

Fig. B6.5

Example 4 Draw a logic network to implement the Boolean expression $\bar{A} \cdot B + \bar{B} \cdot C + \bar{C} \cdot D$.

Seven gates could be used to do this, as shown in fig. B6.6

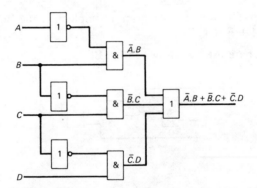

Fig. B6.6

We shall see later that savings in gates can be made by simplifying Boolean expressions before they are implemented.

B6.2 Truth tables from Boolean expressions
As many students will have observed, truth tables are useful in demonstrating the laws of Boolean algebra. They can also be used to show all the output states for possible combinations of input to a given logic network. For example, the Boolean expressions $(A + B) \cdot \bar{C}$ can be implemented with the network in fig. B6.7(a). The truth table in fig. B6.7(b) gives the output state for all eight input combinations of A, B, and C. To make it easier to write down the truth-table values for $(A + B) \cdot \bar{C}$, a column for $(A + B)$ has been included. The inclusion of intermediate terms in this way can avoid errors which may arise if we attempt to write down output values directly from the input states.

84

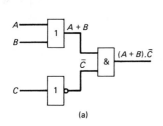

Inputs				Output
A	B	C	(A + B)	(A + B).$\bar{C}$
0	0	0	0	0
0	0	1	0	0
0	1	0	1	1
0	1	1	1	0
1	0	0	1	1
1	0	1	1	0
1	1	0	1	1
1	1	1	1	0

(a)   (b)

Fig. B6.7

Example 1   Construct a truth table from the Boolean expression $(A . \bar{B}) + (\bar{A} . B)$.

With only two variables, A and B, the truth table will have four lines (i.e. 2^n lines for n variables) and is shown below.

A	B	A.$\bar{B}$	$\bar{A}$.B	(A.$\bar{B}$) + ($\bar{A}$.B)
0	0	0	0	0
0	1	0	1	1
1	0	1	0	1
1	1	0	0	0

Example 2   Draw a truth table from the expression $(\bar{A} + B) . (\bar{B} + \bar{C})$.

The truth table has eight lines and is shown below.

A	B	C	$\bar{A}$ + B	$\bar{B}$ + $\bar{C}$	($\bar{A}$ + B) . ($\bar{B}$ + $\bar{C}$)
0	0	0	1	1	1
0	0	1	1	1	1
0	1	0	1	1	1
0	1	1	1	0	0
1	0	0	0	1	0
1	0	1	0	1	0
1	1	0	1	1	1
1	1	1	1	0	0

Example 3   Use a truth table to determine the number of combinations of A, B, C, and D for which $T = 1$, where
$T = A . B . C + \bar{A} . \bar{B} . \bar{D} + B . \bar{C} . D$.

85

With four variables, the truth table has 16 lines as shown below.

A	B	C	D	$A.B.C$	$\bar{A}.\bar{B}.\bar{D}$	$B.\bar{C}.D$	T
0	0	0	0	0	1	0	1
0	0	0	1	0	0	0	0
0	0	1	0	0	1	0	1
0	0	1	1	0	0	0	0
0	1	0	0	0	0	0	0
0	1	0	1	0	0	1	1
0	1	1	0	0	0	0	0
0	1	1	1	0	0	0	0
1	0	0	0	0	0	0	0
1	0	0	1	0	0	0	0
1	0	1	0	0	0	0	0
1	0	1	1	0	0	0	0
1	1	0	0	0	0	0	0
1	1	0	1	0	0	1	1
1	1	1	0	1	0	0	1
1	1	1	1	1	0	0	1

We see from the truth table that there are six combinations for which $T = 1$.

B6.3 Simplifying expressions using Boolean algebra

A summary of the laws of Boolean algebra is given below. We shall now use these laws to simplify expressions involving up to four variables. The methods used here are important in the design of digital equipment, since a simplified Boolean expression can be implemented with fewer gates and therefore more economically.

A summary of the laws of Boolean algebra

$$A + B = B + A$$
$$A.B = B.A$$
commutative laws

$$A + (B + C) = (A + B) + C$$
$$A.(B.C) = (A.B).C$$
associative laws

$$A.(B + C) = A.B + A.C$$
$$A + (B.C) = (A + B).(A + C)$$
distributive laws

$$\left.\begin{array}{l} \overline{A + B} = \overline{A} . \overline{B} \\[2mm] \overline{A . B} = \overline{A} + \overline{B} \end{array}\right\} \text{ De Morgan's theorems}$$

Other useful identities

$A + 0 = A$	$A . 0 = 0$
$A + 1 = 1$	$A . 1 = A$
$A + A = A$	$A . A = A$
$A + \overline{A} = 1$	$A . \overline{A} = 0$

Let us consider the Boolean expression $A . (B + C . A)$ as an example which can be simplified. As it stands, it would take three gates to implement the expression. (You may like to check this by drawing a logic diagram.)

Applying the distributive law to $A . (B + C . A)$ gives

$A . B + A . C . A$

According to the commutative law, $A . C . A = C . A . A$

Now $A . A = A$ and the expression becomes

$A . B + C . A$ or $A . (B + C)$

This expression can now be implemented with two gates instead of the three which were required with the expression in its original form.

Example 1 Simplify the expression $\overline{A} . B . (C . \overline{B} + \overline{A} . B . C)$ using the laws of Boolean algebra.

The distributive law gives

$\overline{A} . B . C . \overline{B} + \overline{A} . B . \overline{A} . B . C$

Applying the associative and commutative laws, we can write the expression as

$\overline{A} . C . (B . \overline{B}) + \overline{A} . \overline{A} . (B . B) . C$

Now $B . \overline{B} = 0$ $B . B = B$ and $\overline{A} . \overline{A} = \overline{A}$

The simplified expression is therefore $\overline{A} . B . C$.

When variables disappear from a Boolean expression during simplification, it shows that they were redundant in the first place and have no effect on the value of the expression.

Example 2 Simplify the equation
$$Q = A \cdot \overline{B} \cdot \overline{C} \cdot \overline{D} + \overline{A} \cdot B \cdot \overline{C} + \overline{A} \cdot B \cdot C + A \cdot \overline{B} \cdot \overline{C} \cdot D$$
and show that one of the variables has no effect on the value of Q.

$$Q = A \cdot \overline{B} \cdot \overline{C} \cdot \overline{D} + \overline{A} \cdot B \cdot \overline{C} + \overline{A} \cdot B \cdot C + A \cdot \overline{B} \cdot \overline{C} \cdot D$$
$$= A \cdot \overline{B} \cdot \overline{C} \cdot (\overline{D} + D) + \overline{A} \cdot B \cdot (\overline{C} + C)$$

But $\quad \overline{D} + D = 1 \quad$ and $\quad \overline{C} + C = 1$

$\therefore \quad Q = A \cdot \overline{B} \cdot \overline{C} + \overline{A} \cdot B$

As D does not appear in the simplified version of the equation, changes in D cannot effect the value of Q.

De Morgan's theorems are also useful in simplifying Boolean expressions.

Example 3 Show using De Morgan's theorem that $\overline{A} \cdot B + \overline{A + B} = \overline{A}$. Check this result using a truth table.

From De Morgan's theorem, $\overline{A + B} = \overline{A} \cdot \overline{B}$ and the expression becomes

$$\overline{A} \cdot B + \overline{A} \cdot \overline{B} \quad \text{or} \quad \overline{A} \cdot (B + \overline{B})$$

Thus $\quad \overline{A} \cdot B + \overline{A + B} = \overline{A} \quad$ (since $\quad B + \overline{B} = 1 \quad$ and $\quad \overline{A} \cdot 1 = \overline{A}$)

The truth table giving values of the original expression has four lines and is shown below.

A	B	$\overline{A} \cdot B$	$A + B$	$\overline{A + B}$	$\overline{A} \cdot B + \overline{A + B}$
0	0	0	0	1	1
0	1	1	1	0	1
1	0	0	1	0	0
1	1	0	1	0	0

The truth table confirms that $\overline{A} \cdot B + \overline{A + B} = \overline{A}$.

B6.4 Karnaugh maps
The Karnaugh map provides a visual method of simplifying Boolean expressions without using the laws and identities discussed in section B6.3.

Before an expression can be simplified using a Karnaugh map, it should be in the form $X + Y + Z + \dots$, where X, Y, and Z may be expressions such as $A \cdot \overline{B} \cdot C$ (we say the expression is in *minterm* form).

Just as there are 2^n lines in a truth table for an expression containing n variables, so a Karnaugh map for the same expression will have 2^n squares. Each square represents a unique combination of variables, and there is a square for every possible combination. Figure B6.8 shows the Boolean expression $\overline{A}.\overline{B}.C + \overline{A}.B.C + A.\overline{B}.\overline{C}$ on a three-variable Karnaugh map.

The layout and notation of the Karnaugh map will take time to get used to. In fig. B6.8, the states of A, B, and C indicated in the rows and columns of the map have been added in brackets, although these are not usually shown. With practice it becomes easier to identify individual squares and groups of squares using the references (i.e. 00, 01, 11, 10) along the top and left side. Each of the three terms in the expression $\overline{A}.\overline{B}.C + A.B.C + A.\overline{B}.\overline{C}$ can be completely represented by placing a '1' in a single square. For example, $\overline{A}.\overline{B}.C$ has been shown with a '1' in the bottom left corner of the Karnaugh map (i.e. first column, second row). This is because all squares in the first column relate to terms containing $\overline{A}.\overline{B}$, while any term which includes C must be shown in the second row.

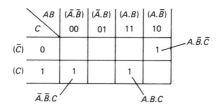

Fig. B6.8 Karnaugh map for three variables

See if you can identify the minterms which would occupy the remaining five squares on the Karnaugh map in fig. B6.8.

Any term which contains every variable identified on a Karnaugh map will be shown as a single square. Terms with fewer variables will

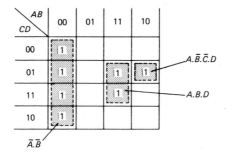

Fig. B6.9 Karnaugh map for four variables

89

occupy more than one square. Figure B6.9 shows the Boolean expression $A \cdot B \cdot D + \bar{A} \cdot \bar{B} + A \cdot \bar{B} \cdot \bar{C} \cdot D$. The term $A \cdot B \cdot D$ occupies two squares, while $\bar{A} \cdot \bar{B}$ takes four squares and $A \cdot \bar{B} \cdot \bar{C} \cdot D$ has a single square. Note that a term involving a single variable would require eight squares on the same Karnaugh map.

Example 1 Draw a Karnaugh map showing the Boolean expression $A \cdot \bar{B} \cdot C + B \cdot \bar{C}$.

With three variables in this example, the Karnaugh map has eight squares as shown in fig. B6.10.

C \ AB	00	01	11	10
0		1	1	
1				1

Fig. **B6.10** Karnaugh map showing $A \cdot \bar{B} \cdot C + B \cdot \bar{C}$

Example 2 Show the expression $A \cdot \bar{D} + A \cdot B \cdot C$ on a suitable Karnaugh map.

The Karnaugh map in this example has sixteen squares (i.e. 2^4 with four variables) and is shown in fig. B6.11.

CD \ AB	00	01	11	10
00			1	1
01				
11			1	
10			1	1

Fig. **B6.11** Karnaugh map showing $A \cdot \bar{D} + A \cdot B \cdot C$

Note that the four squares representing $A \cdot \bar{D}$ in fig. B6.11 are not grouped together, and that one of the squares on the Karnaugh map (fourth row, third column) is shared by both terms represented.

B6.5 Using a Karnaugh map to find the minimum form of a Boolean expression

When all the terms in a Boolean expression have been marked on a Karnaugh map, it is often possible to identify groups of squares which can be related to a simplified version of the expression. The *minimum form* of a Boolean expression found in this way can be implemented with fewer gates at a reduced cost.

Recognising patterns on a Karnaugh map is a skill which requires some practice. We shall look at a few examples of Boolean expressions which can be simplified.

Consider the expression $\bar{A} . B . C + \bar{A} . B . \bar{C} + A . B . C + A . B . \bar{C}$. Each term can be represented by a single square on the Karnaugh map shown in fig. B6.12. The four squares taken together can be defined as B (i.e. they are the four squares we would mark to represent B on the Karnaugh map). Thus

$$\bar{A} . \bar{B} . C + \bar{A} . B . \bar{C} + A . B . C + A . B . \bar{C} = B$$

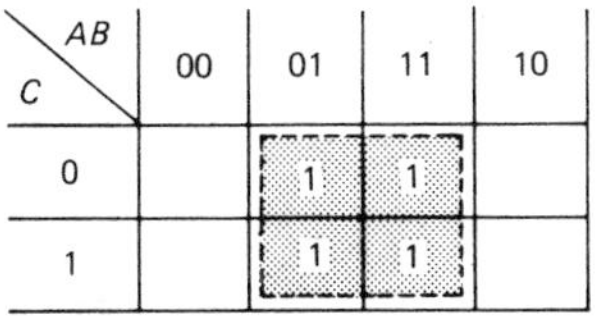

Fig. B6.12 Karnaugh map showing $\bar{A} . B . C + \bar{A} . B . \bar{C} + A . B . C + A . B . \bar{C} = B$

We can check this result using Boolean algebra. Applying the distributive law to the original expression gives

$$B . C . (\bar{A} + A) + B . \bar{C} . (\bar{A} + A)$$

Now $\bar{A} + A = 1$, and the expression is reduced to

$$B . C + B . \bar{C} \quad \text{or} \quad B . (C + \bar{C}) = B$$

Example 1 Find the minimum form of the expression $\bar{A} . B . C + \bar{A} . B . C$ using a Karnaugh map.

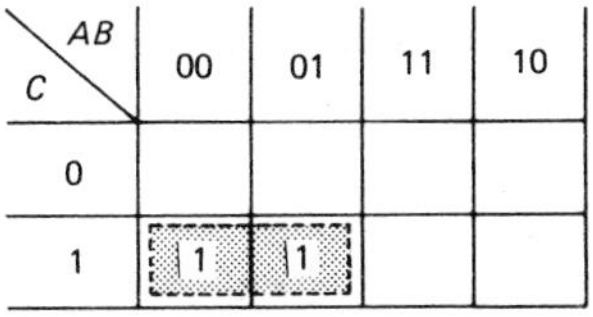

Fig. B6.13 Karnaugh map showing $\bar{A} . \bar{B} . C + \bar{A} . B . C = \bar{A} . C$

91

Each term in the expression is shown as a single square in fig. B6.13. The two squares can be taken together as $\bar{A}.C$. Thus $\bar{A}.\bar{B}.C + \bar{A}.B.C = \bar{A}.C$. This is the minimum form of the expression.

The number of adjacent squares (or minterms) in a defined group should be a power of two (i.e. 2, 4, 8, 16, ...). The groups we identify on a Karnaugh map may overlap when we define the minimum form of a Boolean expression.

Example 2 Use a Karnaugh map to find the minimum form of the Boolean expression

$$A.B.\bar{C} + \bar{A}.C.D + A.B.C.D + A.\bar{B}.C.D + A.B.C.\bar{D}$$

Each of the five terms in the expression is marked on the Karnaugh map in fig. B6.14. Two groups of four squares (i.e. the third column and the third row) can be identified as $A.B$ and $C.D$. The minimum form of the expression is therefore $A.B + C.D$.

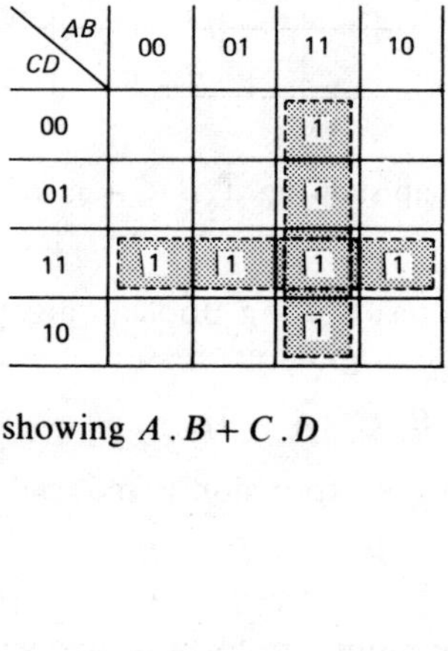

CD \ AB	00	01	11	10
00			1	
01			1	
11	1	1	1	1
10			1	

Fig. B6.14 Karnaugh map showing $A.B + C.D$

Exercise B6

1 Draw logic diagrams using AND, OR, and NOT gates to implement the following Boolean expressions without simplification:

(a) $A.(B + C.D)$ (b) $(A + \bar{B}).C.\bar{D}$ (c) $\bar{A}.B + C.(A + D)$
(d) $(A + B).(C.\bar{D} + C.\bar{A})$ (e) $\overline{A.B + C.D}$

2 Draw truth tables for the following Boolean expressions:

(a) $A.B + \bar{A}.\bar{B}$ (b) $A.\bar{B} + \bar{A}.B.\bar{C}$ (c) $\overline{\bar{A}.B + A.\bar{C}}$
(d) $A.\bar{B}.C + \bar{A}.B.D + A.\bar{C}.\bar{D}$

3 Simplify the following expressions using the laws of Boolean algebra:

    (a) $A.B + C.B$ (b) $A.B.\overline{C} + A.B.C + A.\overline{B}$
    (c) $A.(\overline{B}.C + \overline{A}.B.C)$ (d) $A + C.(A.B + B.C)$
    (e) $A.\overline{B}.C.(\overline{A.D + C.D})$

4 Write down Boolean expressions for the groups on the Karnaugh maps in fig. B6.15.

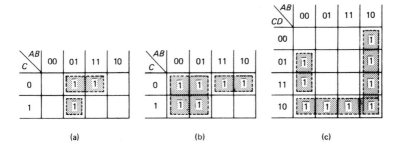

    (a)   (b)   (c)

Fig. B6.15

5 Write down the single term which is represented by the four squares shown on the Karnaugh map in fig. B6.16.

$\backslash AB$ $CD\backslash$	00	01	11	10
00		1	1	
01				
11				
10		1	1	

Fig. B6.16

6 Draw a Karnaugh map showing the expression

    $B.D + \overline{A}.B.\overline{C}.D + \overline{A}.\overline{B}.C$

7 Draw Karnaugh maps for the following Boolean expressions and use them to reduce the expressions to their minimum form:

    (a) $A.B.\overline{C} + \overline{A}.B.\overline{C}$ (b) $\overline{A}.C + \overline{A}.B.\overline{C} + \overline{A}.\overline{B}.\overline{C}$
    (c) $\overline{A}.C.D + \overline{A}.\overline{B}.\overline{C}.D + \overline{A}.B.\overline{C}.D$
    (d) $A.\overline{B}.\overline{C}.\overline{D} + \overline{A}.B.D + \overline{A}.B.C + A.\overline{B}.C.\overline{D} + \overline{A}.B.\overline{C}.\overline{D}$

93

B7 NAND and NOR gates

B7.1 Definitions and logic symbols

NAND

The function $\overline{A.B}$ can be implemented with an inverter and an AND gate as shown in fig. B7.1(a). The term NAND (a shortened form of 'NOT AND') is used to describe the inverted AND function. Alternative symbols for the NAND gate are shown in fig. B7.1(b).

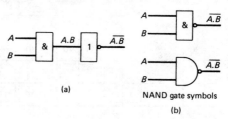

(a)

NAND gate symbols

(b)

Fig. B7.1

The truth-table values for the NAND function are simply inverted AND function values, so the output from a NAND gate is 1 except when all inputs are 1.

Inputs		AND	NAND
A	B	$A.B$	$\overline{A.B}$
0	0	0	1
0	1	0	1
1	0	0	1
1	1	1	0

NOR

The inverted OR function $\overline{A+B}$ is performed by the NOR gate (short for 'NOT OR') shown in fig. B7.2. The small circle in the NOR gate symbol, as in symbols for the NOT and NAND gates, implies an inverted output.

Inputs		OR	NOR
A	B	$A+B$	$\overline{A+B}$
0	0	0	1
0	1	1	0
1	0	1	0
1	1	1	0

NOR gate symbols

Fig. B7.2

94

We shall see in the next two sections that logic circuits can be designed using only NAND gates or NOR gates, and that for economic reasons it may be preferable to use these gates instead of a mixture of AND, OR, and NOT gates.

B7.2 Expressions involving NAND or NOR functions only

Any Boolean expression involving AND, OR, and NOT functions can be converted into an expression involving only NAND functions or NOR functions.

Taking the functions one at a time, we can replace the AND function with NOR functions as follows:

$$\overline{A}.\overline{B} = \overline{A + B} \quad (De\ Morgan's\ theorem)$$

so $\quad A.B = \overline{\overline{A} + \overline{B}} \quad$ (i.e. '$\overline{A}$ NOR $\overline{B}$')

The truth table below confirms this relationship.

A	B	$\overline{A}$	$\overline{B}$	$\overline{A} + \overline{B}$	$\overline{\overline{A} + \overline{B}} = A.B$
0	0	1	1	1	0
0	1	1	0	1	0
1	0	0	1	1	0
1	1	0	0	0	1

We shall see later that single NOR gates or NAND gates can be used as inverters to give $\overline{A}$ and $\overline{B}$ in the above expression for $A.B$.

To replace the AND function with NAND functions, we use the fact that any variable or function which is inverted twice remains unchanged. Thus

$$A.B = \overline{\overline{A.B}}$$

Now $\overline{\overline{A.B}}$ can be implemented using two NAND gates (one acting as an inverter with all inputs linked – see fig. B7.3).

The OR function can be replaced by either NOR or NAND as follows:

$$A + B = \overline{\overline{A + B}}$$

Thus the implementation of $A + B$ requires two NOR gates – one with inputs A and B, the other acting as an inverter on the output of the first.

Replacing OR functions with NAND only,

$$A + B = \overline{\overline{A}.\overline{B}}$$

95

(Check this by applying De Morgan's theorem to the r.h.s. or by using a truth table.)

Now, $\overline{\overline{A} . \overline{B}}$ is '$\overline{A}$ NAND $\overline{B}$', so, by inverting A and B (using two NAND gates), the output of a NAND gate with inputs $\overline{A}$ and $\overline{B}$ will be the same as $A + B$.

Finally, to convert NOT functions into NOR and NAND functions we use identities previously discussed in section B6.3. By inverting both sides of the identity $A + A = A$, we obtain the result

$$\overline{A + A} = \overline{A}$$

Any term $\overline{A}$ in an expression can thus be replaced with $\overline{A + A}$. This function is implemented in a logic circuit using a single NOR gate with linked inputs.

Similarly, from the identity $A . A = A$ we obtain $\overline{A . A} = \overline{A}$, showing that $\overline{A}$ may be converted to $\overline{A . A}$ (representing a NAND gate with inputs linked).

A summary of the conversions described is given in the following table:

		NOR	NAND
AND	$A . B$	$\overline{\overline{A} + \overline{B}}$	$\overline{\overline{A . B}}$
OR	$A + B$	$\overline{\overline{A + B}}$	$\overline{\overline{A} . \overline{B}}$
NOT	$\overline{A}$	$\overline{A + A}$	$\overline{A . A}$

Example 1 Convert the Boolean expression $A . \overline{B}$ into an expression involving NOR functions only.

Converting the AND function gives

$$A . \overline{B} = \overline{\overline{A} + B}$$

Now $\overline{A} = \overline{A + A}$

hence $A . \overline{B} = \overline{\overline{A + A} + B}$

Example 2 Rewrite the expression $A . B + \overline{C}$ using the NAND function only.

$$A . B = \overline{\overline{A . B}}$$

$$\therefore \quad A . B + \overline{C} = \overline{\overline{A . B}} + \overline{C}$$

Finally, we replace the OR function to give

$$\cdot \quad A . B + \overline{C} = \overline{\overline{A . B} . C}$$

Example 3 Write down a Boolean expression involving NAND functions only which is equivalent to $A \cdot (B + C)$.

Converting the OR function,

$$B + C = \overline{\overline{B} \cdot \overline{C}}$$

But $\overline{B} = \overline{B \cdot B}$ and $\overline{C} = \overline{C \cdot C}$

$\therefore$ $A \cdot (B + C) = A \cdot (\overline{\overline{B \cdot B} \cdot \overline{C \cdot C}})$

Converting the remaining AND function gives

$$A \cdot (B + C) = \overline{\overline{A \cdot (\overline{\overline{B \cdot B} \cdot \overline{C \cdot C}})}}$$

B7.3 Logic diagrams with NOR gates or NAND gates only
Many thousands of logic gates can be manufactured as a single integrated circuit. With some of the semiconductor technologies used, NOR gates are preferred; while other technologies lend themselves to making NAND gates easily. It is often more economical to produce logic circuits with NOR or NAND gates only, even though more gates are needed than would be required if AND, OR, and NOT gates were also used.

We can extend the table from section B7.2 to show how the *synthesis* of AND, OR, and NOT gates can be achieved with NOR or NAND gates only. The gate configurations in fig. B7.3 may be used to replace AND, OR, and NOT gates directly. If we wish to implement a Boolean expression using NOR gates or NAND gates only, we can convert the expression and then draw a logic diagram using a single type of gate.

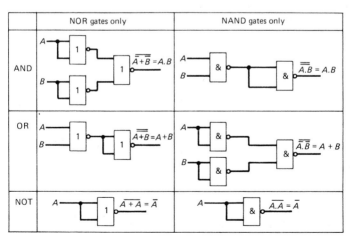

Fig. B7.3 Synthesis of AND, OR, and NOT using NOR and NAND gates

In example 1 of the previous section we showed that
$A \cdot \bar{B} = \overline{\overline{A + A} + B}$. The logic diagram implementing this expression
with NOR gates is shown in fig. B7.4.

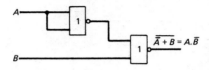

Fig. B7.4

Example 1 Draw a logic diagram using NAND gates only for the
Boolean expression $A + \bar{B}$.

Converting $A + \bar{B}$ into an expression with NAND functions only gives

$$A + \bar{B} = \overline{\overline{A} \cdot B} \quad \text{(remembering that } \bar{A} = \overline{A \cdot A}\text{)}$$

The logic diagram using NAND gates only is shown in fig. B7.5

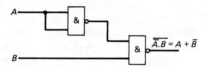

Fig. B7.5

Example 2 Implement the Boolean expression $(A + \bar{B}) \cdot \bar{C}$ using
(a) NOR gates only, (b) NAND gates only.

a) Converting the expression into NOR form gives

$$A + \bar{B} = \overline{\overline{A + \overline{B}}}$$

hence $(A + \bar{B}) \cdot \bar{C} = \overline{\overline{\overline{A + \overline{B}}} + C}$

The circuit using NOR gates only is shown in fig. B7.6.

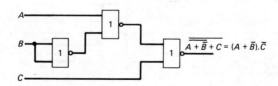

Fig. B7.6

98

b) Converting $(A + \bar{B}) . \bar{C}$ into an expression with NAND functions only gives

$$A + \bar{B} = \overline{\bar{A} . B}$$

hence $(A + \bar{B}) . \bar{C} = \overline{\overline{\bar{A} . B} . \bar{C}}$

The logic circuit for this expression is shown in fig. B7.7.

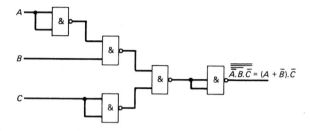

Fig. B7.7

Exercise B7

1 Draw a truth table from the logic diagram in fig. B7.8.

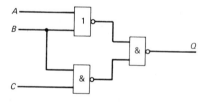

Fig. B7.8

2 Draw a logic diagram to implement the Boolean expression $\overline{A . B . C . D}$ using NAND gates only.

3 Convert the following to give expressions involving NOR functions only, and implement the new expressions using NOR gates: (a) $\bar{A} . B$, (b) $A . (\bar{B} + C)$.

4 Convert the following to give expressions involving NAND functions only, and implement the new expressions using NAND gates: (a) $\bar{A} + B$, (b) $A . \bar{B} + \bar{C} . D$.

C   Calculus

C1   Differentiation of algebraic functions

C1.1   Differential coefficient of ax^n

When variables x and y are related such that the value of y depends on the value of x, we say that y is a *function* of x, and we write $y = f(x)$. Thus if $f(x) = 3x^2$ then $f(4) = 3(4)^2 = 48$. This functional notation is widely used in mathematics, and we shall see its advantages as we study the process of differentiation from first principles.

We are by now familiar with the graphical method of finding the slope (or gradient) of a tangent at a point on a curve, in which the ratio of sides of a triangle is used. Let us consider a general point P at (x, y) on the curve $y = f(x)$ shown in fig. C1.1. Let Q be a point with co-ordinates $(x + \delta x, y + \delta y)$, close to P.

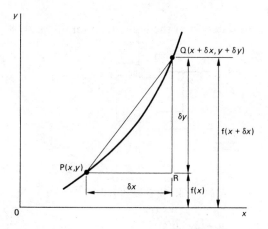

Fig. C1.1

The slope of the chord $PQ = \dfrac{QR}{PR} = \dfrac{\delta y}{\delta x}$

Now $\delta y = f(x + \delta x) - f(x)$ (see fig. C1.1)

$\therefore \quad \dfrac{\delta y}{\delta x} = \dfrac{f(x + \delta x) - f(x)}{\delta x}$

As Q approaches P, so that δx approaches 0 (we write $\delta x \to 0$), the slope of PQ approaches the slope of the tangent to the curve at P. The slope of the curve at P is dy/dx so that, in the limit as $\delta x \to 0$, $\delta y/\delta x \to dy/dx$.

We say that dy/dx is the *differential coefficient* of y with respect to x, or the *derivative* of y with respect to x, where

$$\frac{dy}{dx} = \lim_{\delta x \to 0}\left(\frac{\delta y}{\delta x}\right) = \lim_{\delta x \to 0}\left(\frac{f(x + \delta x) - f(x)}{\delta x}\right)$$

If we take an equation $f(x) = ax^n$ (where a and n are constants), then

$$f(x + \delta x) = a(x + \delta x)^n$$

and

$$\frac{dy}{dx} = \lim_{\delta x \to 0}\left(\frac{a(x + \delta x)^n - ax^n}{\delta x}\right)$$

We shall now find dy/dx for some particular values of n.

$n = 2$ (i.e. $y = ax^2$)

$$\frac{dy}{dx} = \lim_{\delta x \to 0}\left(\frac{a(x + \delta x)^2 - ax^2}{\delta x}\right)$$

Now
$$\frac{a(x + \delta x)^2 - ax^2}{\delta x} = \frac{a(x^2 + 2x\,\delta x + \delta x^2) - ax^2}{\delta x}$$

$$= \frac{2ax\,\delta x + a\,\delta x^2}{\delta x}$$

$$= 2ax + a\,\delta x$$

$\therefore$
$$\frac{dy}{dx} = \lim_{\delta x \to 0}(2ax + a\,\delta x)$$

$$= 2ax$$

$n = 3$ (i.e. $y = ax^3$)

$$\frac{dy}{dx} = \lim_{\delta x \to 0}\left(\frac{a(x + \delta x)^3 - ax^3}{\delta x}\right)$$

and
$$\frac{a(x + \delta x)^3 - ax^3}{\delta x} = \frac{a(x^3 + 3x^2\,\delta x + 3x\,\delta x^2 + \delta x^3) - ax^3}{\delta x}$$

$$= 3ax^2 + 3ax\,\delta x + a\,\delta x^2$$

$\therefore$
$$\frac{dy}{dx} = \lim_{\delta x \to 0}(3ax^2 + 3ax\,\delta x + a\,\delta x^2)$$

$$= 3ax^2$$

$n = 1$ (i.e. $y = ax$)

$$\frac{dy}{dx} = \lim_{\delta x \to 0} \left(\frac{a(x + \delta x)^1 - ax}{\delta x} \right)$$

$$= a$$

(Note that $y = ax$ is a straight line with constant gradient.)

The following table gives a summary of these results, from which we can suggest the general rule for the differentiation of ax^n.

y	dy/dx
ax	a
ax^2	$2ax$
ax^3	$3ax^2$

The general rule can be stated as follows:

if $\quad y = ax^n \quad$ then $\quad \dfrac{dy}{dx} = nax^{n-1}$

Although we have not proved this rule, our three examples obey it and it can be shown to be true for all values of n. Having such a rule makes the differentiation of many algebraic functions easier.

Note that, since $y = f(x)$, $\dfrac{dy}{dx} = \dfrac{d}{dx}f(x)$, which may be written $f'(x)$.

Examples

a) $y = 3x^2 \qquad \dfrac{dy}{dx} = 6x$

b) $y = 5x^4 \qquad \dfrac{dy}{dx} = 20x^3$

c) $y = 8x \qquad \dfrac{dy}{dx} = 8$

d) $y = \dfrac{2}{x^3} = 2x^{-3} \qquad \dfrac{dy}{dx} = -6x^{-4} = \dfrac{-6}{x^4}$

e) $y = 3\sqrt{x} = 3x^{1/2} \qquad \dfrac{dy}{dx} = \tfrac{3}{2}x^{-1/2} = \dfrac{3}{2\sqrt{x}}$

f) $y = 6.5x^{3.2} \qquad \dfrac{dy}{dx} = 20.8x^{2.2}$

g) $y = 7 = 7x^0$ $\dfrac{dy}{dx} = 0$

h) $s = 5t^7$ $\dfrac{ds}{dt} = 35t^6$

C1.2 Differentiation of a sum

The rule is to differentiate term by term and combine the results.

Examples

a) $y = 3x^2 + 2x + 5$ $\dfrac{dy}{dx} = 6x + 2$

b) $v = 4u^3 - u^2 + 5u - 6$ $\dfrac{dv}{du} = 12u^2 - 2u + 5$

c) $z = (t^2 + 5t)^2 = t^4 + 10t^3 + 25t^2$ $\dfrac{dz}{dt} = 4t^3 + 30t^2 + 50t$

d) $f(x) = 6x - \sqrt{x}$ $f'(x) = 6 - \dfrac{1}{2\sqrt{x}}$

In later sections we shall look at some of the many practical applications of differentiation.

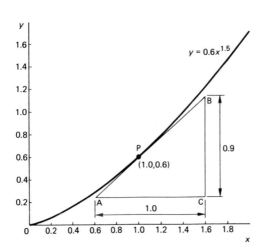

Fig. C1.2

Figure C1.2 shows the curve $y = 0.6x^{1.5}$ with a tangent at P $(1, 0.6)$. The ratio of the sides of triangle ABC gives the slope of the tangent as $BC/CA = 0.9/1.0 = 0.9$. The gradient of the curve at this point can be found more quickly, without drawing a graph, using differentiation as follows:

103

$$y = 0.6x^{1.5}$$

$$\frac{dy}{dx} = 0.9x^{0.5}$$

At $x = 1.0$, $dy/dx = 0.9$, and this is the gradient of the curve.

Example 1 Find the gradient of the curve $y = x^2 - 3x + 2$ at any point (x, y).

The gradient of a curve $y = f(x)$ is given by dy/dx or $f'(x)$. Thus

if $f(x) = x^2 - 3x + 2$

gradient $= f'(x) = 2x - 3$ for any value of x

Example 2 The distance s moved in a time t is given by $s = ut + \frac{1}{2}at^2$, where u and a are constants. Write down an equation for velocity v, if $v = ds/dt$.

$s = ut + \frac{1}{2}at^2$

velocity $v = ds/dt = u + at$ for all values of t

Exercise C1
1 Differentiate the following functions with respect to x: (a) $4x^2$, (b) $6x^3$, (c) $2\sqrt{x}$, (d) $5/x^4$, (e) $3.6x^{1.5}$, (f) $4/x^{1.5}$, (g) $2x^{3/4}$, (h) $-5.4/\sqrt[3]{(x^4)}$.
2 Find the derivatives of the following functions with respect to the variable involved: (a) $5t^3$, (b) $3\sqrt{v}$, (c) $-4z^{1.9}$, (d) $9/u^{0.7}$, (e) $3.5r^{0.4}$, (f) $-2.2/\sqrt{y}$.
3 Find the derivatives of the following functions with respect to x:
    (a) $6x^2 - 4$ (b) $3x^3 + 4x - 5$ (c) $(x + 5)^2$
    (d) $(x^2 - 3x)^2/x$
4 Determine the derivatives shown in brackets in each of the following:
    (a) $f(x) = 2x^5 - 5$ $[f'(x)]$ (b) $f(t) = 2/t^2 - 1/t$ $[f'(t)]$
    (c) $f(v) = (1 - 2v)/\sqrt{v}$ $[f'(v)]$ (d) $f(z) = 1.4z^{0.7} + 5$ $[f'(z)]$
5 Find the gradient of the curve $z = 2t^3 - t^2 + 4t - 1$ at the point $(2,19)$.

C2 Differentiation of exponential, trigonometric, and logarithmic functions

C2.1 Differential coefficient of e^x
Graphical and theoretical methods of differentiation have been studied in earlier sections. The same methods can be applied to determine the differential coefficient of the exponential function e^x.

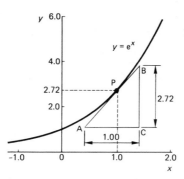

Fig. C2.1 The graph of $y = e^x$

The point P at $(1, 2.72)$ on the graph $y = e^x$ in fig. C2.1 lies on the line AB which is the tangent to the curve at P. To find the slope (or gradient) of this tangent, we use the triangle ABC as follows:

$$\text{slope at P} = \frac{BC}{AC} = \frac{2.72}{1.00} = 2.72$$

Thus the slope of the graph of e^x at $x = 1$ is equal to the value of e^x at $x = 1$ (since $e^1 = 2.72$ to two decimal places).

Drawing triangles at other points would confirm that the slope of the curve at any point is equal to the value of e^x at that point (e.g. the slope at $x = 2$ is equal to $e^2 = 7.39$). Plotting a graph of values of the slope of the exponential curve against x would give the same exponential curve. We conclude that

if $y = e^x$ then $dy/dx = e^x$

(or, if $f(x) = e^x$ then $f'(x) = e^x$)

The exponential function is unique in the way that its value at any point is always the same as its rate of change at that point.

Students familiar with the series for e^x:

$$e^x = 1 + x + \frac{x^2}{2!} + \frac{x^3}{3!} + \dots$$

will note that the series remains unchanged when differentiated term by term.

C2.2 Differential coefficients of $\sin x$, $\cos x$, and $\ln x$

As with previous functions, we shall look at a graphical approach to the determination of derivatives by studying rates of change. Graphs of the functions $\sin x$, $\cos x$, and $\ln x$ are shown in figs C2.2 to C2.4. A point has been selected on each of these curves, so that the slope may be found at the point and we can deduce the derivatives of the

105

functions. Of course, many such points would need to be considered before we could confirm the derivatives with any confidence.

You may find it useful to draw graphs of the functions on graph paper and find gradients at as many points as possible to support the following results. Note that radians must be used to draw the graphs of $\sin x$ and $\cos x$.

$\sin x$

Taking the point P at $(\pi/6, 0.50)$ on the curve $y = \sin x$ in fig. C2.2, the slope at that point, using triangle ABC, is given by

$$\text{slope at P} = \frac{BC}{AC} = \frac{0.69}{0.80} = 0.86$$

Now $\cos(\pi/6) = 0.866$

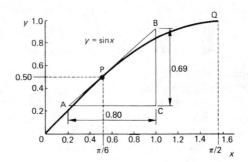

Fig. C2.2

At the point Q, where $x = \pi/2$, the slope is 0 (i.e. the tangent to the curve at Q is parallel to the x-axis), and we know that $\cos(\pi/2) = 0$. By taking many more points we could confirm that the *slope* of the curve $y = \sin x$ for all values of x (in radians) is equal to the *value* of $\cos x$. Hence

if $\quad y = \sin x \qquad$ then $\qquad \dfrac{dy}{dx} = \cos x$

(or, if $\quad f(x) = \sin x \quad$ then $\quad f'(x) = \cos x$)

$\cos x$

The slope of the tangent to the curve $y = \cos x$ in fig. C2.3 at a point R with co-ordinates $(\pi/4, 0.707)$ is found from triangle DEF:

$$\text{slope at R} = -\left(\frac{DE}{DF}\right) = -\left(\frac{0.71}{1.00}\right) = -0.71$$

Now $\sin(\pi/4) = 0.707$, numerically the same as the slope of $\cos x$ at $x = \pi/4$ but with a sign change. Further measurements of the gradient

106

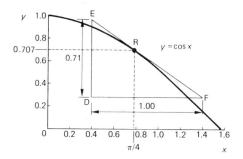

Fig. C2.3

of $y = \cos x$ at other points would confirm that the rate of change of $\cos x$ is $-\sin x$. Hence

$$\text{if} \quad y = \cos x \quad \text{then} \quad \frac{\mathrm{d}y}{\mathrm{d}x} = -\sin x$$

$$(\text{or, if} \quad \mathrm{f}(x) = \cos x \quad \text{then} \quad \mathrm{f}'(x) = -\sin x)$$

ln x

In fig. C2.4, the slope of the tangent to the curve $y = \ln x$ at the point S with co-ordinates $(0.80, -0.223)$ is found using triangle GHI:

$$\text{slope at S} = \frac{\text{HI}}{\text{GI}} = \frac{1.25}{1.00} = 1.25$$

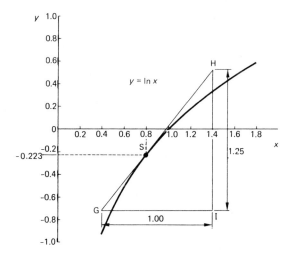

Fig. C2.4

Now 1.25 is the value of $1/x$ when $x = 0.80$. At any point on the graph, we would find that the slope of the tangent to the curve $y = \ln x$ is equal to the value of $1/x$. Thus

107

if $y = \ln x$ then $\dfrac{dy}{dx} = \dfrac{1}{x}$

(or, if $f(x) = \ln x$ then $f'(x) = 1/x$)

These derivatives for $\sin x$, $\cos x$, and $\ln x$ which we have observed using graphical methods can all be proved theoretically and are true for all values of x. The following table gives a summary of the derivatives we are now able to use. The standard derivative for $\tan x$ is included and could be shown in the same way.

y or $f(x)$	dy/dx or $f'(x)$
ax^n	nax^{n-1}
e^x	e^x
$\sin x$	$\cos x$
$\cos x$	$-\sin x$
$\tan x$	$\sec^2 x$
$\ln x$	$1/x$

We can treat these as standard derivatives and use them in a wide range of applications involving rates of change. (See section C3.1 for a table giving differential coefficients for e^{ax}, $\sin ax$, and $\cos ax$.)

In the same way that constants have no effect on the derivative of a simple algebraic function [i.e. if $f(x) = 3x^2$, $f'(x) = 2(3x)$], any constants multiplied by the above functions will remain unchanged during differentiation. For example,

if $f(x) = 5 \sin x$ then $f'(x) = 5 \cos x$

Example 1 If $y = 2x^3 - e^x$, find the value of dy/dx when $x = 1.7$.

$$y = 2x^3 - e^x$$

$$\therefore \frac{dy}{dx} = 6x^2 - e^x$$

When $x = 1.7$, $\dfrac{dy}{dx} = 6(1.7)^2 - e^{1.7} = 11.9$

Example 2 If $f(x) = \sin x - 2 \cos x$, find $f'(\pi/6)$.

$$f(x) = \sin x - 2 \cos x$$

$$\therefore \quad f'(x) = \cos x + 2 \sin x$$

and $f'(\pi/6) = \cos(\pi/6) + 2\sin(\pi/6) = 0.87 + 2(0.50) = 1.87$

108

Example 3 The distance x metres moved by a body in a time t seconds is given by $x = 3t^2 - 2t + 4$. Find the velocity v when $t = 2.2$ s, if $v = \mathrm{d}x/\mathrm{d}t$.

$$x = 3t^2 - 2t + 4$$

$$\therefore \quad v = \frac{\mathrm{d}x}{\mathrm{d}t} = 6t - 2$$

When $t = 2.2$ s, $\dfrac{\mathrm{d}x}{\mathrm{d}t} = 6(2.2) - 2$

The velocity of the body is 11.2 m/s.

Example 4 Given that z and t are related by the equation $z = 3 \ln t + 4$, find $\mathrm{d}z/\mathrm{d}t$ when $t = 1.2$.

$$z = 3 \ln t + 4$$

$$\therefore \quad \frac{\mathrm{d}z}{\mathrm{d}t} = \frac{3}{t}$$

When $t = 1.2$, $\dfrac{\mathrm{d}z}{\mathrm{d}t} = \dfrac{3}{1.2} = 2.5$

Exercise C2

1   Find derivatives with respect to x for the following functions:

   (a) $3\mathrm{e}^x + 5x - 9$ (b) $3\sqrt{x} - 4 \sin x$ (c) $x - (\sqrt{3}/2) \cos x$
   (d) $5 + 8 \ln x$ (e) $2x^{1.8} - \tan x$

2   If $s = 9x - 2\mathrm{e}^x$, find $\mathrm{d}s/\mathrm{d}x$ when $x = 0.50$.
3   Determine the rate of change of z, where $z = 2 \sin t - \sqrt{t} + 2$, when $t = \pi/6$.
4   If $u = \sqrt{2} \ln v + 3v^{1.7} - 6$, calculate the value of $\mathrm{d}u/\mathrm{d}v$ when $v = 7.5$.
5   Given that $w = 1 + \mathrm{e}^t/2$, find the value of t for which $\mathrm{d}w/\mathrm{d}t = 0.8$.

C3 Differentiation of products, quotients, and other functions

C3.1 Differentiation by substitution

We know by now that if $y = x^2 - 3x$, then $\mathrm{d}y/\mathrm{d}x = 2x - 3$. To find $\mathrm{d}y/\mathrm{d}x$ when $y = (x^2 - 3x)^6$ we could multiply $(x^2 - 3x)$ by itself six times, and then differentiate the result term by term. This would take some time, and differentiating $(x^2 - 3x)^{24}$ using this method would take much longer. To make things easier we use a substitution.

$$y = (x^2 - 3x)^6$$

Let $u = x^2 - 3x$

$\therefore \quad y = u^6$

We can now find dy/dx using the rule

$$\frac{dy}{dx} = \frac{dy}{du} \times \frac{du}{dx}$$

To find dy/du we differentiate u^6 with respect to u:

$$\frac{dy}{du} = 6u^5$$

Since $u = x^2 - 3x$, $\quad \dfrac{du}{dx} = 2x - 3$

hence $\quad \dfrac{dy}{dx} = 6u^5(2x - 3)$

Finally, we replace u by the original expression $x^2 - 3x$, giving

$$\frac{dy}{dx} = 6(x^2 - 3x)^5(2x - 3)$$

Making a substitution before differentiating is a useful approach for many types of function. The rule we use is often called the *function of a function rule*. This is because we use a substitution to make y a function of u, while u is itself a function of x. We can remember the rule in the form used earlier:

function of a function rule: $\quad \dfrac{dy}{dx} = \dfrac{dy}{du} \times \dfrac{du}{dx}$

Example 1 Find dy/dx if $y = \sqrt{(x^3 + 5)}$

$$y = \sqrt{(x^3 + 5)} = (x^3 + 5)^{1/2}$$

Let $\quad u = x^3 + 5 \quad$ so that $\quad y = u^{1/2}$

Now $\quad \dfrac{dy}{dx} = \dfrac{dy}{du} \times \dfrac{du}{dx}$

where $\quad \dfrac{dy}{du} = \frac{1}{2}u^{-1/2} \quad$ and $\quad \dfrac{du}{dx} = 3x^2$

$\therefore \quad \dfrac{dy}{dx} = \frac{1}{2}u^{-1/2}(3x^2)$

110

Putting $x^3 + 5$ in place of u gives

$$\frac{dy}{dx} = \frac{3x^2}{2\sqrt{(x^3 + 5)}}$$

Example 2   If $y = \sin(x^2 + 1)$, find dy/dx.

$$y = \sin(x^2 + 1)$$

Let $u = x^2 + 1$ so that $y = \sin u$

Now $\dfrac{dy}{dx} = \dfrac{dy}{du} \times \dfrac{du}{dx}$

$$= \cos u \times 2x$$

$\therefore$ $\dfrac{dy}{dx} = 2x \cos(x^2 + 1)$

Example 3   If $z = e^{3t}$, find the rate of change of z when $t = 0.6\,$s if z is measured in ohms.

$$z = e^{3t}$$

Let $u = 3t$ and $z = e^u$

Now $\dfrac{dz}{dt} = \dfrac{dz}{du} \times \dfrac{du}{dt}$

where $\dfrac{dz}{du} = e^u$ and $\dfrac{du}{dt} = 3$

$\therefore$ $\dfrac{dz}{dt} = 3e^u = 3e^{3t}$

When $t = 0.6\,$s, $\dfrac{dz}{dt} = 3e^{3(0.6)} = 18.1$

i.e. the rate of change of z is $18.1\,\Omega/$s

It is clear from example 3 that, for any function e^{ax} (where a is a constant), the derivative will be $a\,e^{ax}$. Similarly, whenever we differentiate $\sin ax$ and $\cos ax$ with respect to x, we obtain $a \cos ax$ and $-a \sin ax$ respectively. (You may like to check these results by making suitable substitutions to differentiate $\sin 3x$ and $\cos 3x$ for example.) When we recognise functions of this type, we can write down the derivatives directly without carrying out the substitution process. Here is a new version of the table of derivatives first given in section C2.2, amended to include these standard forms.

111

y or $f(x)$	dy/dx or $f'(x)$
ax^n	nax^{n-1}
e^{ax}	$a\,e^{ax}$
$\sin ax$	$a\cos ax$
$\cos ax$	$-a\sin ax$
$\tan ax$	$a\sec^2 ax$
$\ln ax$	$1/x$

Note that $\dfrac{d}{dx}(\ln ax) = \dfrac{1}{x}$ and *not* $\dfrac{a}{x}$. This is because $\ln ax = \ln x + \ln a$, and since $\ln a$ is a constant its derivative is zero.

Example 4 If $y = 2\sin 3x - \cos(x/2) + 5\,e^{2x}$, find dy/dx.

Differentiating each term in turn gives

$$\frac{dy}{dx} = 3(2\cos 3x) - (\tfrac{1}{2})[-\sin(x/2)] + 2(5\,e^{2x})$$

$$= 6\cos 3x + \tfrac{1}{2}\sin(x/2) + 10\,e^{2x}$$

C3.2 Differentiation of a product
When $y = u \times v$, where u and v are both functions of x, we find the derivative of y with respect to x using

$$\frac{dy}{dx} = u\frac{dv}{dx} + v\frac{du}{dx}$$

This is known as the *product rule*.
 If, for example, $y = x^2 \sin x$,

let $u = x^2$ and $v = \sin x$

then $\dfrac{du}{dx} = 2x$ and $\dfrac{dv}{dx} = \cos x$

giving $u\dfrac{dv}{dx} + v\dfrac{du}{dx} = x^2(\cos x) + \sin x(2x)$

$\therefore \quad \dfrac{dy}{dx} = x(x\cos x + 2\sin x)$

Example 1 Find dy/dx if $y = \sqrt{x}\,\ln x$.

112

Let $u = \sqrt{x}$ and $v = \ln x$

then $y = uv$

and $\dfrac{\mathrm{d}y}{\mathrm{d}x} = u\dfrac{\mathrm{d}v}{\mathrm{d}x} + v\dfrac{\mathrm{d}u}{\mathrm{d}x}$

$\qquad = \sqrt{x}\,(1/x) + \ln x(\tfrac{1}{2}x^{-1/2})$

$\therefore \quad \dfrac{\mathrm{d}y}{\mathrm{d}x} = \dfrac{1 + \tfrac{1}{2}\ln x}{\sqrt{x}}$

Example 2 If $y = \mathrm{e}^{3x}\tan 2x$, use the product rule to find $\mathrm{d}y/\mathrm{d}x$.

$y = \mathrm{e}^{3x}\tan 2x$

Let $u = \mathrm{e}^{3x}$ and $v = \tan 2x$

Now $\dfrac{\mathrm{d}y}{\mathrm{d}x} = u\dfrac{\mathrm{d}v}{\mathrm{d}x} + v\dfrac{\mathrm{d}u}{\mathrm{d}x}$

where $\dfrac{\mathrm{d}v}{\mathrm{d}x} = 2\sec^2 2x$ and $\dfrac{\mathrm{d}u}{\mathrm{d}x} = 3\,\mathrm{e}^{3x}$

$\therefore \quad \dfrac{\mathrm{d}y}{\mathrm{d}x} = \mathrm{e}^{3x}(2\sec^2 2x) + \tan 2x(3\,\mathrm{e}^{3x})$

$\qquad = \mathrm{e}^{3x}(2\sec^2 2x + 3\tan 2x)$

C3.3 Differentiation of a quotient

When $y = u/v$, where u and v are both functions of x, we can find the derivative of y with respect to x using

$$\frac{\mathrm{d}y}{\mathrm{d}x} = \frac{v(\mathrm{d}u/\mathrm{d}x) - u(\mathrm{d}v/\mathrm{d}x)}{v^2}$$

This is known as the *quotient rule*.

Example 1 Find $\mathrm{d}y/\mathrm{d}x$ if $y = (\sin x)/x^2$.

We have $y = (\sin x)/x^2$

Let $y = u/v$ where $u = \sin x$ and $v = x^2$

Now $\dfrac{\mathrm{d}y}{\mathrm{d}x} = \dfrac{v(\mathrm{d}u/\mathrm{d}x) - u(\mathrm{d}v/\mathrm{d}x)}{v^2}$

and $\dfrac{\mathrm{d}u}{\mathrm{d}x} = \cos x \qquad \dfrac{\mathrm{d}v}{\mathrm{d}x} = 2x$

$$\therefore \quad \frac{dy}{dx} = \frac{x^2(\cos x) - \sin x(2x)}{x^4}$$

$$= \frac{x \cos x - 2 \sin x}{x^3}$$

Example 2   Use the quotient rule to find $\dfrac{d}{dx}\left(\dfrac{e^{3x}}{x^2 - 1}\right)$.

Let $u = e^{3x}$ and $v = x^2 - 1$

Now $\dfrac{d}{dx}\left(\dfrac{u}{v}\right) = \dfrac{v(du/dx) - u(dv/dx)}{v^2}$

where $\dfrac{du}{dx} = 3\,e^{3x}$ and $\dfrac{dv}{dx} = 2x$

$$\therefore \quad \frac{d}{dx}\left(\frac{e^{3x}}{x^2 - 1}\right) = \frac{(x^2 - 1)\,3\,e^{3x} - e^{3x}(2x)}{(x^2 - 1)^2}$$

$$= \frac{e^{3x}(3x^2 - 2x - 3)}{(x^2 - 1)^2}$$

C3.4 Evaluation of derivatives

It is often necessary to find the value of a derivative at a particular point. We may wish to know the gradient of a curve, or the rate at which one variable is changing with respect to another. All we have to do is to substitute values into an expression after differentiating. A calculator can be most useful here.

Example 1   If $y = 2(x^2 + 1)^{3/2}$, find dy/dx when $x = 2.5$.

First we differentiate, using the substitution

$$u = x^2 + 1$$

so that $y = 2u^{3/2}$

Now $\dfrac{dy}{dx} = \dfrac{dy}{du} \times \dfrac{du}{dx}$ (function of a function – see section C3.1)

$$= 3u^{1/2}(2x)$$

$$= 6x\sqrt{(x^2 + 1)}$$

Substituting $x = 2.5$ gives

$$\frac{dy}{dx} = 40.4$$

114

To evaluate trigonometric functions in derivatives, we use *radians*.

Example 2   Given that the current i, measured in amperes, varies with time according to the equation $i = 12t \sin 3t$, calculate the rate of change of current when $t = 0.1\,\text{s}$.

We have $i = 12t \sin 3t$

Differentiating this as a product with respect to t,

let $u = 12t$ and $v = \sin 3t$

Now $\dfrac{di}{dt} = u\dfrac{dv}{dt} + v\dfrac{du}{dt}$ (product rule – see section C3.2)

where $\dfrac{dv}{dt} = 3\cos 3t$ and $\dfrac{du}{dt} = 12$

$\therefore$ $\dfrac{di}{dt} = 12t(3\cos 3t) + \sin 3t(12)$

$= 12(3t\cos 3t + \sin 3t)$

When $t = 0.1$,

$\dfrac{di}{dt} = 12(0.3\cos 0.3 + \sin 0.3)$

$= 7.0$

i.e. the rate of change of current is $7.0\,\text{A/s}$.

(Working in degrees, $0.3\,\text{rad} = 0.3 \times 57.3° = 17.2°$.)

Example 3   Show that the slope of the curve $y = (\ln x)/x^2$ is zero when $\ln x = \tfrac{1}{2}$.

Let $y = (\ln x)/x^2 = u/v$

where $u = \ln x$ and $v = x^2$

so that $\dfrac{dy}{dx} = \dfrac{v(du/dx) - u(dv/dx)}{v^2}$ (quotient rule – see section C3.3)

$= \dfrac{x^2(1/x) - \ln x(2x)}{x^4} = \dfrac{(1 - 2\ln x)}{x^3}$

When $\ln x = \tfrac{1}{2}$, $1 - 2\ln x = 0$

$\therefore$ $\dfrac{dy}{dx} = 0$

115

i.e. the slope of the curve is zero when $\ln x = \frac{1}{2}$.

Exercise C3

1   Use a suitable substitution to find derivatives of the following with respect to x:

(a) $(5x^4 - 2x)^3$ (b) $4\,e^{0.8x}$ (c) $\sin(3x^2 + 4)$

(d) $2\cos(1/x)$ (e) $1/\sqrt{(8 - 3x^2)}$ (f) $3\ln 2x$

(g) $e^{\tan x}$ (h) $3\sin^2 x$

2   Differentiate the following expressions with respect to the variable involved. (Try these without making a substitution – refer to the table i section C3.1 if necessary.)

(a) e^{7x} (b) $\sin 4x$ (c) $4\cos \omega t$ (ω is constant)

(d) $5\ln 4z$ (e) $3\sin(\theta/4)$ (f) $6\,e^{-t/4}$

3   Use the product rule to differentiate the following with respect to x

(a) $x^3 \cos x$ (b) $3x \ln x$ (c) $e^{2x} \cos(x/2)$

(d) $(x - 4)^3 \sin 2x$ (e) $\sin x \cos x$ (f) $x^4 \ln 2x$

4   Differentiate the following quotients with respect to the variable involved:

(a) $\dfrac{x^2}{x + 1}$ (b) $\dfrac{2\,e^{3t}}{\cos t}$ (c) $\dfrac{\ln 2s}{\sqrt{s}}$

(d) $\dfrac{\sin 2\theta}{e^{4\theta}}$ (e) $\dfrac{(1 + z)^2}{(1 - 2z)}$ (f) $\dfrac{x \cos x}{\sin x}$

5   Show that $\dfrac{d}{dx}(\tan x) = \sec^2 x$, by using the quotient rule to differentiate $\dfrac{\sin x}{\cos x}$. (Remember that $\sin^2 x + \cos^2 x = 1$.)

6   Determine the gradient of the curve $y = \sqrt{(x^2 - 3x)}$ at $x = 4.3$.

7   If $z = e^{2t} \sin 3t$, find dz/dt when $t = 0.2$.

8   Find $f'(1.4)$ if $f(x) = (x^2 - 4)/\ln x$.

C4 Second derivatives

C4.1 Successive differentiation

When a function $y = f(x)$ is differentiated with respect to x, the first derivative or differential coefficient is dy/dx or $f'(x)$:

if $y = 3x^4$ then $\dfrac{dy}{dx} = 12x^3$

Differentiating a second time gives the second derivative, d^2y/dx^2 (we say 'dee two y by dee x squared') or $f''(x)$.

In the above example, where $\dfrac{dy}{dx} = 12x^3$, we have $\dfrac{d^2y}{dx^2} = 36x^2$.

The notation $\dfrac{d^2y}{dx^2}$ is simply a convenient way of expressing the second derivative $\dfrac{d}{dx}\left(\dfrac{dy}{dx}\right)$, showing that y has been differentiated *twice* with respect to x; it is *not* the same as $\left(\dfrac{dy}{dx}\right)^2$.

Successive differentiation of the above function would give

$$\frac{d^3y}{dx^3} = 72x \quad \text{and} \quad \frac{d^4y}{dx^4} = 72 \quad \text{and} \quad \frac{d^5y}{dx^5} = 0$$

Example 1   If $y = x^3 - 2x^2 + 3x - 8$, find d^2y/dx^2.

$$y = x^3 - 2x^2 + 3x - 8$$

Differentiating once gives

$$\frac{dy}{dx} = 3x^2 - 4x + 3$$

Differentiating a second times gives

$$\frac{d^2y}{dx^2} = 6x - 4$$

Example 2   Find the value of d^2z/dt^2 when $t = 0.2$, if $z = t^3 - \ln t + e^{2t}$.

$$z = t^3 - \ln t + e^{2t}$$

$$\therefore \frac{dz}{dt} = 3t^2 - \frac{1}{t} + 2\,e^{2t}$$

and $\dfrac{d^2z}{dt^2} = 6t + \dfrac{1}{t^2} + 4\,e^{2t}$

When $t = 0.2$,

$$\frac{d^2z}{dt^2} = 1.2 + \frac{1}{0.04} + 4\,e^{0.4}$$

$$= 32.2$$

117

Example 3 If $y = 2 \sin 2\theta + \cos 2\theta$, show that $\mathrm{d}^2y/\mathrm{d}\theta^2 + 4y = 0$.

$$y = 2 \sin 2\theta + \cos 2\theta$$

$$\therefore \; \frac{\mathrm{d}y}{\mathrm{d}\theta} = 4 \cos 2\theta - 2 \sin 2\theta$$

and $\quad \dfrac{\mathrm{d}^2y}{\mathrm{d}\theta^2} = -8 \sin 2\theta - 4 \cos 2\theta$

Now $\quad 4y = 8 \sin 2\theta + 4 \cos 2\theta$

$$\therefore \quad \frac{\mathrm{d}^2y}{\mathrm{d}\theta^2} + 4y = 0$$

In later sections we shall study applications in which it is necessary to evaluate second derivatives at given points. In a graph of $y = f(x)$, a positive value of $\mathrm{d}y/\mathrm{d}x$ tells us that the value of y is increasing as x increases, while a positive value of $\mathrm{d}^2y/\mathrm{d}x^2$ indicates that the gradient (i.e. $\mathrm{d}y/\mathrm{d}x$) is increasing as x increases.

Example 4 Use differentiation to find the gradient of the curve $y = 2x^3 - x^2 + 4x - 2$ and to determine how the gradient is changing when $x = 0$ and when $x = 0.2$.

We have $\quad y = 2x^3 - x^2 + 4x - 2$

$$\therefore \qquad \frac{\mathrm{d}y}{\mathrm{d}x} = 6x^2 - 2x + 4$$

and $\quad \dfrac{\mathrm{d}^2y}{\mathrm{d}x^2} = 12x - 2$

When $x = 0$, $\dfrac{\mathrm{d}y}{\mathrm{d}x} = 4$ and $\dfrac{\mathrm{d}^2y}{\mathrm{d}x^2} = -2$

The gradient is therefore positive and decreasing when $x = 0$.

When $x = 0.2$, $\dfrac{\mathrm{d}y}{\mathrm{d}x} = 3.84$ and $\dfrac{\mathrm{d}^2y}{\mathrm{d}x^2} = 0.40$

The gradient is positive and increasing when $x = 0.2$.

Example 5 Given that $z = 2 \sin 3\phi$, show that $\mathrm{d}z/\mathrm{d}\phi = 0$ when $\phi = \pi/6$, and find the value of $\mathrm{d}^2z/\mathrm{d}\phi^2$ at that point.

We have $\quad z = 2 \sin 3\phi$

$$\therefore \qquad \frac{\mathrm{d}z}{\mathrm{d}\phi} = 6 \cos 3\phi$$

When $\phi = \pi/6$, $\quad \dfrac{\mathrm{d}z}{\mathrm{d}\phi} = 6\cos(\pi/2) = 0$

Now $\quad \dfrac{\mathrm{d}^2 z}{\mathrm{d}\phi^2} = -18\sin 3\phi$

When $\phi = \pi/6$,

$$\dfrac{\mathrm{d}^2 z}{\mathrm{d}\phi^2} = -18\sin(\pi/2) = -18$$

Example 6 If $y = \mathrm{e}^{x^2+1}$, find the value of $\mathrm{d}^2 y/\mathrm{d}x^2$ when $x = 0.75$.

$$y = \mathrm{e}^{x^2+1}$$

Let $\quad p = x^2 + 1 \quad$ so that $\quad y = \mathrm{e}^p$

Now $\quad \dfrac{\mathrm{d}y}{\mathrm{d}x} = \dfrac{\mathrm{d}y}{\mathrm{d}p} \times \dfrac{\mathrm{d}p}{\mathrm{d}x} \quad$ (function of a function rule – see section C3.1)

where $\quad \dfrac{\mathrm{d}y}{\mathrm{d}p} = \mathrm{e}^p \quad$ and $\quad \dfrac{\mathrm{d}p}{\mathrm{d}x} = 2x$

$\therefore \quad \dfrac{\mathrm{d}y}{\mathrm{d}x} = 2x\,\mathrm{e}^{x^2+1}$

To find $\mathrm{d}^2 y/\mathrm{d}x^2$, let $\quad u = 2x \quad$ and $\quad v = \mathrm{e}^{x^2+1}$

Now $\quad \dfrac{\mathrm{d}^2 y}{\mathrm{d}x^2} = \dfrac{\mathrm{d}}{\mathrm{d}x}\left(\dfrac{\mathrm{d}y}{\mathrm{d}x}\right)$

$$= u\,\dfrac{\mathrm{d}v}{\mathrm{d}x} + v\,\dfrac{\mathrm{d}u}{\mathrm{d}x} \quad \text{(product rule – section C3.2)}$$

where $\quad \dfrac{\mathrm{d}v}{\mathrm{d}x} = 2x\,\mathrm{e}^{x^2+1} \quad$ and $\quad \dfrac{\mathrm{d}u}{\mathrm{d}x} = 2$

$\therefore \quad \dfrac{\mathrm{d}^2 y}{\mathrm{d}x^2} = 2x(2x\,\mathrm{e}^{x^2+1}) + 2(\mathrm{e}^{x^2+1})$

$$= 2\,\mathrm{e}^{x^2+1}(2x^2 + 1)$$

When $x = 0.75$,

$$\dfrac{\mathrm{d}^2 y}{\mathrm{d}x^2} = 20.3$$

C4.2 Velocity and acceleration

Velocity

If a body, moving in a straight line with constant velocity v, covers a distance x in a time t, then

$$v = \frac{x}{t}$$

Thus a body moving 6 metres in 2 seconds has a velocity $v = 6/2 = 3$ m/s. Under these conditions, a graph of distance against time will be a straight line with slope equal to the velocity.

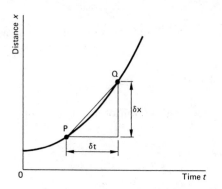

Fig. C4.1

When velocity is not constant but changes with time, a graph of distance moved against time will not be a straight line. In fig. C4.1, two points P and Q are shown on a graph relating distance and time for a moving body. The ratio $\delta x/\delta t$ gives the *average* velocity of the body over the time δt. We define the velocity of the body at P by taking the limit as $\delta t \to 0$ (as we did when differentiating from first principles in section C1.1); so that

$$v = \lim_{\delta t \to 0} \left(\frac{\delta x}{\delta t} \right) = \frac{\mathrm{d}x}{\mathrm{d}t}$$

Thus, by differentiating the function $x = f(t)$ with respect to t, we find the *instantaneous* velocity of the body.

Example 1 A car moves a distance x metres along a straight road in a time t seconds, where x and t are related by the equation $x = t^2 + 2t + 1$. Find the velocity of the car when $t = 0$ s and when $t = 1.2$ s.

We have $x = t^2 + 2t + 1$

120

$$\therefore \quad \text{velocity} = v = \frac{dx}{dt} = 2t + 2$$

When $t = 0\,\text{s}$, $\quad v = 2\,\text{m/s}$

When $t = 1.2\,\text{s}$, $\quad v = 4.4\,\text{m/s}$

Example 2 A stone is dropped from the top of a building, and the distance it falls in a time t seconds is given by $x = 4.9t^2$. Find the velocity of the stone after it has fallen for 2.5 s.

We have $\quad x = 4.9t^2$

$$\therefore \qquad \frac{dx}{dt} = 9.8t$$

When $t = 2.5\,\text{s}$, $\quad \dfrac{dx}{dt} = 24.5\,\text{m/s}$

i.e. the velocity of the stone after falling for 2.5 s is 24.5 m/s.

Angular velocities can be found in the same way from an equation relating angular motion to time.

Example 3 A shaft is rotating such that its angular displacement θ radians at a time t seconds is given by $\theta = 3 \sin 2t$. Find the angular velocity of the shaft when $t = 3.8\,\text{s}$, and show that the shaft comes to rest when $t = \pi/4\,\text{s}$.

$$\theta = 3 \sin 2t$$

$$\therefore \frac{d\theta}{dt} = 6 \cos 2t$$

When $t = 3.8\,\text{s}$, $\quad \dfrac{d\theta}{dt} = 6 \cos 7.6 = 1.51\,\text{rad/s}$

When $t = \pi/4$, $\quad \dfrac{d\theta}{dt} = 6 \cos(\pi/2) = 0\,\text{rad/s}$

i.e. when $t = \pi/4$ the angular velocity is 0 rad/s, so the shaft is at rest.

Acceleration
The rate of change of velocity with respect to time is called *acceleration*. Thus

if $\quad$ velocity $v = \dfrac{dx}{dt}\quad$ then $\quad$ acceleration $a = \dfrac{dv}{dt} = \dfrac{d}{dt}\left(\dfrac{dx}{dt}\right) = \dfrac{d^2x}{dt^2}$

121

The acceleration of a body at time t is therefore given by the slope of the graph of velocity against time at t, and can be found by differentiating the function $v = f(t)$ once or $x = g(t)$ twice, with respect to t.

Example 4   A vehicles moves a distance x metres along a straight track in time t seconds according to the equation $x = 8t + t^3 + 4$. Find (a) the velocity of the vehicle when $t = 0.5\,\text{s}$, (b) the acceleration of the vehicle when $t = 1.5\,\text{s}$.

a) $x = 8t + t^3 + 4$

Velocity is given by

$$v = \frac{dx}{dt} = 8 + 3t^2$$

When $t = 0.5\,\text{s}, \quad v = 8 + 0.75 = 8.75\,\text{m/s}$

i.e. when $t = 0.5\,\text{s}$ the velocity of the vehicle is $8.75\,\text{m/s}$.

b)   Acceleration $a = \dfrac{dv}{dt} = \dfrac{d^2x}{dt^2}$

Now $\dfrac{dx}{dt} = 8 + 3t^2$

$\therefore \qquad a = \dfrac{d^2x}{dt^2} = 6t$

When $t = 1.5\,\text{s}, \quad a = 6(1.5) = 9\,\text{m/s}^2$

i.e. when $t = 1.5\,\text{s}$ the acceleration of the vehicle is $9\,\text{m/s}^2$. (Note that the units of acceleration used here are 'metres per second squared'. A negative value would indicate a *deceleration*.)

Example 5   If $x = 2t^2 - t^3 - t$, where x is the distance in metres move by a body along the x-axis in time t seconds, find (a) the velocity of the body when $t = 0.4\,\text{s}$, (b) the first time at which the velocity is zero, (c) the time at which the acceleration of the body is zero.

a)   We have $x = 2t^2 - t^3 - t$

The velocity of the body is

$$v = \frac{dx}{dt} = 4t - 3t^2 - 1$$

When $t = 0.4\,\text{s}, \quad v = 4(0.4) - 3(0.16) - 1 = 0.12\,\text{m/s}$

b)   The velocity of the body is zero when
$$4t - 3t^2 - 1 = 0$$

122

Factorising this quadratic equation gives

$$(3t - 1)(1 - t) = 0$$

The roots are $t = \frac{1}{3}$ s and $t = 1$ s.

i.e. the first time that the body comes to rest is when $t = \frac{1}{3}$ s.

c) The acceleration of the body is

$$a = \frac{dv}{dt} = \frac{d^2x}{dt^2} = 4 - 6t$$

When $a = 0$, $\quad 4 - 6t = 0$

$$\therefore \quad t = \frac{2}{3} s$$

Angular velocity and acceleration are related in the same way.

Example 6 The angular displacement θ radians of a flywheel varies with time according to the equation $\theta = 8t^2 - t^3$. Find the angular velocity and angular acceleration of the flywheel when $t = 1.2$ s, and determine the time at which the angular acceleration is zero.

We have $\quad \theta = 8t^2 - t^3$

Angular velocity is

$$\frac{d\theta}{dt} = 16t - 3t^2$$

When $t = 1.2$ s, $\quad \dfrac{d\theta}{dt} = 14.9 \, \text{rad/s}$

Angular acceleration is

$$\frac{d^2\theta}{dt^2} = 16 - 6t$$

When $t = 1.2$, $\quad \dfrac{d^2\theta}{dt^2} = 8.80 \, \text{rad/s}^2$

When the angular acceleration is zero,

$$16 - 6t = 0$$

$$\therefore \qquad t = 2.67 \, s$$

Exercise C4

1   Find d^2y/dx^2 from the following equations:
     (a) $y = 3x^5 - x^2 + 9$ (b) $y = \sqrt{x} - \ln x$
     (c) $y = 2 \sin 4x$ (d) $y = 3(x^2 - 1/e^x)$

2 Write down the second derivatives with respect to the variables involved in

    (a) $x = 2\cos 5t$ (b) $z = (1 + s^2)^2$ (c) $r = e^{\sin\theta}$

    (d) $m = \ln(n^2 + 3n)$

3 Evaluate the second derivatives of the following functions at the points indicated:

a) $8x^3 - e^{2x}$ at $x = 0.25$

b) $\sin\theta - 2\cos 2\theta$ at $\theta = \pi/3$

c) $(\sqrt{t} + \ln t)/2$ at $t = 1$

4 If $y = 2e^{3x} + e^{-2x}$, show that $(d^2y/dx^2) - (dy/dx) - 6y = 0$.

5 Determine the gradient of the line $y = x^3 - x^2 + 5x + 2$ at $x = 1$, and state whether the gradient is increasing or decreasing at that point.

6 A particle is moving in a straight line and its distance in metres from a point on the line after t seconds is given by the equation $x = t^3 - 7t^2 + 8t$. Find (a) the velocity and acceleration of the particle when $t = 10\,\text{s}$, (b) the two times at which the velocity of the particle is zero.

7 A car moves so that its distance in metres along a straight road from a position at $t = 0\,\text{s}$ is given by the equation $x = 5t^2 + 8t - t^3/3$. Find how far the car has travelled before it stops accelerating.

8 The angular displacement of a rotating disc at a time t seconds is given by the equation $\theta = 4.5\sin(t/3)$. Find (a) the angular velocity of the disc when $t = 1.80\,\text{s}$, (b) the angular acceleration when $t = 11.5\,\text{s}$, (c) the first time at which the angular acceleration is zero after $t = 0\,\text{s}$.

9 A fuel tank is dropped from a lunar vehicle as it hovers above the surface of the moon. If the tank falls x metres in t seconds according to the equation $x = 0.81t^2$, find its velocity after falling $100\,\text{m}$.

C5 Turning points

C5.1 Defining a turning point

The points P and Q on the graph of $y = x^3 - 12x$ in fig. C5.1 are called *turning points*. At both points, the tangent drawn to the curve would be parallel to the x-axis, and this is one of the necessary conditions at a turning point. The other requirement is that there is a change in the *sign* of the gradient across a turning point.

    If we take the point P at $(-2, 16)$,

$$y = x^3 - 12x$$

the gradient is

$$\frac{dy}{dx} = 3x^2 - 12$$

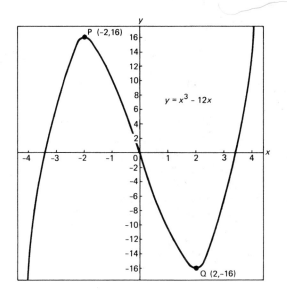

Fig. C5.1 The graph of $y = x^3 - 12x$

at $x = -2$, $\dfrac{\mathrm{d}y}{\mathrm{d}x} = 3(4) - 12 = 0$

This confirms that the tangent at P is parallel to the x-axis.

Taking points on either side of P,

at $x = -2.1$, $\dfrac{\mathrm{d}y}{\mathrm{d}x} = 1.23$

at $x = -1.9$, $\dfrac{\mathrm{d}y}{\mathrm{d}x} = -1.17$

These results confirm what is obvious from the graph, that the gradient changes from being a positive value just before P to a negative value just after P. We call the point P a *maximum*.

Again, at Q $(2, -16)$,

$$\frac{\mathrm{d}y}{\mathrm{d}x} = 3x^2 - 12 = 0$$

at $x = 1.9$, $\dfrac{\mathrm{d}y}{\mathrm{d}x} = -1.17$

and at $x = 2.1$, $\dfrac{\mathrm{d}y}{\mathrm{d}x} = 1.23$

125

Thus the sign of the gradient changes from negative to positive across this turning point. The point Q is a *minimum*.

Using the words 'maximum' and 'minimum' does not imply that the largest and smallest values of y are to be found at P and Q. This is obviously not true. Looking at the graph, we see that when $x > 4$, $y > 16$ and when $x < -4$, $y < -16$.

Stationary points

Turning points are not the only points at which we can have $dy/dx = 0$. There are four situations, shown in fig. C5.2, in which this can occur. Apart from the maximum and minimum points already described and shown in fig. C5.2(a) and (b), there are the *points of inflexion* shown in (c) and (d). At points of inflexion (or contraflexure), the sign of the gradient does *not* change as we move across the point at which $dy/dx = 0$. They can be distinguished from maxima and minima in this way. (Note that we can also have a point of inflexion when $dy/dx \neq 0$.)

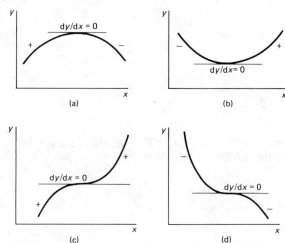

Fig. C5.2 Stationary points

Turning points and points of inflexion are all referred to as *stationary points*.

C5.2 Location of turning points

We could, of course, locate turning points by drawing a graph of the function, but this would take a long time and might require separate graphs showing the vicinity of individual maximum and minimum points. It is usually easier to find by differentiation the points at which $dy/dx = 0$ and then to use one of two methods to decide whether each point is a maximum or a minimum.

126

Example 1 Locate the turning point on the curve $y = 6x - x^2 + 1$. Sketch the curve to find out if the point is a maximum or a minimum.

We have $y = 6x - x^2 + 1$

$\therefore \qquad \dfrac{dy}{dx} = 6 - 2x$

At a turning point, $dy/dx = 0$

$\therefore \quad 6 - 2x = 0$

or $\qquad x = 3$

From the original equation,

at $x = 3$, $\quad y = 6(3) - 9 + 1 = 10$

i.e. the turning point has co-ordinates $(3, 10)$

A sketch of the curve in the vicinity of the turning point (see fig. C5.3) shows that the point is a maximum, since the gradient changes from positive to negative across the point.

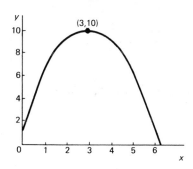

Fig. C5.3 Sketch of $y = 6x - x^2 + 1$

Example 2 Find the maximum and minimum points on the curve $y = x^3 - x^2 - x$.

$\qquad y = x^3 - x^2 - x$

$\therefore \quad \dfrac{dy}{dx} = 3x^2 - 2x - 1$

Now $dy/dx = 0$ at a turning point

$\therefore \quad 3x^2 - 2x - 1 = 0$

or $\quad (3x + 1)(x - 1) = 0$

giving $\quad x = -\frac{1}{3}$ and $\quad x = 1$

Substituting these values of x into the original equation,

at $x = -\frac{1}{3}$, $y = (-\frac{1}{3})^3 - (-\frac{1}{3})^2 - (-\frac{1}{3}) = 0.19$

i.e. the first turning point is $(-0.33, 0.19)$.

To find out if this is a maximum or a minimum we study the gradient on each side of the point:

at $x = -0.40$, $\dfrac{dy}{dx} = 0.28$

at $x = -0.30$, $\dfrac{dy}{dx} = -0.13$

Hence the point $(-0.33, 0.19)$ is a maximum, since the sign of the gradient changes from positive to negative across the point.

At $x = 1$, $y = 1^3 - 1^2 - 1 = -1$

i.e. the second turning point is $(1, -1)$.

Taking points on each side of $x = 1$,

at $x = 0.9$, $\dfrac{dy}{dx} = -0.37$

and at $x = 1.1$, $\dfrac{dy}{dx} = 0.43$

The point $(1, -1)$ is therefore a minimum, since the sign of the gradient changes from negative to positive across the point.

A sketch of the curve is shown in fig. C5.4

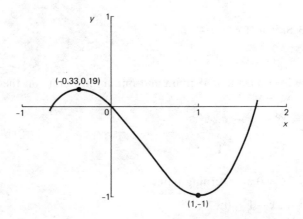

Fig. C5.4 Sketch of $y = x^3 - x^2 - x$

128

C5.3 The use of d^2y/dx^2 to distinguish between maxima and minima

The method used earlier of deciding whether a turning point is a maximum or a minimum by evaluating dy/dx on each side requires several calculations, and may be misleading if points are chosen which are not sufficiently close to the turning point. What we are really trying to determine by these calculations is the way in which the gradient is changing at the turning point. We have already seen in section C4.1 that the second derivative can tell us this.

Once turning points have been located by finding out where $dy/dx = 0$, we can use the *sign* of d^2y/dx^2 to distinguish between maxima and minima. If the second derivative is *positive* at a turning point, it means that dy/dx is increasing and will change from being *negative* before the turning point to *positive* after it. We already know that these conditions indicate a *minimum*. Conversely, a *negative* value of d^2y/dx^2 at a turning point indicates a *maximum*.

In example 2 in the previous section, we found that the turning points on the curve $y = x^3 - x^2 - x$ are at $(-0.33, 0.19)$ and $(1, -1)$, since $dy/dx = 0$ at these points. Let us use the second derivative to test for maximum and minimum points.

We have $y = x^3 - x^2 - x$

$$\therefore \quad \frac{dy}{dx} = 3x^2 - 2x - 1$$

and $\dfrac{d^2x}{dx^2} = 6x - 2$

When $x = -\frac{1}{3}$, $\dfrac{d^2y}{dx^2} = 6(-\frac{1}{3}) - 2 = -4$

The fact that this is *negative* tells us that $(-0.33, 0.19)$ is a *maximum*.

Similarly, when $x = 1$, $\dfrac{d^2y}{dx^2} = 6 - 2 = 4$

The *positive* value indicates that $(1, -1)$ is a *minimum*.

Remember that at a turning point
a *negative* value of the second derivative indicates a *maximum*,
a *positive* value of the second derivative indicates a *minimum*.

Example 1 Show that the curve $y = 8x - 2x^2 + 3$ has a maximum at $(2, 11)$.

From the equation $y = 8x - 2x^2 + 3$

we have $\dfrac{dy}{dx} = 8 - 4x$

At a turning point, $dy/dx = 0$

$\therefore \quad 8 - 4x = 0$

or $\qquad x = 2$

Substituting into the original equation gives $y = 8(2) - 2(4) + 3 = 11$. There is therefore a turning point at $(2, 11)$.

Now $\quad \dfrac{d^2y}{dx^2} = -4 \quad$ (i.e. negative)

The curve therefore has a maximum at $(2, 11)$.

Note that for all quadratic equations $y = ax^2 + bx + c$, the second derivative will be a constant $(d^2y/dx^2 = 2a)$; thus the sign of the coefficient a tells us if the single turning point on a quadratic curve is a maximum or a minimum. A negative value of a indicates a maximum (as in the above example with $a = -2$), while a positive value of a indicates a minimum

Example 2 Find the values of z at the maximum and minimum points on the curve $z = 2t^3 + t^2 - t + 1$.

We have $\quad z = 2t^3 + t^2 - t + 1$

$\therefore \qquad \dfrac{dz}{dt} = 6t^2 + 2t - 1$

At a turning point, $dz/dt = 0$

$\therefore \quad 6t^2 + 2t - 1 = 0$

Using the formula method to solve this quadratic equation,

$$t = \frac{-2 \pm \sqrt{(4 + 24)}}{12} = \frac{-2 \pm 5.29}{12}$$

$\therefore \quad t = -0.61 \quad$ and $\quad t = 0.27$

Considering the turning points one at a time,

at $t = -0.61, \quad z = 2(-0.61)^3 + (-0.61)^2 - (-0.61) + 1 = 1.53$

Now $\quad \dfrac{d^2z}{dt^2} = 12t + 2$

At $t = -0.61, \quad \dfrac{d^2z}{dt^2} = 12(-0.61) + 2 = -5.32$

The point $(-0.61, 1.53)$ is therefore a maximum, since d^2z/dt^2 is negative.

At the second turning point, $t = 0.27$

$\therefore \quad z = 2(0.27)^3 + (0.27)^2 - (0.27) + 1 = 0.84$

and $\quad \dfrac{\mathrm{d}^2 z}{\mathrm{d}t^2} = 12(0.27) + 2 = 5.24$

The point $(0.27, 0.84)$ is therefore a minimum, since $\mathrm{d}^2 z/\mathrm{d}t^2$ is positive.

Thus $z = 1.53$ at the maximum point and $z = 0.84$ at the minimum point.

C5.4 Problems involving maxima and minima

The methods for finding maxima and minima discussed in previous sections can be used in many engineering applications. The first step is to establish an equation relating one variable to another. This often requires the elimination of other variables involved.

Example 1   An open tank with a volume of $2.5\,\mathrm{m}^3$ has a square base and is to be made from sheet steel. Find the dimensions of the tank, to the nearest centimetre, for which the area of steel plate used is a minimum.

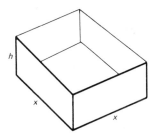

Fig. C5.5

Let the square base of the tank have sides x metres and let the tank height be h metres as shown in fig. C5.5. The volume of the tank is

$$hx^2 = 2.5\,\mathrm{m}^3$$

$$\therefore \quad h = \dfrac{2.5}{x^2}$$

The total area of four sides and the base is

$$A = x^2 + 4xh$$

or $\quad A = x^2 + 4x\left(\dfrac{2.5}{x^2}\right) = x^2 + \dfrac{10}{x}$

Now $\quad \dfrac{\mathrm{d}A}{\mathrm{d}x} = 2x - \dfrac{10}{x^2}$

131

When A is minimum, $dA/dx = 0$

$$\therefore \quad 2x - \frac{10}{x^2} = 0$$

or $\quad 2x^3 = 10$

giving $\quad x = \sqrt[3]{5} = 1.71\,m$

Now $\quad \dfrac{d^2A}{dx^2} = 2 + \dfrac{20}{x^3}$

When $\quad x = 1.71$, $\quad \dfrac{d^2A}{dx^2} = 2 + \dfrac{20}{5} = 6$

The area of steel plate is therefore a minimum when $x = 1.71\,m$, since d^2A/dx^2 is positive. (Note that, as an alternative to using the second derivative, we could show that the values of dA/dx at say $x = 1.70$ and $x = 1.72$ are respectively negative and positive, indicating that the turning point is a minimum.)

Now $\quad h = \dfrac{2.5}{x^2} = \dfrac{2.5}{(1.71)^2} = 0.85\,m$

The dimensions of the tank are therefore $1.71\,m \times 1.71\,m \times 0.85\,m$.

Example 2 The velocity of a motor cycle in metres per second varies with time t seconds according to the equation $v = 11t - 3t^2 + 2$. Find the maximum velocity of the motor cycle in km/h.

$$v = 11t - 3t^2 + 2$$

At maximum velocity, $dv/dt = 0$

$$\therefore \quad 11 - 6t = 0$$

or $\quad t = 1.83\,s$

Now $\quad \dfrac{d^2v}{dt^2} = -6$

hence the velocity is maximum at $t = 1.83\,s$, since d^2v/dt^2 is negative, and so

$$v = 11(1.83) - 3(1.83)^2 + 2 = 12.1\,m/s$$

$$= 12.1 \times \frac{60 \times 60}{1000} = 43.6\,km/h$$

i.e. the maximum velocity of the motor cycle is $43.6\,km/h$.

Example 3 The rate at which a ship's engine consumes fuel is given by $30 + 0.002v^3$ tonnes/hour, where v is the speed of the ship in km/h.

Determine the speed at which the minimum amount of fuel is used on a voyage of 1500 km, and find the amount of fuel used to the nearest tonne.

At a constant speed v, the time taken to sail 1500 km is

$$\frac{\text{distance}}{\text{velocity}} = \frac{1500}{v} \text{ hours}$$

The amount of fuel used is given by

$$F = (30 + 0.002v^3) \times \frac{1500}{v} \text{ tonnes}$$

$$= \frac{45\,000}{v} + 3v^2$$

For minimum fuel use, $dF/dv = 0$

$$\therefore \quad -\frac{45\,000}{v^2} + 6v = 0$$

$$\text{or} \quad v^3 = \frac{45\,000}{6} = 7500$$

giving $v = 19.6 \text{ km/h}$

Now $\dfrac{d^2 F}{dv^2} = \dfrac{90\,000}{v^3} + 6$

When $v = 19.6$, d^2F/dv^2 is positive and therefore F has a minimum value which is given by

$$F = \frac{45\,000}{19.6} + 3(19.6)^2 = 3448 \text{ tonnes}$$

i.e. the speed for greatest fuel economy is 19.6 km/h, when 3448 tonnes of fuel are consumed.

Exercise C5
1   What are the necessary conditions at a turning point for a function $y = f(x)$? Explain the difference between a turning point and a point of inflexion.
2   Locate turning points for the following functions, without stating whether they are maxima or minima:

(a) $y = 5 + 6x^2 - 3x$ (b) $y = 4x^2 + 2x - 3$
(c) $z = 2 \sin 2\theta$ (in the range $0 < \theta < \pi/2$)
(d) $x = t^3/3 - 2t^2 + 3t - 5$ (e) $v = u + 9/u$

3   Show that there is a turning point on the curve $y = 3 - 4x^2 + 10x$ at $(1.25, 9.25)$ and state whether it is a maximum or a minimum.

4 Find the minimum value of $y = 5x^2 + 2x - 3$.

5 Locate the turning points on the curve $y = 9x - 3x^2 - x^3 + 4$ and distinguish between them.

6 Locate and identify the turning points on the curve $y = 9x + 1/x$. Sketch the curve.

7 Locate and identify turning points on the curve $y = x^3 + 2x^2 - 4x - 8$. Sketch the curve.

8 Show that the curve $y = x^3 - 4$ has no maximum or minimum value.

9 A rectangular area is formed by bending a 20 cm long piece of wire in three places. Show that the area enclosed by the wire is maximum when all four sides are 5 cm long.

10 A stone is thrown upwards so that its height x metres after t seconds is given by $x = 18t - 4t^2$. Find the maximum height reached by the stone.

11 A rectangular steel plate measuring 3 m by 2 m has four identical squares of side x m cut from its corners, as shown in fig. C5.6. The plate is then made into a tank, on a press. Find the value of x for which the volume of the tank is maximum.

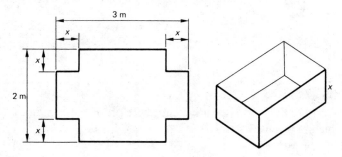

Fig. C5.6

12 If the resistance to motion, F newtons, of a moving vehicle is given by the equation $F = 10/x + 120x$, find the minimum value of F if x is always positive.

13 A closed cylinder with a volume of 0.5 m^3 is to be made from a sheet of copper. Find, to the nearest 10 mm, the height and radius of the cylinder for which the area of material used is minimum.

C6 Indefinite and definite integration

Starting with an equation expressing y in terms of x, we have seen how to differentiate y with respect to x to obtain the differential coefficient denoted by the symbol dy/dx. We shall now consider the reverse process, which is known as *integration*.

C6.1 Indefinite integration

An expression which becomes y when it is differentiated with respect to x is known as 'the *integral* of y with respect to x' and is denoted by the symbol

$$\int y \, dx$$

For example, if $y = x^3$ then $\dfrac{dy}{dx} = 3x^2$

i.e. $\int 3x^2 \, dx = x^3$ or 'the integral of $3x^2$ with respect to x is x^3'

However, if $y = x^3 + C$, where C is any constant, once again $dy/dx = 3x^2$. If, therefore, we are asked to integrate $3x^2$ with respect to x, i.e. to find $\int 3x^2 \, dx$, and we are not given any corresponding values of x and y, the result could be

$$y = x^3$$

or $\quad y = x^3 + 1$

or $\quad y = x^3 + \text{any constant}$

As we cannot give a definite relationship from which to calculate values of y for particular values of x, this result is known as an *indefinite integral* and is usually presented as

$$\int 3x^2 \, dx = x^3 + C$$

where C is known as the *arbitrary constant* and is added to cover the possibility of there having been a constant term in the relationship between x and y which was originally differentiated.

Differentiating $ax + \text{any constant}$ with respect to x, where a is also a constant, gives a; so

$$\int a \, dx = ax + C$$

whatever the value of the constant a.

C6.2 General form of the indefinite integral

Since $\dfrac{dx^n}{dx} = nx^{n-1}$, we can obtain x^n by differentiating $\dfrac{x^{n+1}}{n+1} + C$.

In reverse, therefore,

$$\int x^n \, dx = \frac{x^{n+1}}{n+1} + C$$

This result is true for all values of n, including negative and fraction values, *except* the case $n = -1$, when the denominator in the expression becomes zero. We will briefly mention this special case later, but the following examples illustrate the use of this result for some other values of n.

a) $\int x^4 \, dx = \dfrac{x^5}{5} + C$

b) $\int \dfrac{dx}{x^3} = \int x^{-3} \, dx = \dfrac{x^{-2}}{-2} + C = -\dfrac{1}{2x^2} + C$

c) $\int \sqrt{x} \, dx = \int x^{1/2} \, dx = \dfrac{x^{3/2}}{\frac{3}{2}} + C = \frac{2}{3}\sqrt{x^3} + C$

It should be noted that, when a power of x is multiplied by a constant, that constant remains unchanged by the process of integration and can be placed outside the integration sign,

e.g. $\int 6x^2 \, dx = 6 \int x^2 \, dx = \dfrac{6 \times x^3}{3} + C = 2x^3 + C$

Exception to the general form
The one exception to the general form above is the case where $n = -1$. In this case the integral is of logarithmic form and will be dealt with more fully in later sections:

$$\int \frac{dx}{x} = \ln x + C$$

Integration of a sum
When a sum of several terms is integrated, the result will be the sum of the integrals of the separate terms. Only one arbitrary constant is required.

Examples
a) $\int (3x^2 - 8x + 4) \, dx = x^3 - 4x^2 + 4x + C$

b) $\int (5x - \sqrt{x})^2 \, dx = \int (25x^2 - 10x^{3/2} + x) \, dx$

$$= \frac{25x^3}{3} - 4x^{5/2} + \frac{x^2}{2} + C$$

C6.3 Definite integrals – area under a curve
In fig. C6.1, we wish to find the area under the curve between the limits $x = a$ and $x = b$. Consider a strip of width δx (where δx is very small) at a distance x from the y-axis. The area of this narrow strip is approximately $y\delta x$ and the total area of the section required is given approximately by the sum of all such strips of area $y\delta x$, from $x = a$ to $x = b$.

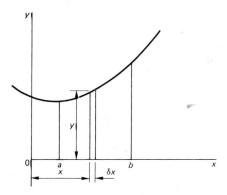

Fig. C6.1

Now the accuracy would be increased by increasing the number of strips, i.e. by reducing the value of δx. Taking this to the limit, the area is given accurately by an infinite number of strips of which the width δx has become the infinitesimal dx. For the sum of these strips we use the long s which has already been introduced as the symbol of integration, and the limits are placed at the head and foot of this symbol. In this notation,

$$\text{area} = \int_a^b y \, dx$$

b and a are referred to as the upper and lower *limits* of the integral.

To calculate the area, the expression obtained after integration is evaluated first with the upper limit (b) substituted for x and then with the lower limit (a) substituted for x. The difference of these results (i.e. the evaluation using b minus the evaluation using a) is the area.

The process of evaluating the integral using the upper limit and then subtracting the evaluation using the lower limit is symbolised by enclosing the integral within square brackets with the upper and lower limits written outside. Thus

if $\qquad y = x^2$

then $\qquad \displaystyle\int_a^b y \, dx = \int_a^b x^2 \, dx$

$$= \left[\frac{x^3}{3} + C \right]_a^b = \left(\frac{b^3}{3} + C \right) - \left(\frac{a^3}{3} + C \right)$$

$$= \frac{b^3}{3} - \frac{a^3}{3} = \tfrac{1}{3}(b^3 - a^3)$$

137

Notice that for any particular curve the arbitrary constant will be the same for both evaluations and so does not enter into the result. An integral between limits is therefore known as a *definite* integral, and, as in the following example, it is not usual to introduce the arbitrary constant at all.

Example 1   Find the area between the curve $y = 2x^2 + 3x + 1$ and the x-axis between the limits $x = 1$ and $x = 2$.

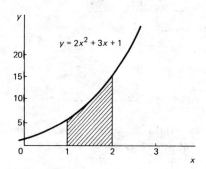

Fig. C6.2

The area is shown shaded in fig. C6.2.

$$\text{Area} = \int_1^2 (2x^2 + 3x + 1)\,dx$$

$$= \left[\frac{2x^3}{3} + \frac{3x^2}{2} + x \right]_1^2$$

$$= \left(\frac{16}{3} + 6 + 2 \right) - \left(\frac{2}{3} + \frac{3}{2} + 1 \right)$$

$$= 10.17 \text{ sq. units}$$

Areas above the axis come out positive, while parts of an area which are below the axis come out negative. This illustrates the necessity of checking whether or not a given curve crosses the axis within the given limits.

Example 2   Find the sum of the three shaded areas enclosed by the curve $y = x^2 - 3x$ and the x-axis in fig. C6.3. Compare this total area with the evaluation of $\displaystyle\int_{-1}^{5} (x^2 - 3x)\,dx$.

138

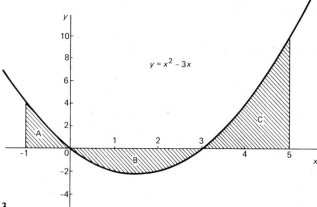

Fig. C6.3

The areas A, B, and C can be calculated separately by choosing as limits of integration $x = -1$ to $x = 0$, $x = 0$ to $x = 3$, and $x = 3$ to $x = 5$ respectively.

$$\text{Area } A = \int_{-1}^{0} (x^2 - 3x)\,dx = \left[\frac{x^3}{3} - \frac{3x^2}{2}\right]_{-1}^{0}$$

$$= (0) - \left(\frac{(-1)^3}{3} - \frac{3(-1)^2}{2}\right)$$

$$= 1.83 \text{ sq. units}$$

$$\text{Area } B = \int_{0}^{3} (x^2 - 3x)\,dx = \left[\frac{x^3}{3} - \frac{3x^2}{2}\right]_{-1}^{3}$$

$$= \left(\frac{(3)^3}{3} - \frac{3(3)^2}{2}\right) - (0)$$

$$= -4.50 \text{ sq. units}$$

$$\text{Area } C = \int_{3}^{5} (x^2 - 3x)\,dx = \left[\frac{x^3}{3} - \frac{3x^2}{2}\right]_{3}^{5}$$

$$= \left(\frac{(5)^3}{3} - \frac{3(5)^2}{2}\right) - \left(\frac{(3)^3}{3} - \frac{3(3)^2}{2}\right)$$

$$= 8.67 \text{ sq. units}$$

(Note that B, the area below the x-axis, is negative while the other two areas which are above the x-axis are positive.)

The *numerical* sum of the areas A, B, and C is
$1.83 + 4.50 + 8.67 = 15$ sq. units.
The *algebraic* sum is $1.83 - 4.50 + 8.67 = 6.0$ sq. units.
Integrating between limits $x = -1$ and $x = 5$ gives the algebraic sum, as follows:

$$\int_{-1}^{5} (x^2 - 3x)\, dx = \left[\frac{x^3}{3} - \frac{3x^2}{2} \right]_{-1}^{5}$$

$$= \left(\frac{(5)^3}{3} - \frac{3(5)^2}{2} \right) - \left(\frac{(-1)^3}{3} - \frac{3(-1)^2}{2} \right)$$

$$= 4.17 - (-1.83)$$

$$= 6.0 \text{ sq. units}$$

Exercise C6
1   Integrate with respect to x (a) $4x$, (b) $8x^3$, (c) $x + 2$, (d) $6x^2 - 4x + 3$.
2   If $dy/dx = 9x^2 + 6x - 10$, find y, given that $y = 0$ when $x = 1$.
3   Given that $s = 0$ when $t = 0$, and $ds/dt = 49 - 9.8t$, find s in terms of t. Hence determine the value of s when $ds/dt = 0$.
4   Integrate the following functions with respect to x:
     (a) $9x^2 - 4x^3$ (b) $4(x - 2)$ (c) $1.8x^2 - 2.2x$
5   Find (a) $\int 4\pi r^2\, dr$, (b) $\int (4 - 10.8t^2)\, dt$.
6   Evaluate

(a) $\displaystyle\int_{1}^{2} (3x^2 - 4x)\, dx$ (b) $\displaystyle\int_{0}^{2} (2 + 3x)^2\, dx$

(c) $\displaystyle\int_{-1}^{3} (x^2 + 2x + 1)\, dx$ (d) $\displaystyle\int_{-2}^{0} (x^2 + 2x - 3)\, dx$

(e) $\displaystyle\int_{1}^{2} (t^{2.5} - 1)\, dt$ (f) $\displaystyle\int_{4}^{9} (2\sqrt{z} - 1/\sqrt{z})dz$

(Use positive values of square roots in (f).)
7   Find the area under the line $y = x$ between $x = 0$ and $x = 3$ by integration. Check the answer by using a formula for the area of a triangle.
8   Find the area enclosed between the x-axis and the curve $y = 7x - x^2 - 6$ by integrating between the limits of $x = 1$ and $x = 6$.
9   Find by integration the shaded area in fig. C6.4(a).
10   Evaluate the shaded area in fig. C6.4(b).
11   Sketch the curve $y = x^2 - 2x$ between $x = 0$ and $x = 4$. Integrate to find the numerical sum of the areas enclosed by the curve, both above and below the x-axis, between $x = 0$ and $x = 2$ and between

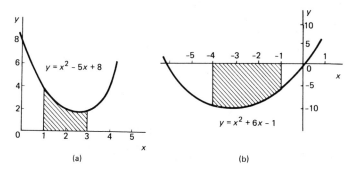

Fig. C6.4

$x = 2$ and $x = 4$. Compare your answer with the evaluation of $\int_0^4 (x^2 - 2x)\,dx$.

12 Sketch the curve $y = x - x^2 + 2$ between $x = -2$ and $x = 4$. Choose suitable limits and find the numerical sum of the three sections of the area enclosed by the curve and the x-axis between $x = -2$ and $x = 4$.

C7 Integration of trigonometric and exponential functions

C7.1 Standard integrals

We can deduce a number of standard integrals, since we now know that integration is the reverse process of differentiation. (You may need to refer to the list of standard derivatives in section C3.1.)

a) $\dfrac{d}{dx}(\cos ax) = -a \sin ax$

$\therefore \quad \int (-a \sin ax)\,dx = \cos ax + C$

or $\qquad \int \sin ax\,dx = -\dfrac{1}{a}\cos ax + C$

b) $\dfrac{d}{dx}(\sin ax) = a \cos ax$

$\therefore \quad \int a \cos ax\,dx = \sin ax + C$

141

or $\quad \displaystyle\int \cos ax \, dx = \frac{1}{a} \sin ax + C$

c) $\quad \dfrac{d}{dx}(\tan ax) = a \sec^2 ax$

$\therefore \quad \displaystyle\int \sec^2 ax \, dx = \frac{1}{a} \tan ax + C$

d) $\quad \dfrac{d}{dx}(e^{ax}) = a \, e^{ax}$

$\therefore \quad \displaystyle\int e^{ax} \, dx = \frac{1}{a} e^{ax} + C$

e) $\quad \dfrac{d}{dx}(\ln ax) = \dfrac{1}{x}$

$\therefore \quad \displaystyle\int \frac{1}{x} \, dx = \ln x + C$

(Note that we need not write $\ln ax + C$, since $\ln ax = \ln x + \ln a$ and the constant $\ln a$ can be included in the arbitrary constant C.)

A summary of these results is given in the following table of useful standard integrals.

y	$\int y \, dx$
ax^n	$\dfrac{a}{n+1} x^{n+1}$
$\sin ax$	$-\dfrac{1}{a} \cos ax$
$\cos ax$	$\dfrac{1}{a} \sin ax$
$\sec^2 ax$	$\dfrac{1}{a} \tan ax$
e^{ax}	$\dfrac{1}{a} e^{ax}$
$\dfrac{1}{x}$	$\ln x$

Example 1 Integrate the following functions with respect to x:

(a) $2x^3 - 4 \sin 5x$ (b) $3 \cos 2x + 2 \sec^2 3x$ (c) $6 e^{1.5x} - 5/x$

a) $\displaystyle\int (2x^3 - 4 \sin 5x)\, dx = \dfrac{2x^{3+1}}{3+1} - 4(-\tfrac{1}{5}\cos 5x) + C$

$$= \dfrac{x^4}{2} + \tfrac{4}{5}\cos 5x + C$$

b) $\displaystyle\int (3 \cos 2x + 2 \sec^2 3x)\, dx = 3(\tfrac{1}{2}\sin 2x) + 2(\tfrac{1}{3}\tan 3x) + C$

$$= \tfrac{3}{2}\sin 2x + \tfrac{2}{3}\tan 3x + C$$

c) $\displaystyle\int (6 e^{1.5x} - 5/x)\, dx = 6\left(\dfrac{1}{1.5}e^{1.5x}\right) - 5(\ln x) + C$

$$= 4 e^{1.5x} - 5 \ln x + C$$

Sometimes the arbitrary constant C can be evaluated, and it is not used at all with definite integrals. Remember to use radians when evaluating trigonometrical functions.

Example 2 Write down an equation for z if $dz/ds = (3s^3 + 1)/s$ and $z = 3$ when $s = 1$.

We have $\dfrac{dz}{ds} = \dfrac{3s^3 + 1}{s} = 3s^2 + \dfrac{1}{s}$

hence $z = \displaystyle\int \left(3s^2 + \dfrac{1}{s}\right) ds$

Integrating gives

$z = s^3 + \ln s + C$

Now $z = 3$ when $s = 1$

$\therefore$ $3 = 1 + 0 + C$ or $C = 2$

giving the equation

$z = s^3 + \ln s + 2$

Example 3 Evaluate the following definite integrals:

(a) $\displaystyle\int_0^1 (4x - e^{3x})\, dx$ (b) $\displaystyle\int_{\pi/4}^{\pi/2} (1 + 3 \cos 4\theta)\, d\theta$

(c) $\displaystyle\int_2^3 \left(\dfrac{3}{t} + 2 \sec^2 \dfrac{t}{4}\right) dt$

143

a) $\displaystyle\int_0^1 (4x - e^{3x})\,dx = [2x^2 - \tfrac{1}{3} e^{3x}]_0^1$

$$= (2 - \tfrac{1}{3} e^3) - (0 - \tfrac{1}{3} e^0)$$

$$= -4.36$$

b) $\displaystyle\int_{\pi/4}^{\pi/2} (1 + 3 \cos 4\theta)\,d\theta = [\theta + \tfrac{3}{4} \sin 4\theta]_{\pi/4}^{\pi/2}$

$$= (\pi/2 + \tfrac{3}{4} \sin 2\pi) - (\pi/4 + \tfrac{3}{4} \sin \pi)$$

$$= 0.785$$

c) $\displaystyle\int_2^3 \left(\frac{3}{t} + 2 \sec^2 \frac{t}{4}\right) dt = \left[3 \ln t + 8 \tan \frac{t}{4}\right]_2^3$

$$= (3 \ln 3 + 8 \tan \tfrac{3}{4}) - (3 \ln 2 + 8 \tan \tfrac{1}{2})$$

$$= 4.30$$

Integration can, of course, be used to determine areas enclosed by trigonometrical and exponential curves. It is often useful to draw a sketch of the function.

Example 4 Find the area enclosed between the curve $y = 2\,e^{x/2} + 1$ and the x-axis between $x = 1$ and $x = 2$.

The area is shown shaded in the sketch in fig. C7.1.

$$\text{Area} = \int_1^2 (2\,e^{x/2} + 1)\,dx = [4\,e^{x/2} + x]_1^2$$

$$= (4\,e^1 + 2) - (4\,e^{1/2} + 1)$$

$$= 5.28 \text{ sq. units}$$

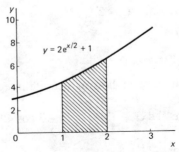

Fig. C7.1 Sketch of the curve $y = 2\,e^{x/2} + 1$

144

It is clear from the sketch that the area will have a value between 4 sq. units and 6 sq. units. A rough check like this can avoid mistakes.

C7.2 Mean and root-mean-square values

Mean value

You are no doubt familiar with the process of finding the mean (or average) value of a list of ten numbers by simply adding them together and dividing the total by ten. Integration can be used to find the mean value of a continuous function over a given range.

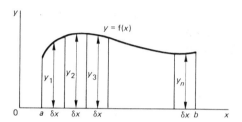

Fig. C7.2

Figure C7.2 shows the area below a curve $y = f(x)$ divided into thin strips, each of width δx. Let $y_1, y_2, y_3, ..., y_n$ be the mid-ordinates of the strips; $\bar{y}$, the mean value of these mid-ordinates, is then given by

$$\bar{y} = \frac{y_1 + y_2 + y_3 + ... + y_n}{n}$$

If we multiply the numerator and the denominator by δx,

$$\bar{y} = \frac{y_1 \, \delta x + y_2 \, \delta x + y_3 \, \delta x + ... + y_n \, \delta x}{n \, \delta x}$$

Now $y_1 \, \delta x$ is approximately the area of the first strip, so, by taking the limit as $\delta x \to 0$, the numerator approaches the total area below the curve between $x = a$ and $x = b$. We can define this area by an integral. The denominator, $n \, \delta x$, is equal to $b - a$; hence

$$\bar{y} = \frac{\int_a^b y \, dx}{b - a}$$

Example 1 Find the mean value of $y = x^2 + 1$ between $x = 1$ and $x = 3$.

$$\text{Mean value } \bar{y} = \frac{1}{3 - 1} \int_1^3 (x^2 + 1) \, dx = \frac{1}{2}\left[\frac{x^3}{3} + x\right]_1^3$$

$$= \tfrac{1}{2}[(9 + 3) - (\tfrac{1}{3} + 1)]$$

$$= 5.33$$

Example 2 The voltage v across a capacitor after a time t seconds is given by the equation $v = 12\,e^{-0.6t}$. Find the mean value of the voltage between $t = 2.0\,\text{s}$ and $t = 2.5\,\text{s}$.

The mean value of v is given by

$$\bar{v} = \frac{1}{2.5 - 2.0} \int_{2.0}^{2.5} v\,dt = \frac{1}{0.5} \int_{2.0}^{2.5} 12\,e^{-0.6t}\,dt$$

$$= \frac{12}{0.5} \left[\frac{-1}{0.6}\,e^{-0.6t} \right]_{2.0}^{2.5}$$

$$= \frac{-12}{0.3} (e^{-1.5} - e^{-1.2})$$

$$= 3.12\,\text{V}$$

Root-mean-square (r.m.s.) value

The root-mean-square value is used for periodic functions when the mean value may be zero. It provides a useful measure for alternating currents and voltages and can be related to electrical power. The r.m.s. value is defined as the square root of the mean value of the square of the function.

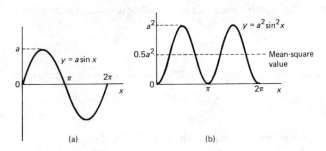

Fig. C7.3

Take as a simple example the function $y = a \sin x$. A complete cycle of the curve is shown in fig. C7.3(a), and we see, of course, that the peak value is a. From a sketch of the *square* of the function (i.e. $y = a^2 \sin^2 x$) shown in fig. C7.3(b), we see that the curve lies entirely above the x-axis and that the peak value is a^2. It is clear from this sketch that the mean-square value is $0.5a^2$ (the curve $y = a^2 \sin^2 x$ is symmetrical about this line). We obtain the r.m.s. value by taking the square root of this mean-square value; hence

r.m.s. value $= \sqrt{(0.5a^2)} = 0.707a$

To find the r.m.s. value of a function $y = f(x)$ analytically, we obtain the mean of all values of y^2 by integration and then take the square

146

root of this mean-square value. Thus the r.m.s. value between $x = a$ and $x = b$ can be stated as follows:

$$\text{r.m.s. value} = \sqrt{\left(\frac{1}{b-a}\int_a^b y^2 \, dx\right)}$$

Example The instantaneous current i amperes in a circuit is given by $i = 5 \sin \omega t$. Find the r.m.s. value of the current between $t = 0\,$s and $t = 2\pi/\omega\,$s.

The current is $\quad i = 5 \sin \omega t$

$$\text{Mean-square value} = \frac{1}{2\pi/\omega - 0}\int_0^{2\pi/\omega} (5 \sin \omega t)^2 \, dt$$

$$= \frac{25\omega}{2\pi}\int_0^{2\pi/\omega} \sin^2 \omega t \, dt$$

Now $\quad \sin^2 \omega t = \dfrac{1 - \cos 2\omega t}{2}$

(This comes from the identities $\cos 2x = \cos^2 x - \sin^2 x$ and $\sin^2 x + \cos^2 x = 1$ – see section D6.1.)

The integral becomes $\quad \dfrac{25\omega}{4\pi}\displaystyle\int_0^{2\pi/\omega} (1 - \cos 2\omega t) \, dt$

Integration gives

$$\text{mean-square value} = \frac{25\omega}{4\pi}\left[t - \frac{1}{2\omega}\sin 2\omega t\right]_0^{2\pi/\omega}$$

$$= \frac{25\omega}{4\pi}\left[\left(\frac{2\pi}{\omega} - 0\right) - (0 - 0)\right]$$

$$= \frac{25}{2}$$

$$\therefore \quad \text{r.m.s. value} = \sqrt{\frac{25}{2}} = \frac{5}{\sqrt{2}}\,\text{A}$$

Note that this is a well known result. The peak value of a current waveform $i = I \sin \omega t$ is I amperes and the r.m.s. value is $I/\sqrt{2}$ or $0.707I$. A direct current of $0.707I$ amperes will deliver the same power in a given time as an alternating current with peak value I amperes.

C7.3 Approximate methods of integration

You may by now have studied some approximate methods of finding areas, such as the mid-ordinate rule, the trapezoidal rule, and Simpson's rule. These involve dividing the area up into thin strips and using a

147

numerical method to sum the areas of the strips. The accuracy of the results obtained using these methods depends upon the nature of the area and the number of strips used. (You may remember that for some functions Simpson's rule gives exact values for the area.) By contrast, integration will always give answers which are exactly correct.

To find the area under one loop of a sine wave by integration

$$\text{area} = \int_0^\pi \sin x \, dx = [-\cos x]_0^\pi$$

$$= -(-1) - (-1)$$

$$= 2 \text{ sq. units}$$

Compare this true value with those in the following table, obtained using the three approximate methods discussed with different numbers of strips.

Rule	Area		
	Number of strips		
	2	4	6
Mid-ordinate	2.221	2.052	2.023
Trapezoidal	1.571	1.896	1.954
Simpson's	2.094	2.005	2.001

The approximate methods can be used to find areas when a function is difficult to integrate, or when a numerical method is needed for computer solution.

Exercise C7

1 Integrate the following functions with respect to x:
   (a) $2x^{0.8} + 6 \cos 2x$ (b) $4 \sin(x/3) - 3 e^{-2.1x} + 1$
   (c) $(1 + x)/x^2$

2 Given that $ds/dt = 1 - 2 \cos 2t$, and if $s = 0$ when $t = \pi/2$, write down an equation for s.

3 Evaluate the following definite integrals:

   (a) $\int_1^4 (3x - x^2 + 2) \, dx$ (b) $\int_{0.1}^{0.3} 3 e^{5z} \, dz$

   (c) $\int_{3.1}^{6.8} (2 + 3/t) dt$ (d) $\int_{-\pi/4}^{\pi/2} 2 \cos x \, dx$

   (e) $\int_{\pi/6}^{\pi/3} 5 \sin 3\theta \, d\theta$ (f) $\int_{1.1}^{2.1} \frac{2 \, d\phi}{1 - \sin^2 \phi}$

148

4 Sketch the curve $y = 4 - 3\,\mathrm{e}^{-2x}$. Find by integration the area enclosed by the curve and the x-axis between $x = 1$ and $x = 2$. Use your sketch to make a rough check of the area.

5 The work done by a force F which moves a body through a distance $(b - a)$ from $x = a$ to $x = b$ is given by $\int_a^b F\,\mathrm{d}x$. Find the work done when a force given by $F = 3/x + 1$ newtons moves a body a distance from $x = 2.5$ metres to $x = 8.5$ metres.

6 Find the mean values of the following functions between the given limits:

a) $y = 3x + 2$, from $x = 2$ to $x = 5$
b) $z = t - 4/t$, from $t = 1$ to $t = 11$
c) $v = 1 + 2.8 \sin 4\theta$, from $\theta = \pi/4$ to $\theta = \pi/2$
d) $r = 2.4\,\mathrm{e}^{-0.6s} + 1/s^2$, from $s = 2.2$ to $s = 4.1$

7 The velocity v metres per second of a train as it slows down before a station is given by $v = 5 - t^3/30$. Find the average velocity over the first five seconds of deceleration.

8 Find the r.m.s. value of $y = 1 + x$ between $x = 1$ and $x = 3$.

9 Determine the r.m.s. value of $2\,\mathrm{e}^x$ between $x = 1.5$ and $x = 1.8$.

10 The instantaneous potential difference v in a circuit is given by the equation $v = 3 \cos 2t$. Find, using integration, the r.m.s. value of the voltage from $t = 0\,\mathrm{s}$ to $t = \pi\,\mathrm{s}$. [Note that $\cos^2 x = (1 + \cos 2x)/2$.]

C8 Volumes by integration

C8.1 Volume of a solid of revolution
Integration can be applied to finding volumes as well as areas. The area shown in fig. C8.1(a) lies below a curve $y = f(x)$ between $x = a$ and

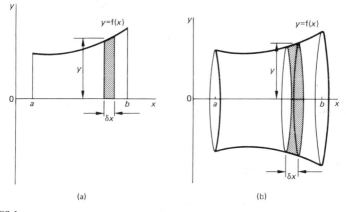

(a)　　　　　(b)

Fig. C8.1

$x = b$. If we rotate this area about the x-axis through 360°, the *solid of revolution* shown in fig. C8.1(b) is produced.

Consider the area in fig. C8.1(a) to be made up of a large number of thin strips. A typical strip is shown shaded and has an area of approximately $y\,\delta x$. When rotation of the area takes place to give the solid of revolution, a thin disc is swept out by the strip. The volume of this *elemental* disc (see fig. C8.1(b)) is approximately $\pi y^2 \delta x$. The total volume of the solid is given by the sum of the volumes of all the elemental discs between $x = a$ and $x = b$; hence

$$\text{total volume} = \sum_{x=a}^{x=b} \pi y^2\, \delta x \quad \text{(approximately)}$$

This approximation becomes more accurate as the number of discs is increased. Taking the limit as $\delta x \to 0$, the volume can be defined exactly by an integral:

$$\text{volume } V = \int_a^b \pi y^2\, \mathrm{d}x$$

The following examples show how to use this expression to find volumes of revolution. As when finding areas, it is often helpful to draw a sketch.

Example 1   Find the volume of the solid of revolution produced when the area below the line $y = x$ between $x = 0$ and $x = 3$ is rotated through 360° about the x-axis.

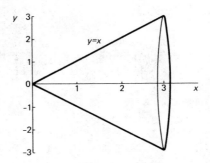

Fig. C8.2

The volume required is shown in the sketch in fig. C8.2:

$$\text{volume} = \int_0^3 \pi y^2\, \mathrm{d}x = \int_0^3 \pi x^2\, \mathrm{d}x$$

$$= \pi \left[\frac{x^3}{3} \right]_0^3 = \pi(9 - 0)$$

$$= 9\pi \quad \text{or} \quad 28.3 \text{ cubic units}$$

In this case we can verify the answer, since the volume of revolution is of course a cone. The volume of a cone is $\frac{1}{3}\pi r^2 h$, where $r = 3$ (i.e. $y = 3$ when $x = 3$) and $h = 3$,

$\therefore \quad \frac{1}{3}\pi r^2 h = \frac{1}{3}\pi(27) = 9\pi$ cubic units

Example 2 What is the volume generated when the area below the curve $y = x^2 + 2$ between $x = 1$ and $x = 2$ is rotated through one complete revolution?

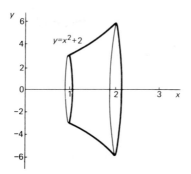

Fig. C8.3

The volume is shown in fig. C8.3:

$$\text{required volume} = \int_1^2 \pi y^2 \, dx$$

Now $y = x^2 + 2$

$\therefore \quad y^2 = (x^2 + 2)^2 = x^4 + 4x^2 + 4$

hence volume $= \pi \int_1^2 (x^4 + 4x^2 + 4) \, dx$

$$= \pi \left[\frac{x^5}{5} + \frac{4x^3}{3} + 4x \right]_1^2$$

$$= \pi \left[\left(\frac{32}{3} + \frac{32}{3} + 8 \right) - \left(\frac{1}{5} + \frac{4}{3} + 4 \right) \right]$$

$$= 19.5\pi \quad \text{or} \quad 61.3 \text{ cubic units}$$

The volume of solids of revolution about the y-axis can be found by integration in the same way. If an area enclosed by a curve $x = f(y)$ and the y-axis between $y = c$ and $y = d$ rotates about the y-axis through $360°$, the volume generated is given by

151

$$\text{volume} = \int_c^d \pi x^2 \, dy$$

Example 3 Show that the volume produced by the rotation through one complete revolution of the area enclosed between the curve $x^2 + y^2 = r^2$ and the y-axis from $y = -r$ to $y = r$ is equal to $\tfrac{4}{3}\pi r^3$.

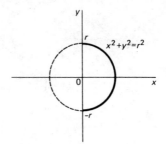

Fig. C8.4

The curve $x^2 + y^2 = r^2$ is shown in fig. C8.4. The volume required is given by

$$V = \int_{-r}^r \pi x^2 \, dy$$

Now $x^2 = r^2 - y^2$

$$\therefore \quad V = \pi \int_{-r}^r (r^2 - y^2) \, dy = \pi \left[r^2 y - \frac{y^3}{3} \right]_{-r}^r$$

$$= \pi \left[\left(r^3 - \frac{r^3}{3} \right) - \left(-r^3 + \frac{r^3}{3} \right) \right]$$

$$= \tfrac{4}{3}\pi r^3 \text{ cubic units}$$

Note that the curve $x^2 + y^2 = r^2$ is a circle with radius r, and the volume we have found is, of course, that of a sphere.

Example 4 Figure C8.5 shows the area enclosed by the curve $y = 4/x^2$ and the x-axis between $x = 1$ and $x = 2$. Find the volume of the solid produced by the rotation of this area through one revolution about the x-axis. Find also the volume generated when the area enclosed between the same section of the curve and the y-axis is rotated through a complete revolution about the y-axis.

Rotation about the x-axis

$$\text{Volume} = \int_1^2 \pi y^2 \, dx = \pi \int_1^2 \frac{16}{x^4} \, dx$$

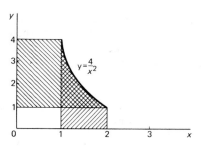

ig. C8.5

$$= \pi \left[\frac{-16}{3x^3} \right]_1^2 = \pi \left[\frac{-16}{24} - \left(\frac{-16}{3} \right) \right]$$

$$= 4.67\pi \quad \text{or} \quad 14.7 \, \text{cubic units}$$

Rotation about the y-axis

We have $y = 4/x^2$ or $x^2 = 4/y$

When $x = 1$, $y = 4$; when $x = 2$, $y = 1$.

The volume required is given by

$$\text{volume} = \int_1^4 \pi x^2 \, \mathrm{d}y = \pi \int_1^4 \frac{4}{y} \, \mathrm{d}y$$

$$= \pi [4 \ln y]_1^4 = \pi (4 \ln 4 - 4 \ln 1)$$

$$= 5.55\pi \quad \text{or} \quad 17.4 \, \text{cubic units}$$

C8.2 The centroid of a solid of revolution

An introduction to the *centroid* can be found in *Mathematics for level-2 technicians*, section D3. Section D1 in this book deals with the location of centroids of plane areas. You may find it useful to read these before starting this section, which is concerned with centroids of volumes of revolution.

Many calculations in engineering and science are made easier when we can consider all the mass of a body to be concentrated at a point. We call this point the *centre of gravity* (or centre of mass) of the body. When the material of the body is *homogeneous* (i.e. there is a constant density throughout the body), the centre of gravity coincides with the geometric centre of the space occupied by the body, which we call the centroid. For example, the centre of gravity and the centroid of a steel ball are at the same point, whereas the centre of gravity of a cylindrical can half-filled with oil will be at a point below the centroid. We shall treat all volumes of revolution as homogeneous solids in this section, so that centroids and centres of gravity will always coincide.

153

If we let the centroid of a solid of revolution be a point $(\bar{x}, \bar{y})$, it is obvious (from the symmetry of the volume) that the centroid of a solid of revolution formed by rotation about the x-axis will lie on the x-axis (i.e. $\bar{y} = 0$). If the volume is V, then

$$V\bar{x} = M$$

where M is the total *moment* of the volume with respect to a plane perpendicular to the x-axis passing through the origin. This equation arises from taking moments about the origin, when the moments of masses acting at known distances are equated. Having established, however, that the solids of revolution are homogeneous, we have replaced *mass* with *volume* by ignoring an identical density factor on both sides of the equation.

Consider the solid of revolution in fig. C8.6, formed by rotating the area below the curve $y^2 = 4x$ between $x = 1$ and $x = 4$ through 360° about the x-axis. Let the centroid be at the point G $(\bar{x}, 0)$.

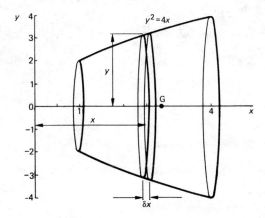

Fig. C8.6

Taking an elemental disc with volume approximately $\pi y^2 \, \delta x$ at a distance x along the x-axis, the moment of the disc about the origin is given by

moment of the disc $= x(\pi y^2 \, \delta x)$

The value of M for the whole volume is obtained by taking the limit as $\delta x \to 0$, when the total moment of an infinite number of discs between $x = 1$ and $x = 4$ is given by the integral

$$M = \int_1^4 \pi x y^2 \, \mathrm{d}x$$

154

Now $y^2 = 4x$

$$\therefore \quad M = 4\pi \int_1^4 x^2 \, dx = 4\pi \left[\frac{x^3}{3} \right]_1^4$$

$$= 4\pi \left(\frac{64}{3} - \frac{1}{3} \right) = 263.9$$

We know that V, the volume of the solid of revolution, is given by

$$V = \int_1^4 \pi y^2 \, dx = 4\pi \int_1^4 x \, dx$$

$$= 4\pi \left[\frac{x^2}{2} \right]_1^4 = 4\pi(8 - \tfrac{1}{2})$$

i.e. $V = 94.3$

Now $V\bar{x} = M$

$$\therefore \quad \bar{x} = \frac{M}{V} = \frac{263.9}{94.3} = 2.80$$

i.e. the centroid of the volume of revolution is at the point $(2.80, 0)$.

Example Locate the centroid of the solid produced by rotating about the x-axis the area below the curve $y = 4 - x^2$ between $x = 1.0$ and $x = 1.5$.

The centroid will lie on the x-axis at $(\bar{x}, 0)$, where $\bar{x}$ is given by the equation $\bar{x} = M/V$ relating the volume V and the total moment of the volume M.

The value of M for the solid is given by

$$M = \int_{1.0}^{1.5} \pi x y^2 \, dx = \pi \int_{1.0}^{1.5} x(4 - x^2)^2 \, dx$$

$$= \pi \int_{1.0}^{1.5} (x^5 - 8x^3 + 16x) \, dx = \pi \left[\frac{x^6}{6} - 2x^4 + 8x^2 \right]_{1.0}^{1.5}$$

$$= \pi(9.773 - 6.167) = 11.3$$

The volume of the solid is given by

$$V = \int_{1.0}^{1.5} \pi y^2 \, dx = \pi \int_{1.0}^{1.5} (x^4 - 8x^2 + 16) \, dx$$

$$= \pi \left[\frac{x^5}{5} - \frac{8x^3}{3} + 16x \right]_{1.0}^{1.5} = 9.93$$

155

Hence $\bar{x} = \dfrac{M}{V} = \dfrac{11.3}{9.93} = 1.20$

i.e. the centroid of the solid of revolution is at the point $(1.20, 0)$.

Exercise C8

1   Find the volumes of the solids of revolution formed when areas below the following curves, between the limits given, are rotated through one complete revolution about the x-axis. (Try to draw a rough sketch and check your answer wherever possible.)

a) $y = 4$, between $x = 1$ and $x = 3$
b) $y = 3x$, between $x = 2$ and $x = 4$
c) $y = 10/x^2$, between $x = 2.5$ and $x = 3.5$
d) $y = x^3/2$, between $x = 0$ and $x = 2$
e) $y = 2\,e^{x/2}$, between $x = 0.5$ and $x = 1.5$
f) $y^2 = 3/x$, between $x = 2.2$ and $x = 4.8$

2   Find the volume of the solid formed when the area between the curve $y = x^2$ and the x-axis from $x = 2$ to $x = 3$ is rotated about the x-axis through $360°$. Find also the volume generated when the area enclosed by the same section of the curve and the y-axis rotates about the y-axis.

3   The area between the curve $x\sqrt{y} = 1$ and the y-axis from $y = 1.35$ to $y = 2.75$ is rotated through one complete revolution about the y-axis. Find the volume of the resulting solid.

4   A solid of revolution is formed by rotating the area below the line $y = 2x + 1$ between $x = 0$ and $x = 2$ through $360°$ about the x-axis. Find the co-ordinates of the centroid of the solid.

5   Find the co-ordinates of the centroid of the hemisphere formed when the shaded area in fig. C8.7 is rotated through one complete revolution about the x-axis.

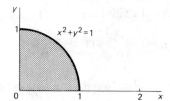

Fig. C8.7

C9 Differential equations

C9.1 Families of curves

If we were asked to write down an equation $y = f(x)$ given that $dy/dx = 2$, we could integrate both sides with respect to x to give

156

$$y = \int 2 \, dx = 2x + C$$

where C is an arbitrary constant. We cannot identify a single equation relating y and x unless the value of C is known. Among the possible equations are $y = 2x$, $y = 2x + 1$, $y = 2x + 4$, and $y = 2x - 3$. There is, of course, an infinite number of these equations, all with the form $y = 2x + C$ and all of them satisfying the equation $dy/dx = 2$. They represent straight lines with a gradient of 2, and some of them are shown in fig. C9.1.

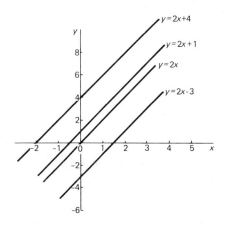

Fig. C9.1 Four members of the family $y = 2x + C$

We say that the equation $y = 2x + C$ represents a *family* of curves. A single member of the family can be identified if we know a point through which the curve passes. Thus, if we are told that the graph of $y = 2x + C$ passes through the point $(2, 5)$, we have

$$y = 2x + C \quad \text{and} \quad x = 2 \text{ when } y = 5$$

$$\therefore \quad 5 = (2 \times 2) + C \quad \text{giving} \quad C = 1$$

The equation is therefore $y = 2x + 1$.

Example Sketch the family of curves given by the equation $dy/dx = 6x$, and find the equation of one of these curves which passes through the point $(1, 2)$.

We have $\dfrac{dy}{dx} = 6x$

$$\therefore \qquad y = \int 6x \, dx = 3x^2 + C$$

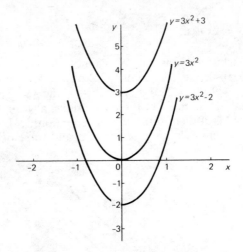

Fig. C9.2 Members of the family of curves $y = 3x^2 + C$

Some members of the family of curves with an equation of the form $y = 3x^2 + C$ are shown in fig. C9.2. To find out which curve passes through the point $(1, 2)$, we substitute $x = 1$ and $y = 2$ into the equation

$$y = 3x^2 + C$$

giving $2 = 3 + C$ or $C = -1$

i.e. the equation of the curve is $y = 3x^2 - 1$

C9.2 Differential equations of the form $dy/dx = f(x)$

Equations involving differential coefficients are called *differential equations*. They occur frequently in engineering and science.

The equation $dy/dx = 6x$ involves the first derivative, dy/dx, and is known as a *first-order* differential equation. (Note that second-order differential equations contain a second derivative such as d^2y/dx^2. We are not concerned with these here.) Solutions to first-order differential equations of the form $dy/dx = f(x)$ can usually be found directly by integrating.

Thus, in our example, $\dfrac{dy}{dx} = 6x$

Integrating gives $y = \displaystyle\int 6x \, dx = 3x^2 + C$

This solution, which we have seen in section C9.1, contains an arbitrary constant and is known as a *general solution*. Additional information or *boundary conditions* will enable us to evaluate C and to write down the *particular solution*. This will be an equation

158

representing a single member of the family of curves defined by the general solution. Thus, if we have the general solution $y = 3x^2 + C$ and are given the boundary conditions $y = 16$ when $x = 2$, then

$$y = 3x^2 + C$$

gives $16 = 3(2)^2 + C$ or $C = 4$

i.e. the particular solution is $y = 3x^2 + 4$.

Example 1 Find the general solution to the differential equation $dy/dx = 4x + 1$. Determine the particular solution given the boundary conditions $y = 4$ when $x = -1$.

We have $\dfrac{dy}{dx} = 4x + 1$

Integrating both sides with respect to x,

$$y = \int (4x + 1)\, dx = 2x^2 + x + C$$

i.e. the general solution to the differential equation is $y = 2x^2 + x + C$.

Substituting the boundary conditions $y = 4$ when $x = -1$ gives

$$4 = 2 - 1 + C$$

$$\therefore \quad C = 3$$

i.e. the particular solution is $y = 2x^2 + x + 3$.

Example 2 A vehicle, moving in a straight line, is x metres from a fixed point after t seconds. The velocity of the vehicle along the x-axis is given by the differential equation $dx/dt = 3t + 2$. If $x = 25$ m when $t = 3$ s, find the value of x when $t = 10$ s.

We have the differential equation

$$\frac{dx}{dt} = 3t + 2$$

Integrating both sides with respect to t gives

$$x = \frac{3t^2}{2} + 2t + C$$

When $t = 3$ s, $x = 25$ m

$$\therefore \quad 25 = \frac{27}{2} + 6 + C$$

and so $C = 5.5$

i.e. the distance x is given by the equation

$$x = \frac{3t^2}{2} + 2t + 5.5$$

When $t = 10\,\text{s}$,

$$x = \frac{3(10)^2}{2} + 2(10) + 5.5 = 175.5\,\text{m}$$

i.e. when $t = 10\,\text{s}$, the distance of the vehicle from the fixed point is $x = 175.5\,\text{m}$.

C9.3 Differential equations of the form $dQ/dt = kQ$

We cannot simply integrate both sides of a differential equation $dQ/dt = kQ$ with respect to t for a solution of the form $Q = \mathrm{f}(t)$ – to do this we would need to be able to express Q on the r.h.s. as a function of t, and this would be the solution we are looking for in the first place! Methods of solving this type of differential equation by integration following the separation of variables are beyond the scope of this book.

The general solution of a differential equation of the form $dQ/dt = kQ$ is in fact $Q = A\,e^{kt}$, where A is a constant. We can show that this is true by differentiating both sides of the solution with respect to t:

if $\quad Q = A\,e^{kt} \quad$ then $\quad \dfrac{dQ}{dt} = kA\,e^{kt} = kQ$

i.e. $dQ/dt = kQ$, which is the original differential equation.

By assuming a general solution of the form $Q = A\,e^{kt}$, we can substitute boundary conditions to evaluate A and find the particular solution.

Example 1 Find the particular solution of the differential equation $dQ/dt = 4Q$ given that $Q = 5.2$ when $t = 0.1$.

We have $\quad \dfrac{dQ}{dt} = 4Q$

The general solution is $Q = A\,e^{4t}$, where A is a constant.

Substituting $t = 0.1$ and $Q = 5.2$ gives

$$5.2 = A\,e^{0.4} = 1.49A$$

$$\therefore \quad A = \frac{5.2}{1.49} = 3.49$$

The particular solution to the differential equation is therefore $Q = 3.49\,e^{4t}$.

In section B2 there are many examples of natural laws of growth and decay which can be defined by equations of the form $Q = A e^{kt}$. From the work in this section, it is clear that $Q = A e^{kt}$ is the general solution of the differential equation $dQ/dt = kQ$. We can deduce that the natural laws relate to situations in which the rate of change of a variable Q at a given time t is proportional to the *value* of Q at that time.

Example 2   Newton's law of cooling states that the rate at which a body cools is proportional to the temperature difference between the body and its surroundings. For a temperature difference $\Delta\theta$ between a body and its surroundings, the cooling rate is given by $d(\Delta\theta)/dt = k\Delta\theta$. Write down the general solution to this differential equation and find the value of k if the temperature difference drops from $\Delta\theta = 50\,°C$ to $\Delta\theta = 48\,°C$ in the first four minutes of cooling. Use the solution to determine the temperature difference after 10 minutes of cooling.

We have the differential equation $\dfrac{d(\Delta\theta)}{dt} = k\Delta\theta$

The general solution is $\Delta\theta = A e^{kt}$

When $t = 0$, $\Delta\theta = 50\,°C$ and so $50 = A e^0 = A$

Substituting $A = 50$ gives the particular solution to the differential equation:

$\Delta\theta = 50 e^{kt}$

Now when $t = 4$ minutes, the temperature has fallen so that $\Delta\theta = 48\,°C$,

$\therefore$ $48 = 50 e^{4k}$

giving $e^{4k} = 0.96$

Rearranging this into logarithmic form,

$4k = \ln 0.96$

$\therefore$ $k = \frac{1}{4} \ln 0.96 = -0.04/4 = -0.01$

Hence $\Delta\theta = 50 e^{-0.01t}$

To find the temperature difference after ten minutes of cooling, substitute $t = 10$ minutes, giving

$\Delta\theta = 50 e^{-0.1} = 45.2\,°C$

i.e. after a total of ten minutes cooling, the temperature of the body is 45.2 °C above room temperature.

Example 3   At a time t after the switch in fig. C9.3 is moved from A to B, the current i is given by the equation

161

$$iR + L\frac{di}{dt} = 0$$

Obtain the general solution for the current i in terms of R, L, and t. If $R = 10\,\Omega$, $L = 4\,H$, and $i = 2\,A$ when $t = 0\,s$, find the current flowing when $t = 0.3\,s$ and the time taken for the current to fall to $0.1\,A$.

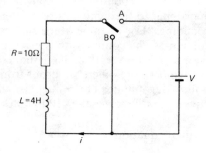

Fig. C9.3

The general solution to the differential equation $\dfrac{di}{dt} = -\dfrac{R}{L}i$ is

$\quad i = I\,e^{-(Rt/L)}$ where I is a constant

Now $i = 2\,A$ when $t = 0\,s$,

$\therefore\quad 2 = I\,e^0$ or $I = 2$ (note incidentally that $I = V/R$)

giving the particular solution

$\quad i = 2\,e^{-(Rt/L)} = 2\,e^{-(10t/4)}$ since $R = 10\,\Omega$ and $L = 4\,H$

Substituting $t = 0.3$ to find the current flowing after 0.3 seconds gives

$\quad i = 2\,e^{-3/4} = 0.945\,A$

To find the time taken for the current to fall to $0.1\,A$, we substitute $i = 0.1$ into the equation $i = 2\,e^{-(10t/4)}$, giving

$\quad 0.1 = 2\,e^{-2.5t}$

or $\quad e^{-2.5t} = 0.05$

Rearranging this into logarithmic form,

$$t = -\frac{1}{2.5}\ln 0.05 = -\frac{(-3.00)}{2.5} = 1.20\,s$$

i.e. the current will have fallen to $0.1\,A$ after 1.20 seconds.

Exercise C9

1   Sketch the family of curves represented by each of the following differential equations:

(a) $dy/dx = 3$ (b) $dy/dx = 4x$ (c) $dy/dx = 2x + 1$

2   Write down the general solution to the differential equation $dy/dx = 6x^2 - 4$, and sketch the family of curves it represents.

3   Write down the particular solution to the differential equation $dy/dx = 2x - 1$, given that $y = 5$ when $x = 2$.

4   Solve the differential equation $dz/dt - t^2 = 5$, if $z = 18$ when $t = 3$.

5   Find the particular solution to the equation $dr/d\theta = 2\cos\theta$, given that $r = 3$ when $\theta = \pi/2$.

6   If $dx/dt = kt + 1$, where k is a constant, write down the particular solution, given that $x = 1$ when $t = 0$. Find k if $x = 13$ when $t = 4$.

7   A ball is thrown vertically upwards with an initial velocity $u = 18\,\text{m/s}$. If the motion of the ball is described by the differential equation $dx/dt = u - gt$, where x is the height of the ball at time t, and $g = 9.8\,\text{m/s}^2$, find the height of the ball after 2.5 seconds if $x = 0\,\text{m}$ when $t = 0\,\text{s}$.

8   Find the particular solution to the equation $dy/dx = 3y$ if $y = 500$ when $x = 2$.

9   If $dz/dt = kz$, find the particular solution, given that $z = 5$ when $t = 0$. Determine the value of k if $z = 15$ when $t = 1$.

10   The current i amperes in a conductor at a time t seconds is given by the differential equation $di/dt + ki = 0$, where k is a constant. If $i = 3.5\,\text{A}$ when $t = 0\,\text{s}$, and $i = 1.4\,\text{A}$ when $t = 1.5\,\text{s}$, find the value of k and determine the current flowing when $t = 2\,\text{s}$.

11   The motion of a body moving with a velocity v against a resistance which is proportional to v is described by the differential equation $dv/dt = -kv$. If the initial velocity of the body is $150\,\text{m/s}$, and the velocity when $t = 2.8\,\text{s}$ is $80\,\text{m/s}$, find the time at which the velocity is reduced to $15\,\text{m/s}$.

12   For an object at a temperature $\Delta\theta$ above that of its surroundings, the rate of cooling is given by the differential equation $d(\Delta\theta)/dt = -k\Delta\theta$. If $\Delta\theta = 65\,°\text{C}$ when $t = 5$ minutes, and $\Delta\theta = 47\,°\text{C}$ when $t = 22$ minutes, find the time taken for $\Delta\theta$ to fall to $30\,°\text{C}$.

13   The radioactive decay of an isotope is described by the differential equation $dQ/dt = -\lambda Q$, where λ is the decay constant for the isotope and Q is the quantity of radioactive material remaining at a time t. Find an expression for the original quantity when $t = 0$, and show that half the radioactive material will remain when $t = (1/\lambda)\ln 2$.

D   Geometry and trigonometry

D1 The centroid of a plane area

D1.1 Centroids and first moments of area

The *centroid* of a lamina (like the *centre of gravity* of a solid object) is
the point at which, for the purposes of calculation, we can consider all
the mass to be located. (You may recall that a *lamina* is a plane area
with constant thickness and density which is so thin that we can equate
mass and area in our calculations.) An introduction to the centroid can
be found in *Mathematics for level-2 technicians*, section D3.

Practical problems in bending and stress analysis require us to be
able to locate the centroids of plane areas. Figure D1.1 shows an
irregular lamina with area A and centroid at G, which has co-ordinates
$(\bar{x}, \bar{y})$. We define the *first moment of area* about an axis as the product
of the area and the perpendicular distance of its centroid from the axis.
While we normally associate taking moments with the product of
distance and force (e.g. weight), the mass of a lamina depends only on
its area and, from our definition, we can consider the whole mass to be
concentrated at the centroid. In all cases the axes must be in the plane
of the area.

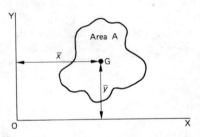

Fig. D1.1 Location of the centroid of a lamina

The first moment of area about the OY axis for the lamina in fig.
D1.1 is therefore $A\bar{x}$, and about the OX axis $A\bar{y}$.

You should be familiar with the way in which centroids of simple
composite areas can be found by equating the first moment of area
about a chosen axis to the product of the total area and the distance of
the centroid from that axis. It is worthwhile looking at an example of

164

this method before going on to deal with irregular areas using integration.

Example Locate the centroid of the plane area in fig. D1.2.

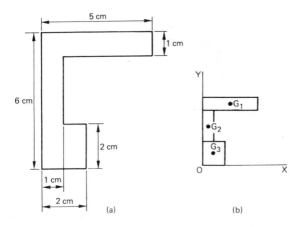

Fig. D1.2

We divide the composite shape into three rectangles with centroids G_1, G_2, G_3 and draw axes OX and OY as shown. The centroid of the composite is at the point $(\bar{x}, \bar{y})$ and is located using the values in Table D1.1.

Section	Area (cm²)	Distance of centroid from OY (cm)	Distance of centroid from OX (cm)	Moment of area about OY (cm³)	Moment of area about OX (cm³)
▭	5	2.5	5.5	12.5	27.5
▯	3	0.5	3.5	1.5	10.5
▢	4	1	1	4	4
⌐	12	$\bar{x}$	$\bar{y}$	$12\bar{x}$	$12\bar{y}$

Table D1.1

165

Equating moments of area about OY (see Table D1.1 for values),

$$12\bar{x} = 12.5 + 1.5 + 4$$

$$\therefore \quad \bar{x} = \frac{18}{12} = 1.5\,\text{cm}$$

and about OX,

$$12\bar{y} = 27.5 + 10.5 + 4$$

$$\therefore \quad \bar{y} = \frac{42}{12} = 3.5\,\text{cm}$$

i.e. the centroid is located 1.5 cm from the left edge and 3.5 cm from the base of the figure.

Note that in this example the centroid lies outside the material of the section.

D1.2 Locating centroids by integration

Consider the area below a curve $y = f(x)$ between $x = a$ and $x = b$ shown in fig. D1.3. To find the position of the centroid, we must determine the first moment of area about axes OY and OX. We divide the area into a large number of approximately rectangular strips like the one shown in fig. D1.3, which has height y and width δx. The area of the strip is $y\,\delta x$ and its centroid G has co-ordinates $(x, y/2)$ as shown.

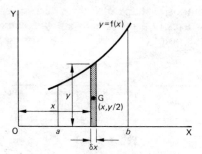

Fig. D1.3

The first moment of the area of the strip about the axis OY is given by the product of the area and the perpendicular distance between G and the axis,

$\therefore$ first moment of the area of the strip about OY $= (y\,\delta x)\,x = xy\,\delta x$

$\therefore$ total first moment of area between $x = a$ and $x = b = \sum_{x=a}^{x=b} xy\,\delta x$

Taking the limit as $\delta x \to 0$,

first moment of area about the axis OY $= \displaystyle\int_a^b xy\,\mathrm{d}x$

Similarly, the first moment of area of the strip about the axis OX is

$$(y\,\delta x)\frac{y}{2} = \tfrac{1}{2}y^2\,\delta x$$

Taking the limit as $\delta x \to 0$ of a summation for all strips between $x = a$ and $x = b$ gives the first moment of area about the axis OX:

$$\text{first moment of area about the axis OX} = \frac{1}{2}\int_a^b y^2\,\mathrm{d}x$$

If the centroid of the area has co-ordinates $(\bar{x}, \bar{y})$ and the total area is A, taking moments about the axis OY gives

$$A\bar{x} = \int_a^b xy\,\mathrm{d}x$$

Now A can be found by integration, since

$$\text{area } A = \int_a^b y\,\mathrm{d}x$$

hence $\quad \bar{x} = \dfrac{\int_a^b xy\,\mathrm{d}x}{\int_a^b y\,\mathrm{d}x}$

Taking moments about the axis OX,

$$A\bar{y} = \frac{1}{2}\int_a^b y^2\,\mathrm{d}x$$

$$\therefore \quad \bar{y} = \frac{\tfrac{1}{2}\int_a^b y^2\,\mathrm{d}x}{\int_a^b y\,\mathrm{d}x}$$

These expressions for $\bar{x}$ and $\bar{y}$ can be used to locate centroids of areas bounded by curves which we can define as $y = f(x)$.

Example 1 Locate the centroid of the area below the line $y = 2x$ between $x = 0$ and $x = 3$.

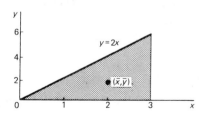

Fig. D1.4

167

The area is shown shaded in fig. D1.4. Let the centroid have co-ordinates $(\bar{x}, \bar{y})$, then

$$\bar{x} = \frac{\int_0^3 xy \, dx}{\int_0^3 y \, dx} = \frac{\int_0^3 x(2x) \, dx}{\int_0^3 2x \, dx} = \frac{[2x^3/3]_0^3}{[x^2]_0^3}$$

$$= \frac{18}{9} = 2$$

and $\quad \bar{y} = \frac{\frac{1}{2}\int_0^3 y^2 \, dx}{\int_0^3 y \, dx} = \frac{\frac{1}{2}\int_0^3 (2x)^2 \, dx}{9} = \frac{\frac{1}{2}[4x^3/3]_0^3}{9}$

$$= \frac{18}{9} = 2$$

i.e. the centroid is at the point $(2, 2)$.

(Note that the area is a triangle and we know that the centroid of a triangle is one-third of the perpendicular height above the base. Thus $\bar{x} = 3 - \frac{1}{3}(3) = 2$, and $\bar{y} = \frac{1}{3}(6) = 2$, confirming our results by integration.)

Example 2　Locate the centroid of the area below the curve $y = x^2 + 1$ between $x = 1$ and $x = 4$.

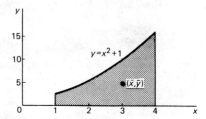

Fig. D1.5

The area is shown in fig. D1.5.

$$\bar{x} = \frac{\int_1^4 xy \, dx}{\int_1^4 y \, dx} = \frac{\int_1^4 x(x^2 + 1) \, dx}{\int_1^4 (x^2 + 1) \, dx} = \frac{\int_1^4 (x^3 + x) \, dx}{\int_1^4 (x^2 + 1) \, dx}$$

$$= \frac{[x^4/4 + x^2/2]_1^4}{[x^3/3 + x]_1^4} = \frac{71.25}{24} = 2.97$$

and $\quad \bar{y} = \frac{\frac{1}{2}\int_1^4 y^2 \, dx}{\int_1^4 y \, dx} = \frac{\frac{1}{2}\int_1^4 (x^2 + 1)^2 \, dx}{24} = \frac{\frac{1}{2}\int_1^4 (x^4 + 2x^2 + 1) \, dx}{24}$

$$= \frac{\frac{1}{2}[x^5/5 + 2x^3/3 + x]_1^4}{24} = \frac{124.8}{24} = 5.20$$

i.e. the centroid of the area is at the point $(2.97, 5.20)$.

D1.3 Locating the centroids of common shapes
The centroids of many simple shapes can be located from their symmetry. In other cases we can use integration or the theorem of Pappus which states that

> when a plane area rotates about an axis which does not cut the area, the volume generated is equal to the product of the area and the distance through which the centroid of the area moves.

If the area is A and the volume generated is V, then $V = 2\pi\bar{y}A$, where $\bar{y}$ is the distance between the centroid and the axis about which the area rotates. You may have used this theorem before to determine volumes of revolution.

The semicircle
Consider the semicircle with radius r and centroid at $(0, \bar{y})$ in fig. D1.6.

If we rotate the semicircle about the x-axis, the volume of the sphere generated is $V = \frac{4}{3}\pi r^3$. The area of the semicircle is $A = \frac{1}{2}\pi r^2$.

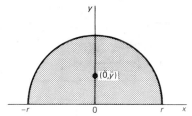

Fig. D1.6

From the theorem of Pappus,

$$V = 2\pi\bar{y}A$$

$$\therefore \quad \tfrac{4}{3}\pi r^3 = 2\pi\bar{y}(\tfrac{1}{2}\pi r^2)$$

hence $\quad \bar{y} = \dfrac{4r}{3\pi} = 0.424r$

A summary of the locations of centroids of some common shapes is given in Table D1.2.

Sector of a circle
Consider the sector of a circle with its centroid at the point $(0, \bar{y})$ shown in fig. D1.7. The volume generated when this area rotates about the x-axis through one complete revolution is given by $V = \frac{4}{3}\pi r^3 \sin\theta$. (Students familiar with the method of finding volumes by integration may like to confirm this.) The area of the sector is $A = \frac{1}{2}r^2(2\theta) = r^2\theta$.

Applying the theorem of Pappus,

$$V = 2\pi\bar{y}A$$

169

Title	Figure	Centroid location
Rectangle		$\bar{x} = \dfrac{a}{2}$ $\bar{y} = \dfrac{b}{2}$
Triangle		$BE = \dfrac{BA}{2}$ and $EG = \dfrac{EC}{3}$ $CD = \dfrac{CA}{2}$ and $DG = \dfrac{DB}{3}$ $\bar{y} = h/3$
Isosceles triangle		$\bar{x} = \dfrac{BA}{2}$ $\bar{y} = \dfrac{CD}{3}$
Circle		$\bar{x} = r$ $\bar{y} = r$
Semicircle		$\bar{x} = r$ $\bar{y} = \dfrac{4r}{3\pi}$ or $0.42r$

Table D1.2

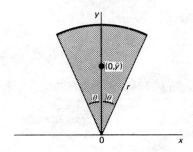

Fig. D1.7 Centroid of a sector of a circle

$$\therefore \quad \tfrac{4}{3}\pi r^3 \sin\theta = 2\pi\bar{y}(r^2\theta)$$

hence
$$\bar{y} = \frac{2r\sin\theta}{3\theta}$$

170

(Note that when $\theta = \pi/2$ the sector is in fact a semicircle and $\bar{y} = 4r/3\pi$ as we have shown earlier.)

Example 3   Find the position of the centroid of the cross-sectional area shown in fig. D1.8.

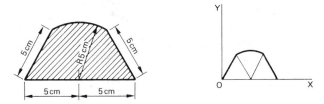

Fig. D1.8

Dividing the cross-section into three parts as shown, we can see from the symmetry of the area that $\bar{x} = 5.0$ cm. Using our knowledge of the location of the centroids of a triangle and of a sector of a circle, we can complete a table giving the first moment of area of each of the three parts.

Section	Area (cm^2)	Distance of centroid from OX (cm)	First moment of area about OX (cm^3)
△	½(25)sin 60° = 10.83	⅓(5)sin 60° = 1.44	10.83 x 1.44 = 15.60
▽	25(π/6) = 13.09	$\dfrac{10 \sin 30°}{3(\pi/6)}$ = 3.18	13.09 x 3.18 = 41.63
◁▷	2(10.83)+13.09= 34.75	$\bar{y}$	34.75 $\bar{y}$

Table D1.3

Equating moments of area about the axis OX (see Table D1.3),

$$34.75\bar{y} = 2(15.60) + 41.63$$

$$= 72.83$$

$$\therefore \quad \bar{y} = \frac{72.83}{34.75} = 2.10 \text{ cm}$$

The centroid is therefore 2.10 cm above the base.

171

Exercise D1
In questions 1 to 5, use integration to find the co-ordinates of the centroid of the area which lies below the curve between the given limits.
1   $y = 4$, between $x = 0$ and $x = 6$
2   $y = 3x$, between $x = 0$ and $x = 2$
3   $y = x$, between $x = 2$ and $x = 5$
4   $y = 2x^2$, between $x = 0$ and $x = 3$
5   $y = x^3 - 1$, between $x = 1$ and $x = 2$

In questions 6 to 9, locate the centroid of the cross-sectional area with reference to the axes defined. (All dimensions in centimetres.)

6

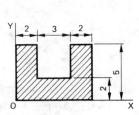

7

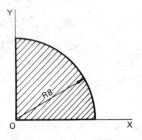

8

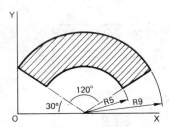

9

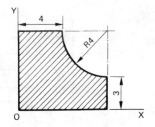

D2 Second moments of area

D2.1 Definition and units of the second moment of area
Second moments of area have many applications, including the determination of bending moments and stresses in mechanical engineering. In the well known formula $M/I = \sigma/y = E/R$ used in bending calculations, I is the second moment of area. The letter J is often used to denote the *polar second moment of area*, which is used in torsion calculations.

   In section D1 we defined the first moment of area by considering a thin strip with area $y\,\delta x$ (see fig. D1.3). The *first* moment of area of the strip about the axis OY is $xy\,\delta x$ (i.e. the product of the area of the strip and the perpendicular distance between the centroid of the strip and the axis OY). The *second* moment of area of the same strip about OY is given by $x^2 y\,\delta x$ (i.e. the product of the area of the strip and the *square* of the distance between the strip and the axis OY).

To find I_{OY}, the second moment of the total area between $x = a$ and $x = b$ about axis OY, we make a summation of the contributions of all similar strips between $x = a$ and $x = b$. As $\delta x \to 0$, we define I_{OY} as an integral:

$$I_{OY} = \int_a^b x^2 y \, dx$$

The second moment of area is always given in relation to an axis and has units consistent with (area) × (distance)^2, such as mm^4.

For plane areas, measurements of mass and area are interchangeable and we can use the term *moment of inertia* for second moment of area. (Note that the moment of inertia of a solid body about an axis is defined as the second moment of the *mass* of the body about that axis. It is a quantity widely used in dynamics.)

Values of I expressed in mm^4 can become very large when dimensions are measured in millimetres, and cm^4 are often used for convenience (e.g. values of I for universal beams in BS 4: part 1).

The following example shows how the second moment of an area below a curve can be found by integration using the method described above.

Example Determine the second moment of the area below the curve $y = x^2$ between $x = 1$ and $x = 2$ about the y-axis.

The area is shown in fig. D2.1.

$$I_{OY} = \int_1^2 x^2 y \, dx = \int_1^2 x^4 \, dx$$

$$= \left[\frac{x^5}{5}\right]_1^2 = 6.2\,(\text{units})^4$$

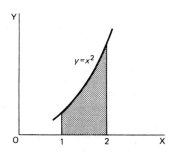

Fig. D2.1

Second moments of area of some common shapes are considered in the following sections.

D2.2 Second moment of area of a rectangle about an edge

Figure D2.2 shows a rectangle with dimensions b and d. A thin strip with area $b\,\delta x$ is parallel to the axis OY at a distance x.

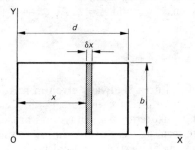

Fig. D2.2

The second moment of area of the strip about the axis OY is given by

(area of strip) × (distance from OY)^2 = $(b\,\delta x)\,x^2$

Integrating for the second moment of area of the rectangle gives

$$I_{OY} = \int_0^d bx^2\ \mathrm{d}x = b\left[\frac{x^3}{3}\right]_0^d$$

$$= \frac{bd^3}{3}$$

This is a well known result which will be useful later when we find the second moments of area of some simple composite shapes.

You may like to show that the second moment of area of the same rectangle about the axis OX is $db^3/3$, by considering a horizontal strip with area $d\,\delta y$ at a distance y from the axis OX.

Example Find the second moment of area of the cross-section in fig. D2.3(a) about the base.

Dividing the cross-sectional area into three parts and setting up axes OX and OY as shown in fig. D2.3(b), we can add the individual second moments of area about the base, giving

$$I_{OX} = 2\left(\frac{b_1 d_1^3}{3}\right) + \left(\frac{b_2 d_2^3}{3}\right)$$

$$= 2\left(\frac{2 \times 4^3}{3}\right) + \left(\frac{5 \times 3^3}{3}\right) = 130.3\,\mathrm{cm}^4$$

174

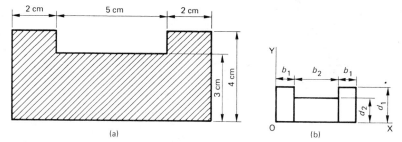

Fig. D2.3

D2.3 Second moment of area of a triangle about an edge

Figure D2.4 shows a triangular area on which we have drawn a thin strip with area $y \, \delta x$. As in previous cases, the second moment of area of the strip about the axis OY is $x^2 y \, \delta x$. For the whole triangle, therefore,

$$I_{OY} = \int_0^h x^2 y \, dx$$

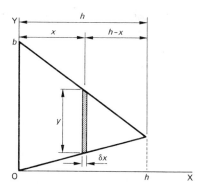

Fig. D2.4

Before we can integrate with respect to x, we must express y as a function of x. The strip is parallel to the axis OY, and so

$$\frac{h}{b} = \frac{h - x}{y} \quad \text{(similar triangles in fig. D2.4)}$$

$$\therefore \quad y = \frac{b(h - x)}{h}$$

Substituting for y in the integral gives

$$I_{OY} = \int_0^h \frac{x^2 b(h - x)}{h} \, dx = \frac{b}{h} \int_0^h (hx^2 - x^3) \, dx$$

175

$$= \frac{b}{h} \left[\frac{hx^3}{3} - \frac{x^4}{4} \right]_0^h = \frac{b}{h} \left(\frac{h^4}{3} - \frac{h^4}{4} \right)$$

$$= \frac{bh^3}{12}$$

Thus the second moment of area of any triangle about its base is $bh^3/12$, where b is the base length and h is the perpendicular height.

Example   Find the second moment of area of the cross-sectional area in fig. D2.5(a) about the base.

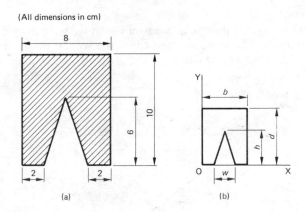

(All dimensions in cm)

(a)

(b)

Fig. D2.5

Setting up the axes OX and OY as shown in fig. D2.5(b), we subtract the second moment of area of the triangle about the axis OX from that of the complete rectangle, to give

$$I_{OX} = \frac{bd^3}{3} - \frac{wh^3}{12}$$

$$= \frac{8(10)^3}{3} - \frac{4(6)^3}{12}$$

$$= 594.7 \, \text{cm}^4$$

D2.4 Polar second moment of area of a circle
We will now consider the second moment of area of a circle about the *polar axis*, which is the axis passing through the centre of the circle and perpendicular to its plane.

176

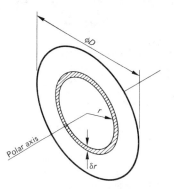

Fig. D2.6

The circle in fig. D2.6 has a diameter D. A thin circular strip or *annulus* with width δr is shown on the circle at a radius r from the polar axis. The area of the annulus is $2\pi r\,\delta r$ (i.e. circumference × width) and its second moment of area about the polar axis is $(2\pi r\,\delta r)r^2$. The total polar second moment of area for the circle is given by

$$I_{\text{polar}} = \int_0^{D/2} 2\pi r^3\,\mathrm{d}r = 2\pi \left[\frac{r^4}{4}\right]_0^{D/2}$$

$$= 2\pi\left(\frac{D^4}{64}\right) = \frac{\pi D^4}{32}$$

As stated earlier, the letter J is often used for the polar second moment of area of the cross-sections of circular shafts.

Example Find the polar second moment of area of the propeller-shaft cross-section in fig. D2.7.

The polar second moment of area of the cross-sectional area is given by

$$J = \frac{\pi(50)^4}{32} - \frac{\pi(40)^4}{32}$$

$$= 3.62 \times 10^5\ \text{mm}^4$$

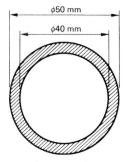

$\phi 50$ mm

$\phi 40$ mm

Fig. D2.7 Propeller-shaft cross-section

Exercise D2

1 Using integration, find the second moments of area about the y-axis of the areas enclosed by the following curves and the x-axis between the given limits.

a) $y = 4$, between $x = 1$ and $x = 3$
b) $y = 2x$, between $x = 2$ and $x = 3$
c) $y = 1/x$, between $x = 3$ and $x = 5$
d) $y = 4 + x$, between $x = 0$ and $x = 2$
e) $y = x^2 + 1$, between $x = -1$ and $x = 3$

In questions 2 to 5, find the second moments of area of the cross-sectional areas about the base. (All dimensions are in cm.)

2
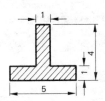

3
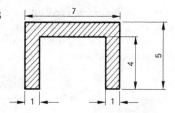

4
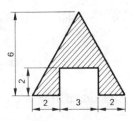

5
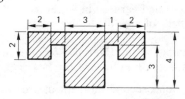

6 A torque T is applied to one end of a steel shaft of length l. The other end is firmly fixed. The angle of twist is given by $\theta = Tl/JG$, where J is the polar second moment of area of the shaft cross-section and G is the modulus of rigidity of the steel. Find the diameter of the shaft if $\theta = 0.01$ rad when $G = 7.5 \times 10^{10}$ N/m^2, $l = 1.40$ m, and $T = 150$ N m.

D3 The parallel-axis and perpendicular-axis theorems

D3.1 The parallel-axis theorem
Consider the area A in fig. D3.1 with its centroid at G. If we know the second moment of the area about an axis BB which passes through G,

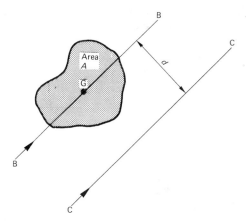

Fig. D3.1

we can determine I_{CC}, the second moment of the area about an axis CC which is parallel to BB, using the *parallel-axis theorem*. This states that

$$I_{CC} = I_{BB} + Ad^2$$

where d is the perpendicular distance between the parallel axes.

This is a most useful theorem which enables us to determine the second moment of an area about an axis through its centroid if we already know the second moment of the area about a parallel axis. In bending theory, it is the value of I about an axis through the centroid of a cross-sectional area which is used to calculate stresses and bending moments. (Note that when a beam is subjected to bending forces, the centroidal axis of the beam cross-section perpendicular to the plane of bending coincides with the *neutral axis* at which there is no stress or strain.)

It is usual to let I_{XX} and I_{YY} be the second moments of area of a cross-sectional area about the horizontal and vertical axes which pass through the centroid.

Example 1 Show that $I_{XX} = bd^3/12$ for the rectangular area in fig. D3.2.

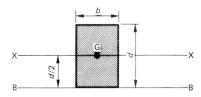

Fig. D3.2

179

The axis XX passes through the centroid of the rectangle. We know that $I_{BB} = bd^3/3$ (see section D2.2).

From the parallel-axis theorem,

$$I_{BB} = I_{XX} + (bd)\left(\frac{d}{2}\right)^2$$

$$\therefore \quad I_{XX} = I_{BB} - \frac{bd^3}{4}$$

$$= \frac{bd^3}{3} - \frac{bd^3}{4}$$

$$= \frac{bd^3}{12}$$

Example 2 Determine I_{YY} and I_{ZZ} for the triangular area in fig. D3.3, if $I_{BB} = bh^3/12$.

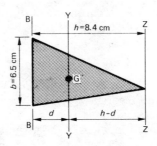

Fig. D3.3

The centroid G of the triangle is a distance $d = h/3$ from axis BB, and the area of the triangle is $A = \frac{1}{2}bh$.

Using the parallel-axis theorem,

$$I_{BB} = I_{YY} + Ad^2$$

$$\therefore \quad I_{YY} = I_{BB} - Ad^2$$

$$= \frac{bh^3}{12} - \tfrac{1}{2}bh\left(\frac{h}{3}\right)^2$$

$$= \frac{bh^3}{36} = 107.0 \, \text{cm}^4$$

Now, the axis ZZ is also parallel to YY and we use the parallel-axis theorem a second time to give

$$I_{ZZ} = I_{YY} + A(h - d)^2$$

180

$$= \frac{bh^3}{36} + \tfrac{1}{2}bh\left(\frac{2h}{3}\right)^2$$

$$= \frac{bh^3}{4} = 963.1\,\text{cm}^4$$

Further use of the parallel-axis theorem is made in section D3.3, to find second moments of area of composite cross-sectional areas about their centroidal axes.

D3.2 The perpendicular-axis theorem

The axes OX and OY are drawn at right angles on the plane area in fig. D3.4. A third axis, OZ, is drawn at right angles to the plane area. We say that OX, OY, and OZ are *mutually perpendicular axes*.

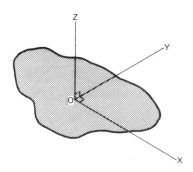

Fig. D3.4

The *perpendicular-axis theorem* states that

$$I_{OZ} = I_{OX} + I_{OY}$$

The second moment of area of a circle about a diameter

We have already seen that the polar second moment of area of a circle with diameter D is given by

$$I_{\text{polar}} = \frac{\pi D^4}{32}$$

The circle in fig. D3.5 has axes XX and YY at right angles to each other and to the polar axis. From the perpendicular-axis theorem,

$$I_{\text{polar}} = I_{XX} + I_{YY}$$

Now $I_{XX} = I_{YY}$ (from the symmetry of the circle), and so the second moment of area of a circle about a diameter is given by

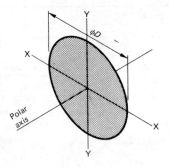

Fig. D3.5

$$I_{xx} = \frac{I_{\text{polar}}}{2} = \frac{\pi D^4}{64}$$

This is a well known result which can be used in calculations involving circular shafts subjected to bending forces.

Note that the second moment of area of a semicircle about its diameter is $\pi D^4/128$, half the value for the circle.

Table D3.1 shows the second moments of area of some common shapes.

Example Determine the polar second moment of area of the cross-sectional area in fig. D3.6.

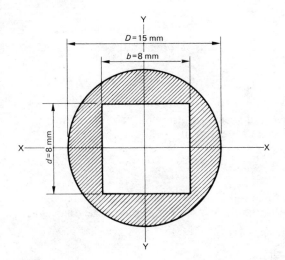

Fig. D3.6

Title	Figure	Second moments of area
Rectangle		$I_{AB} = \dfrac{bd^3}{3}$ $I_{XX} = \dfrac{db^3}{12}$ $I_{YY} = \dfrac{bd^3}{12}$
Triangle		$I_{AB} = \dfrac{bh^3}{12}$ $I_{YY} = \dfrac{bh^3}{36}$ $I_{CD} = \dfrac{bh^3}{4}$
Circle		I_{Polar} (or J) $= \dfrac{\pi D^4}{32}$ $I_{XX} = I_{YY} = \dfrac{\pi D^4}{64}$
Semicircle		$I_{AB} = \dfrac{\pi r^4}{8}$ $I_{XX} = \dfrac{\pi r^4}{8}$ $I_{YY} = r^4 \left(\dfrac{\pi}{8} - \dfrac{8}{9\pi} \right)$ $= 0.110 r^4$

Table D3.1 Second moments of area of common shapes

We have
$$I_{XX} = \frac{\pi D^4}{64} - \frac{bd^3}{12} \quad \text{(see Table D3.1)}$$
$$= \frac{\pi(15)^4}{64} - \frac{8(8)^3}{12}$$
$$= 2144 \text{ mm}^4$$

183

The cross-section is symmetrical and so $I_{XX} = I_{YY}$.

From the perpendicular-axis theorem,

$$I_{polar} = I_{XX} + I_{YY}$$

hence $I_{polar} = 2(2144) = 4288\,\text{mm}^4$

D3.3 Second moments of area of composite areas

The parallel-axis theorem discussed in section D3.1 enables us to find the second moments of area of composite cross-sectional areas about their centroidal (or neutral) axes. When the location of the centroid of the composite is known, we simply divide the area into common shapes and use known values of second moments of area, about selected axes, for these shapes to evaluate the total second moment of area for the cross-section.

Example 1 Find I_{XX} and I_{YY} for the cross-sectional area in fig. D3.7.

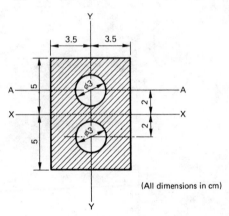

(All dimensions in cm)

Fig. D3.7

To find I_{XX}

Consider the complete rectangular area without holes. Its centroid lies on axis XX and its second moment of area is given by

$$I_{XX} = \frac{bd^3}{12} = \frac{7(10)^3}{12} = 583.3\,\text{cm}^4$$

Consider the circle with its centre on axis AA:

$$I_{AA} = \frac{\pi D^4}{64} = \frac{\pi(3)^4}{64} = 3.98\,\text{cm}^4$$

Axes XX and AA are parallel, and applying the parallel-axis theorem the circular area gives

184

$$I_{XX} = I_{AA} + Ad^2$$

where A is the area of the circle and d is the distance between XX and AA

$$\therefore \quad I_{XX} = 3.98 + \pi(1.5)^2\,(2)^2$$
$$= 32.25\,\text{cm}^4$$

For the cross-section given,

$$I_{XX} = I_{XX}\ \text{of rectangle} - 2(I_{XX}\ \text{of circle})$$
$$= 583.3 - 2(32.25)$$
$$= 518.8\,\text{cm}^4$$

To find I_{YY}

$$I_{YY} = I_{YY}\ \text{of rectangle} - 2(I_{YY}\ \text{of circle})$$

The centroids of both the rectangle and the circle lie on axis YY,

$$\therefore \quad I_{YY} = \frac{db^3}{12} - 2\left(\frac{\pi D^4}{64}\right)$$
$$= \frac{10(7)^3}{12} - 2\left(\frac{\pi (3)^4}{64}\right)$$
$$= 277.9\,\text{cm}^4$$

A tabular method is often used to find I_{XX} and I_{YY} for composite areas. We will use the cross-sectional area in fig. D3.8(a) in an example of this method.

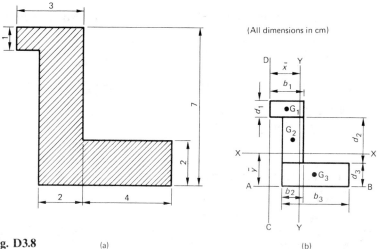

Fig. D3.8   (a)   (b)

185

To find I_{XX}

First we divide the area into three rectangular parts and draw axes XX and AB (see fig. D3.8(b)). We know that the second moment of area of a rectangle about its neutral axis is $bd^3/12$, and we can use the parallel-axis theorem to find the total second moment of area for the three rectangles about axis AB, since, for each rectangular area,

$$I_{AB} = I_G + Ay^2$$

where I_G is the second moment of area of the rectangle about an axis through G parallel to AB, A is the area of the rectangle, and y is the distance between the axis through G and the parallel axis AB. Table D3.2 contains all the relevant information.

Section	A (cm^2)	y (cm)	Ay (cm^3)	Ay^2 (cm^4)	I_G (cm^4)
[rectangle]	$b_1d_1 = 3.0$	6.5	19.5	126.8	$\frac{b_1d_1^3}{12} = 0.25$
[rectangle]	$b_2d_2 = 8.0$	4.0	32.0	128.0	$\frac{b_2d_2^3}{12} = 10.7$
[rectangle]	$b_3d_3 = 12.0$	1.0	12.0	12.0	$\frac{b_3d_3^3}{12} = 4.0$
	$\Sigma A = 23.0$		$\Sigma Ay = 63.5$	$\Sigma Ay^2 = 266.8$	$\Sigma I_G = 15.0$

Table D3.2

The distance of the centroid of the cross-section from AB is given by

$$\bar{y} = \frac{\sum Ay}{\sum A} = \frac{63.5}{23.0} = 2.76 \, \text{cm}$$

The second moment of area about axis AB is given by

$$I_{AB} = \sum I_G + \sum Ay^2$$
$$= 15.0 + 266.8$$
$$= 281.8 \, \text{cm}^4$$

Using the parallel-axis theorem again,

$$I_{XX} = I_{AB} - \sum A(\bar{y})^2$$
$$= 281.8 - (23)(2.76)^2$$
$$= 106.6 \, \text{cm}^4$$

Section	A (cm^2)	x (cm)	Ax (cm^3)	Ax^2 (cm^4)	I_G (cm^4)
	$b_1 d_1 = 3.0$	1.5	4.5	6.75	$\dfrac{d_1 b_1^3}{12} = 2.25$
	$b_2 d_2 = 8.0$	2.0	16.0	32.0	$\dfrac{d_2 b_2^3}{12} = 2.67$
	$b_3 d_3 = 12.0$	4.0	48.0	192.0	$\dfrac{d_3 b_3^3}{12} = 36.00$
	$\Sigma A = 23.0$		$\Sigma Ax = 68.5$	$\Sigma Ax^2 = 230.8$	$\Sigma I_G = 40.9$

Table D3.3

To find I_{YY}

A similar table (Table D3.3) is drawn giving values of A, x, Ax, Ax^2, and I_G with reference to the vertical axis CD at the far left of fig. D3.8(b). (Note that in practice the two tables can be combined.)

From Table D3.3,

$$\bar{x} = \frac{\sum Ax}{\sum A} = \frac{68.5}{23.0} = 2.98 \, \text{cm}$$

The second moment of area about axis CD is given by

$$I_{CD} = \sum I_G + \sum Ax^2$$
$$= 40.9 + 230.8$$
$$= 271.7 \, \text{cm}^4$$

From the parallel-axis theorem,

$$I_{YY} = I_{CD} - \sum A(\bar{x})^2$$
$$= 271.7 - (23.0)(2.98)^2$$
$$= 67.5 \, \text{cm}^4$$

Example 2 Find I_{XX} and I_{YY} for the cross-sectional area in fig. D3.9(a).

Values in Table D3.4 relate to axes AB and CD shown in fig. D3.9(b).

To find I_{XX}

$$\bar{y} = \frac{\sum Ay}{\sum A} = \frac{167.7}{48.93} = 3.43 \, \text{cm}$$

187

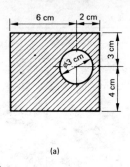

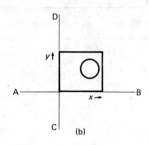

(a)

(b)

Fig. D3.9

Section	A (cm^2)	x (cm)	y (cm)	Ax (cm^3)	Ay (cm^3)	Ax^2 (cm^4)	Ay^2 (cm^4)	I_{G1} about a vertical axis (cm^4)	I_{G2} about a horizontal axis (cm^4)
▭	56.0	4.0	3.5	224.0	196.0	896.0	686.0	298.7	228.7
○	7.07	6.0	4.0	42.4	28.3	254.5	113.1	3.98	3.98
Σ	48.93			181.6	167.7	641.5	572.9	294.7	224.7

Table D3.4

The second moment of area about AB is

$$I_{AB} = \sum I_{G2} + \sum Ay^2$$
$$= 224.7 + 572.9$$
$$= 797.6 \, \text{cm}^4$$

Applying the parallel-axis theorem,

$$I_{XX} = I_{AB} - \sum A(\bar{y})^2$$
$$= 797.6 - (48.93)(3.43)^2$$
$$= 222 \, \text{cm}^4$$

To find I_{YY}

$$\bar{x} = \frac{\sum Ax}{\sum A} = \frac{181.6}{48.93} = 3.71 \, \text{cm}$$

188

The second moment of area about CD is

$$I_{CD} = \sum I_{G1} + \sum Ax^2$$
$$= 294.7 + 641.5$$
$$= 936.2 \, \text{cm}^4$$

From the parallel-axis theorem

$$I_{YY} = I_{CD} - \sum A(\bar{x})^2$$
$$= 936.2 - (48.93)(3.71)^2$$
$$= 263 \, \text{cm}^4$$

Exercise D3

You may assume values of second moments of area of the common shapes in Table D3.1.

1 State the parallel-axis theorem and use it to find the second moment of area of a plane circular area with diameter 22 mm about an axis which is a tangent to the circle in the same plane.

2 Use the parallel-axis theorem twice to find I_{DC} of the area in fig. D3.10 if $I_{AB} = 4450 \, \text{mm}^4$.

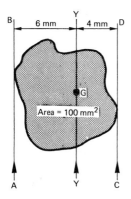

Fig. D3.10

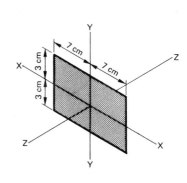

Fig. D3.11

3 State the perpendicular-axis theorem and use it to find I_{ZZ} for the rectangular area in fig. D3.11.

4 Find I_{ZZ} for the semicircular area in fig. D3.12.

5 Find I_{XX}, I_{YY}, and the polar second moment of area of the cross-sectional area in fig. D3.13.

6 Find I_{XX} for the cross-sectional area in fig. D3.14.

7 Find I_{XX} and I_{YY} for the cross-sectional area in fig. D3.15.

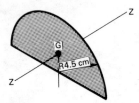

Fig. D3.12

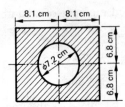

Fig. D3.13

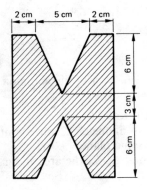

Fig. D3.14

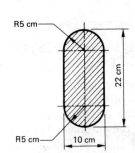

Fig. D3.15

In questions 8, 9, and 10, use a tabular method to determine I_{xx}.

8

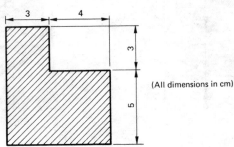

(All dimensions in cm)

9

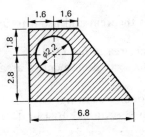

(All dimensions in cm)

190

10

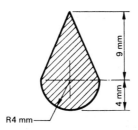

R4 mm

11 Use a table to find I_{YY} for the cross-sectional area in question 8.
12 Use a table to find I_{YY} for the cross-sectional area in question 9.

D4 Three-dimensional trigonometry

D4.1 Solution of triangles
Much of the work in this chapter involves the solution of triangles. A right-angled triangle may be solved using the trigonometric ratios together with the theorem of Pythagoras. For a triangle with no right angle, we may use the sine rule and the cosine rule. These two rules are introduced in *Mathematics for level-2 technicians*, section D6, and are summarised below.

Fig. D4.1

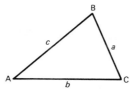

For the triangle ABC in fig. D4.1, the *sine rule* states that

$$\frac{a}{\sin A} = \frac{b}{\sin B} = \frac{c}{\sin C}$$

The *cosine rule* states that

$$a^2 = b^2 + c^2 - 2bc \cos A$$

or $\quad b^2 = a^2 + c^2 - 2ac \cos B$

or $\quad c^2 = a^2 + b^2 - 2ab \cos C$

Example 1 In a triangle ABC, $A = 116°$, $B = 38°$, and $a = 12\,\text{mm}$. Find b.

191

Using the sine rule,
$$\frac{a}{\sin A} = \frac{b}{\sin B}$$

$$\therefore \quad \frac{12}{\sin 116°} = \frac{b}{\sin 38°}$$

$$b = \frac{12 \sin 38°}{\sin 116°} = 8.22 \, \text{mm}$$

Example 2   In a triangle DEF, $e = 4.8\,\text{m}$, $f = 6.4\,\text{m}$, $D = 128°$. Find d.

Using the cosine rule,
$$d^2 = e^2 + f^2 - 2ef \cos D$$
$$= (4.8)^2 + (6.4)^2 - 2(4.8)(6.4) \cos 128°$$
$$= 101.83$$
$$\therefore \quad d = 10.1 \, \text{m}$$

Any triangle for which we know two sides and an angle, two angles and a side, or all three sides may be solved. There is an *ambiguous case* which arises when we are given two sides and an angle which is not included between the two given sides.

Example 3   In a triangle ABC, $a = 7\,\text{mm}$, $b = 11\,\text{mm}$, and $A = 29°$. Find B.

Using the sine rule,

$$\frac{a}{\sin A} = \frac{b}{\sin B}$$

$$\therefore \quad \frac{7}{\sin 29°} = \frac{11}{\sin B}$$

giving $\sin B = \dfrac{11 \sin 29°}{7} = 0.7618$

Using tables or your calculator,

$$B = 49.6° \quad \text{or} \quad 130.4°$$

You may like to sketch these two triangles.

192

In many ambiguous cases which arise in engineering and science, one of the mathematically possible results may be physically impossible and the ambiguity can be resolved.

D4.2 The angle between a line and a plane

The line AB in fig. D4.2 meets a plane at A. To define the angle between this line and the plane, we draw from C on the plane a perpendicular which meets the line at B. The angle between the line AB and the plane is $\angle$ BAC.

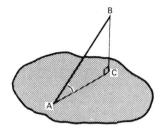

Fig. D4.2 The angle between a line and a plane

Example Find the angle between the line AE and the plane ABC in fig. D4.3.

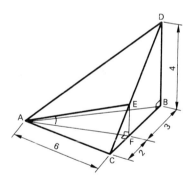

Fig. D4.3

The angle between the line AE and the plane ABC is $\angle$ EAF, since EF is drawn at right angles to the plane ABC.

Triangles CBD and CEF are similar,

$$\therefore \quad \frac{DB}{EF} = \frac{BC}{FC}$$

193

giving $\dfrac{4}{EF} = \dfrac{5}{2}$

and $\quad EF = \dfrac{8}{5} = 1.60$

Applying the theorem of Pythagoras to triangle AFC gives

$$AF^2 = FC^2 + CA^2$$
$$= 2^2 + 6^2$$
$$\therefore \quad AF = 6.325$$

In the right-angled triangle AEF,

$$\angle EAF = \arctan \dfrac{EF}{AF} = \arctan \dfrac{1.60}{6.325}$$

$$= 14.20°$$

i.e. the angle between the line AE and the plane ABC is 14.20°, or 14° 12′.

D4.3 The angle between two intersecting planes

When two planes intersect they do so along a straight line. Planes ABCD and BEFC in fig. D4.4 intersect along the line BC.

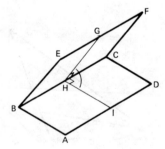

Fig. D4.4 The angle between two intersecting planes

The angle between the planes is defined as the angle between any two lines, drawn one on each plane, which meet at and are perpendicular to the line of intersection of the planes. The angle between the planes in fig. D4.4 is therefore $\angle$ GHI, the angle between the lines GH and HI.

Example 1 What is the angle between the sloping sides and the base of a right pyramid with a square base of side 20 mm and a perpendicular height of 35 mm?

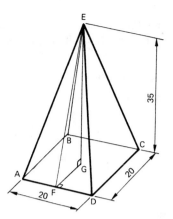

Fig. D4.5

The pyramid is shown in fig. D4.5. The angle between the side AED and the base ABCD is ∠EFG, where EF and FG are perpendicular to the line of intersection AD.

From the symmetry of the pyramid, side FG = 10 mm in the right-angled triangle EFG,

$$\therefore \quad \angle EFG = \arctan \frac{EG}{FG} = \arctan \frac{35}{10}$$

$$= 74.05°$$

i.e. the angle between the sloping sides and the base is 74.05°, or 74° 3′.

Example 2 Find the angle between the planes IEJ and JGI if points I and J bisect sides AD and AB respectively in the 8 mm cube in fig. D4.6.

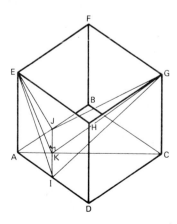

Fig. D4.6

195

The angle between planes IEJ and JGI is ∠EKG, since EK and KG are perpendicular to IJ, the line at which the planes intersect.

In the right-angled triangle AKI, AI = 4 mm and ∠KAI = 45°,

∴   AK = AI cos KAI = 4 cos 45° = 2.828

In the right-angled triangle AEK,

$$\angle EKA = \arctan \frac{EA}{AK} = \arctan \frac{8}{2.828} = 70.53°$$

Applying the theorem of Pythagoras to triangle ABC,

$$AC^2 = AB^2 + BC^2 = 8^2 + 8^2$$

∴   AC = 11.31 mm

Now   KC = AC − AK

$$= 11.31 - 2.828$$

$$= 8.482 \text{ mm}$$

In the right-angled triangle GCK,

$$\angle CKG = \arctan \frac{GC}{KC} = \arctan \frac{8.0}{8.482}$$

$$= 43.32°$$

Now   ∠EKG = 180° − (∠EKA + ∠CKG)

$$= 180° - (70.53° + 43.32°)$$

$$= 66.15°$$

i.e. the angle between the planes IEJ and JGI is 66.15°, or 66° 9′.

Example 3   Figure D4.7 shows a rectangular block with AB = 6 mm, BC = 4 mm, and CG = 5 mm. If BF = 2 mm and DE = 3 mm, find the angle between the planes ABFED and EFG.

In the right-angled triangle EFC,

$$\angle FEC = \arctan \frac{FC}{EC} = \arctan \frac{2}{3}$$

$$= 33.69°$$

In the right-angled triangle EHC,

$$\sin HEC = \frac{HC}{EC}$$

∴   HC = 3 sin 33.69° = 1.664 mm

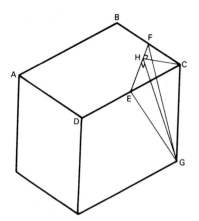

Fig. D4.7

In the right-angled triangle CGH,

$$\angle CHG = \arctan \frac{CG}{HC} = \arctan \frac{5}{1.664}$$

$$= 71.59°$$

The angle between the planes ABFED and EFG is given by

$$180° - \angle CHG = 180° - 71.59°$$

$$= 108.4° \quad \text{or} \quad 108°\,24'.$$

D4.4 Three-dimensional triangulation problems

We are by now familiar with the use of trigonometric methods of finding lengths and angles in three-dimensional space. Problems of this type arise frequently in engineering and science and so it is essential that we can visualise and draw diagrams of solid objects. We have seen that much of the analysis depends on our ability to solve triangles, and an accurately drawn diagram is needed to select the most useful triangles. Remember that we can use the trigonometric ratios and the theorem of Pythagoras only with *right-angled* triangles.

Example Figure D4.8 shows a rectangular block containing a triangular plane AGI. If BI = IC = 7 mm, find (a) the length of the line AG, (b) $\angle AGI$, (c) the angle between the planes AGI and ABCD.

a) In the right-angled triangle AGC,

$$AG^2 = AC^2 + CG^2$$

Now $AC^2 = AB^2 + BC^2$ (from the right-angled triangle ABC)

$$= 9^2 + 14^2 = 277$$

197

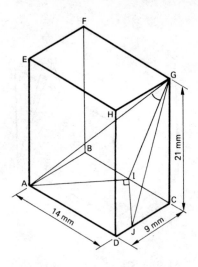

Fig. D4.8

hence $AG^2 = 277 + 21^2 = 718$

giving $AG = 26.80$ mm

b) In the right-angled triangle IGC,

$$IG^2 = IC^2 + CG^2$$
$$= 7^2 + 21^2$$

$$\therefore \quad IG = 22.14 \text{ mm}$$

In the right-angled triangle ABI,

$$AI^2 = AB^2 + BI^2$$
$$= 9^2 + 7^2$$

$$\therefore \quad AI = 11.40 \text{ mm}$$

Applying the cosine rule to triangle AGI,

$$AI^2 = AG^2 + GI^2 - 2(AG)(GI) \cos AGI$$

$$\therefore \quad (11.40)^2 = (26.80)^2 + (22.14)^2 - 2(26.80)(22.14) \cos AGI$$

giving $\angle AGI = \arccos 0.9088 = 24.66°$ or $24° 39'$.

c) The angle between planes AGI and ABCD is $\angle GIJ$, where IJ is perpendicular to the line of intersection of the planes, AI.

In the right-angled triangle ABI,

$$\angle AIB = \arctan \frac{AB}{BI} = \arctan \frac{9}{7}$$

$$= 52.13°$$

198

In the right-angled triangle JIC,

$$\angle JIC = 90° - \angle AIB = 90° - 52.13°$$
$$= 37.87°$$

Now $JC = IC \tan JIC = 7 \tan 37.87°$

$$= 5.443 \, mm$$

Applying the theorem of Pythagoras,

$$JI^2 = IC^2 + JC^2 = 7^2 + 5.443^2$$

$\therefore$ $JI = 8.867 \, mm$

In the right-angled triangle GCJ,

$$GJ^2 = GC^2 + CJ^2$$
$$= 21^2 + 5.443^2$$

$\therefore$ $GJ = 21.69 \, mm$

Applying the cosine rule to triangle GIJ,

$$GJ^2 = JI^2 + IG^2 - 2(JI)(IG) \cos GIJ$$

$\therefore$ $(21.69)^2 = (8.867)^2 + (22.14)^2 - 2(8.867)(22.14) \cos GIJ$

giving $\angle GIJ = \arccos 0.2505 = 75.49°$ or $75° 29'$.

D4.5 Navigational bearings

Defining the location, speed, and direction of moving objects such as ships and aircraft often involves the solution of three-dimensional triangulation problems of the type we have studied in earlier sections. Special terms are used to make the descriptions of these movements clear and unambiguous.

The angles of *elevation* and *depression* are angles measured relative to a horizontal plane at the point of observation. They give the true angle between the horizontal plane and the straight line between the observer and the object.

Bearings provide a simple way of specifying the position of an object with respect to the points of the compass. The bearings of the three points A, B, and C in fig. D4.9 with respect to O are N 46° E, S 28° W, and N 35° W respectively.

An observer on the ground can locate an object in three-dimensional space by knowing its bearings, angle of elevation, and altitude.

Example 1   A balloon is observed from a point A on level ground in a direction S 16° E. The angle of elevation is 24° and the altitude of the balloon is 1500 m. After moving in a straight line for 30 minutes, the balloon has climbed to 1850 m and, when observed from the same point

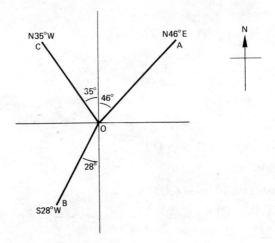

Fig. D4.9 Navigational bearings

A, its direction is S 12° W, with an angle of elevation of 27°. Find the speed of the balloon in km/h.

The balloon moves from E to D in fig. D4.10, and we must find the distance between these two points to determine its speed.

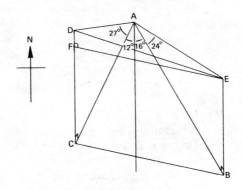

Fig. D4.10

Using the right-angled triangles AEB and ADC,

$$AB = 1500/\tan 24° = 3369 \text{ m}$$

$$AC = 1850/\tan 27° = 3631 \text{ m}$$

In triangle CAB,

$$\angle CAB = 16° + 12° = 28°$$

From the cosine rule,

$$CB^2 = AC^2 + AB^2 - 2(AC)(AB) \cos CAB$$
$$= 3631^2 + 3369^2 - 2(3631)(3369) \cos 28°$$
$$\therefore \quad CB = 1712 \, m$$

In the right-angled triangle DEF, FE = CB = 1712 m, and
DF = DC − EB = 350 m (since FEBC is a rectangle).
From the theorem of Pythagoras,

$$DE^2 = FE^2 + DF^2$$
$$= 1712^2 + 350^2$$
$$\therefore \quad DE = 1747 \, m$$

The balloon has travelled 1747 m in 30 minutes. Its speed in km/h is
given by

$$\text{speed} = \frac{1747}{1000} \times \frac{60}{30} = 3.5 \, km/h$$

Wind effect on the navigation of aircraft

The course or *heading* of an aircraft tells us the direction in which the
aircraft is pointing. This angle is measured clockwise from north and is
given as a three-digit reading between 000 and 360. For example,
N 35° E becomes 035 using this type of navigational bearing.

A wind which has the same direction as an aircraft will increase the
ground speed of the aircraft but will cause no navigational problems.
Similarly a wind blowing from directly in front of the aircraft will only
reduce the ground speed. Any winds with directions other than these
will require corrections to the heading of the aircraft to achieve the
required *track* (the name given to the true path of the aircraft over the
ground).

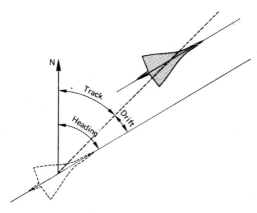

Fig. D4.11

201

The angle between heading and track is called the *drift*. Figure D4.11 shows the relationship between heading, track, and drift.

Early navigators were required to solve triangles trigonometrically to determine, for example, the heading of an aircraft given its air speed, the required track, and the wind direction and speed. Modern instrumentation used in many aircraft is designed to carry out these computations automatically, but it is worthwhile looking at a typical problem.

Example 2 The airspeed of an aircraft is 280 km/h. Find the heading and ground speed when the required track is 255, if the wind direction is 320 and the wind speed is 65 km/h.

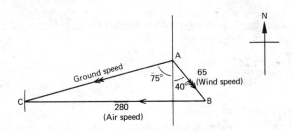

Fig. D4.12

From the information given, triangle ABC in fig. D4.12 can be drawn as follows:

 i) Draw AB with length 65 mm in the direction shown to represent the wind speed. (The bearing 320 gives the direction *from* which the wind is blowing. Note the convention of drawing three arrowheads on this line.)

 ii) Draw a line from A in the direction given by the track (i.e. at an angle 255° clockwise from north. Note the two arrowheads on this line.)

iii) Draw an arc of radius 280 mm from B to C. (A single arrowhead is used on this line representing air speed.)

To determine the heading and ground speed, we must find the direction of CB and the length of AC. If triangle ABC is drawn accurately as described, the angle between AB and CB and the length of AC can be measured to give the answers. To calculate the required values,

$$\angle CAB = 75° + 40° = 115°$$

Using the sine rule,

$$\sin C = \frac{65 \sin 115°}{280} = 0.210$$

$$\therefore \quad \angle C = 12.1°$$

202

The heading of the aircraft is therefore 267 (i.e. 255° + 12.1° to the nearest degree).

Now $\angle ABC = 180° - (115° + 12.1°)$

$$= 52.9°$$

Using the sine rule again,

$$AC = \frac{280 \sin 52.9°}{\sin 115°} = 246.4$$

i.e. the ground speed is approximately 246 km/h.

Exercise D4
1   Solve the following triangles ABC:
  (a) $a = 2.1$, $C = 90°$, $B = 37°$ (b) $a = 8.7$, $c = 11.4$, $C = 50°$
  (c) $a = 2.7$, $c = 3.1$, $B = 48°$ (d) $b = 14.7$, $c = 7.3$, $A = 55°$
  (e) $a = 5.3$, $b = 6.1$, $A = 52°$
2   In fig. D4.13, ABCD is a rectangular base with AD = 12 mm and DC = 8 mm. The triangles AEB and DFC are both perpendicular to the base. Find the angle between the line AG and the base if $\angle GAD = 40°$.
3   Find the true angle between the planes ACD and BCD in fig. D4.14.

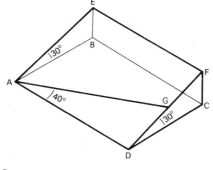

Fig. D4.13

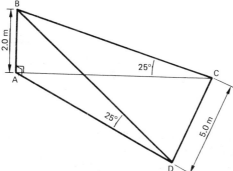

Fig. D4.14

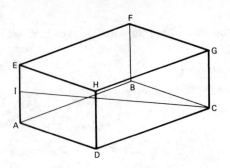

Fig. D4.15

4 The dimensions of the rectangular block in fig. D4.15 are
AB = 150 mm, BC = 100 mm, and CG = 70 mm. If IA = 40 mm, find
the angles between the line IC and the planes ABCD, BFGC, and
DHGC.
5 A right pyramid has a square base with sides 22 mm and has a
height of 16 mm. Find (a) the angle between any of the triangular faces
and the base, (b) the angle between two adjacent triangular faces.
6 The prism in fig. D4.16 has a horizontal base ABC which is an
equilateral triangle of side 20 mm. The three rectangular sides are
perpendicular to the base and 15 mm in height. If AG = GC and
DH = HE, find the length of the line GH and the angle this line makes
with side ADFC.

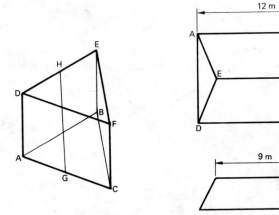

Fig. D4.16   **Fig. D4.17**

7 Figure D4.17 shows the side elevation and plan of the roof of a
house. Determine the angles between (a) side AED and the base ABCD,
(b) side ABFE and the base ABCD, (c) sides AED and DEFC.

204

8 Define the terms heading, track, and drift as applied to aircraft navigation. Find the heading of an aircraft if the required track is 155, the wind direction is 268, the wind speed is 76 km/h, and the air speed of the aircraft is 425 km/h.

9 Calculate the ground speed and track of an aircraft flying with air speed 355 km/h, heading 048, if the wind is from 335 and the wind speed is 65 km/h.

D5 Graphs of trigonometric functions

D5.1 Angular velocity, periodic time, and frequency

Sine curves and cosine curves can be constructed by relating the angle of a rotating radius or *phasor* to its vertical and horizontal projections respectively. The phasor OP in fig. D5.1 is moving anticlockwise with *angular velocity* ω radians per second

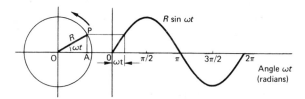

Fig. D5.1 The sine curve $R \sin \omega t$ from projections of a phasor

In the position shown, the phasor has been moving for t seconds and has turned through an angle ωt radians from its starting point. We can see from triangle OPA that $AP = OP \sin \omega t$ and, if we let $OP = R$, then $AP = R \sin \omega t$. By projecting values of AP across to corresponding points along an axis representing angular movement of the phasor, the curve $R \sin \omega t$ can be drawn as shown.

The peak value or *amplitude* of the sine curve is R, so that, when $\omega t = \pi/2$ and the phasor is in a vertical position, $R \sin \omega t = R$.

Periodic time

The phasor will have completed one revolution when $\omega t = 2\pi$ radians. We define the time taken for the phasor to complete a revolution and for $R \sin \omega t$ to complete one *cycle* as the *periodic time*, for which we use the letter T.

Thus $\omega T = 2\pi$

or $T = \dfrac{2\pi}{\omega}$ seconds

Frequency

The frequency f is defined as the number of cycles completed in one second. The unit of frequency is the *hertz* (Hz), where 1 Hz represents one cycle per second.

Now we have already seen that one cycle is completed in the periodic time T seconds. It follows that $1/T$ cycles will be completed every second,

$$\therefore \quad f = \frac{1}{T} \text{ Hz}$$

But $\quad T = \frac{2\pi}{\omega} \text{ s}$

$$\therefore \quad f = \frac{\omega}{2\pi} \text{ Hz} \quad \text{or} \quad \omega = 2\pi f \text{ rad/s}$$

Note that we can now express $R \sin \omega t$ in terms of frequency f as $R \sin 2\pi f t$. This is a common way of representing sinusoidally varying quantities, including voltage, current, and magnetic flux density.

Example The instantaneous value of a sinusoidal voltage is given by $v = 12 \sin 100t$ volts. Determine (a) the peak voltage, (b) the frequency, (c) the periodic time.

a) Let $\quad v = 12 \sin 2\pi f t$
The peak voltage is 12 V, when $\sin 2\pi f t = 1$

b) If $\quad 12 \sin 2\pi f t = 12 \sin 100t$

then $\qquad\qquad 2\pi f = 100$

or $\qquad\qquad f = \frac{100}{2\pi} = 15.9 \text{ Hz}$

i.e. the frequency is 15.9 Hz.

c) We know that $f = 1/T$, where T is the periodic time,

$$\therefore \quad T = \frac{1}{f} = \frac{1}{15.9} = 0.0628 \text{ s} \quad \text{or} \quad 62.8 \text{ ms}$$

i.e. the periodic time is 0.0628 s, or 62.8 ms.

D5.2 Graphs of sin ωt and cos ωt

We now consider the effect which varying the value of ω has on the graph of $R \sin \omega t$.

We know that the periodic time T is the time taken to complete one cycle, and that $T = 2\pi/\omega$. If $\omega = 1 \text{ rad/s}$, then

$$T = 2\pi = 6.28 \text{ s}$$

If $\omega = 2\,\text{rad/s}$,

$$T = \pi = 3.14\,\text{s}$$

If $\omega = 3\,\text{rad/s}$,

$$T = 2\pi/3 = 2.09\,\text{s}$$

If $\omega = 0.5\,\text{rad/s}$,

$$T = 4\pi = 12.57\,\text{s}$$

Figure D5.2 shows graphs of $\sin \omega t$ against time with $\omega = 0.5, 1, 2$, and $3\,\text{rad/s}$. The smaller the value of ω, the longer it takes to complete one cycle, as the above values of T show. Note also that, since $f = 1/T$, if the periodic time is increased, the frequency is reduced. The frequency of $\sin t$ is *half* that of $\sin 2t$, so $\sin 2t$ completes *twice* as many cycles as $\sin t$ in a given time.

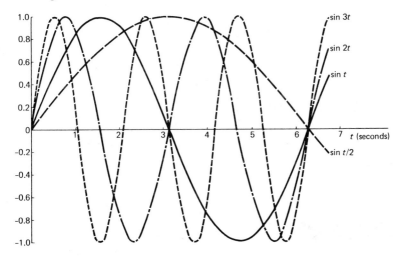

Fig. D5.2 Graphs of $\sin(t/2)$, $\sin t$, $\sin 2t$, and $\sin 3t$

D5.3 Graphs of $\sin^2 \omega t$ and $\cos^2 \omega t$

The graph of $\sin^2 t$ against time between $t = 0\,\text{s}$ and $t = 7\,\text{s}$ is shown in fig. D5.3. Although $\sin^2 t$ is a periodic function, it is not *sinusoidal*. The graph can be drawn by plotting values of $\sin^2 t$ against t, but not by using projections of a phasor.

It is clear from the graph that the periodic time of $\sin^2 t$ is $\pi\,\text{s}$ (approximately $3.14\,\text{s}$), since one cycle is completed in this time. The frequency is thus

$$f = \frac{1}{T} = \frac{1}{3.14} = 0.318\,\text{Hz}$$

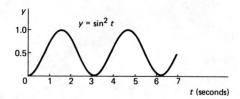

Fig. D5.3 The graph of $\sin^2 t$

The graph of $\sin^2 2t$ in fig. D5.4 shows that the periodic time of $\sin^2 2t$ is 1.57 s (the approximate value of $\pi/2$), so that

$$f = \frac{1}{T} = \frac{1}{1.57} = 0.637 \text{ Hz}$$

We can conclude that, in general, the periodic time of $\sin^2 \omega t$ is given by $T = \pi/\omega$, and that the frequency is $f = \omega/\pi$.

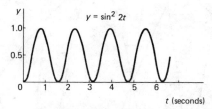

Fig. D5.4 The graph of $\sin^2 2t$

D5.3 Phase relationships
Two sine curves with the same frequency which reach peak values at exactly the same time are said to be *in phase*. When the waveforms are not in phase, so that one curve reaches a peak before the other, we say that the first curve *leads* the second or, alternatively, that the second curve *lags* the first. The phase relationship between periodic functions is most important in engineering and science.

Graphs of $R \sin(\omega t \pm \alpha)$ and $R \cos(\omega t \pm \alpha)$
We can easily show that a graph of $R \sin(\omega t + \alpha)$ against time t, which has an amplitude R and periodic time $2\pi/\omega$, will have exactly the same shape as the curve $R \sin \omega t$ but will be displaced along the t-axis. As an example, we will plot values of $3 \sin(2t + 0.85)$ against t between $t = 0$ s and $t = 3.5$ s.

The table of values is produced using a calculator (set to work in radians) or tables. Values are shown every 0.5 s, although more points would be required to draw the graph accurately.

208

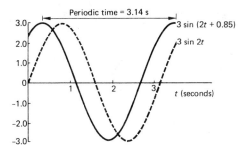

Fig. D5.5 Graphs of 3 sin 2*t* and 3 sin(2*t* + 0.85)

t (seconds)	0.00	0.50	1.00	1.50	2.00	2.50	3.00	3.50
3 sin(2t + 0.85)	2.25	2.88	0.86	−1.95	−2.97	−1.26	1.61	3.00

The graph of 3 sin(2*t* + 0.85) is shown as the solid line in fig. D5.5, with 3 sin 2*t* shown for comparison as a broken line.

We know that the periodic time of $R \sin \omega t$ is $2\pi/\omega$ seconds. For the curve 3 sin 2*t*, $\omega = 2$ rad/s and therefore $T = 2\pi/2 = 3.14$ s. This is confirmed by the graph of 3 sin 2*t* in fig. D5.5, since the curve (shown as the broken line) completes one cycle in 3.14 s. The periodic time of 3 sin(2*t* + 0.85) is also 3.14 s. This can be confirmed by measuring the time for one complete cycle of the curve (e.g. the time between two adjacent peaks, as shown on the graph). It is clear from the graph that the curve 3 sin(2*t* + 0.85) reaches a peak before 3 sin 2*t*. We can calculate exactly when these peaks occur as follows.

For 3 sin 2*t*, the peak value occurs when

$$2t = \pi/2$$

$$\therefore \quad t = \pi/4 = 0.785 \text{ s}$$

Similarly, for 3 sin(2*t* + 0.85) the peak value occurs when

$$2t + 0.85 = \pi/2$$

$$\therefore \quad t = \frac{\pi/2 - 0.85}{2} = 0.360 \text{ s}$$

Thus the leading curve 3 sin(2*t* + 0.85) reaches a peak 0.425 seconds before 3 sin 2*t*. It is usual to give this lead as a *phase angle* α in radians or degrees rather than as a time. We multiply 0.425 by $\omega = 2$ rad/s to give $\alpha = 0.85$ rad. The result can be remembered as follows:

the curve $R \sin(\omega t + \alpha)$ leads the curve $R \sin \omega t$ by the phase angle α;
the curve $R \sin(\omega t - \alpha)$ lags the curve $R \sin \omega t$ by the phase angle α.

These phase relationships can be seen clearly in the diagrams in fig. D5.6.

In the upper of the two diagrams, the phasor OQ leads OP by an angle α. The phasors have magnitude R as before, so that projections

209

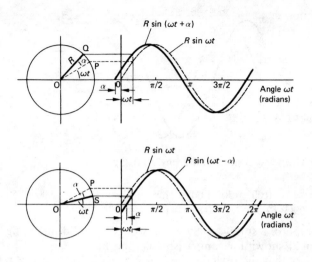

Fig. D5.6 The curves $R \sin(\omega t + \alpha)$ and $R \sin(\omega t - \alpha)$

from phasor OP give the curve $R \sin \omega t$ while projections from OQ give the curve $R \sin(\omega t + \alpha)$. With an angular horizontal axis measured in radians, the phase lead α, discussed earlier, is apparent.

In the lower diagram, phasor OS has moved through an angle $\omega t - \alpha$ in the same time that OP has moved through an angle ωt. The curve $R \sin(\omega t - \alpha)$ can be seen to lag the curve $R \sin \omega t$, as we would expect, by the angle α.

Exercise D5

1 Draw one complete cycle of the curve $40 \sin t$ by relating projections of a phasor with length 40 mm to the angle in radians through which it moves in an anticlockwise direction.

2 Plot values of $\cos t$ against time t between $t = 0$ s and $t = 3.5$ s.

3 Draw the curves $\cos 2t$ and $\cos(t/3)$ on the same axes between $t = 0$ s and $t = 7.0$ s.

4 State the amplitude, periodic time, and frequency of the following waveforms: (a) $2 \sin 3t$, (b) $240 \sin 100\pi t$, (c) $3 \cos(t/2)$, (d) $0.5 \sin(2t + 1.3)$.

5 Find the frequency of the sinusoidal voltage with peak value 12 V if the instantaneous value is 0 V at $t = 0$ s rising to 5.2 V when $t = 15$ ms.

6 The instantaneous value of an alternating current is given by

$$i = 6 \sin 157.1t$$

Find (a) the peak current, (b) the frequency, (c) the periodic time.

7 Draw the curves $\cos^2 t$ and $\cos^2 3t$ on the same axes for values of t between $t = 0$ s and $t = 7$ s.

8 Determine the periodic time and the frequency of the curves (a) $2 \sin^2 2t$, (b) $100 \cos^2 \pi t$.

9 How many cycles of the curve $3 \sin^2 5t$ are completed in 2π seconds? Sketch the curve between $t = 0\,\text{s}$ and $t = 2\,\text{s}$.

10 Define the terms phase lead and phase lag. Use projections of a 50 mm radius rotating through 2π radians to draw the curve $50 \sin(t + \pi/6)$. (Your horizontal axis should give the angle in radians through which the radius moves.)

11 Plot values of $\sin(\omega t + \pi/3)$ and $\sin(\omega t - \pi/6)$ against ωt between $\omega t = 0\,\text{rad}$ and $\omega t = 3\pi\,\text{rad}$. Use the same axes for both curves and identify angles of phase lead and phase lag when the curves are compared with $\sin \omega t$.

12 The instantaneous value of an alternating voltage is given by the equation $v = 120 \sin(377t + 0.45)$ volts. Determine (a) the amplitude and frequency of the oscillation, (b) the voltages when $t = 0\,\text{s}$ and when $t = 2.5\,\text{ms}$, (c) the time taken for the voltage to reach peak value, (d) the phase angle between the given waveform and $120 \sin 377t$.

13 Plot values of $2.5 \sin(3t - 0.75)$ against t between $t = 0\,\text{s}$ and $t = 4\,\text{s}$.

D6 Compound-angle formulae

D6.1 $\sin(A \pm B)$ and $\cos(A \pm B)$

In this section we look at uses of the following *compound-angle* formulae for sines and cosines of the sum and difference of two angles A and B:

$$\sin(A + B) = \sin A \cos B + \cos A \sin B$$
$$\sin(A - B) = \sin A \cos B - \cos A \sin B$$
$$\cos(A + B) = \cos A \cos B - \sin A \sin B$$
$$\cos(A - B) = \cos A \cos B + \sin A \sin B$$

The proof of these formulae is beyond the scope of this book, but we can easily demonstrate that they are true for any values of A and B we select. For example if $A = 54°$ and $B = 28°$, using four-figure tables or a calculator gives $\sin 54° = 0.8090$, $\cos 54° = 0.5878$, $\sin 28° = 0.4695$, and $\cos 28° = 0.8829$. Substituting these values into the first of the above compound-angle formulae,

$$\sin(54° + 28°) = \sin 54° \cos 28° + \cos 54° \sin 28°$$

$$= (0.8090)(0.8829) + (0.5878)(0.4695)$$

$$= 0.9902$$

This agrees with the value of $\sin 82°$ (correct to three significant figures) obtained from tables or a calculator. You should use the three remaining formulae to confirm the following results:

$$\sin 26° = 0.438 \qquad \cos 82° = 0.139 \quad \text{and} \quad \cos 26° = 0.899$$

The compound-angle formulae are easy to remember but many mistakes are made involving the $+$ and $-$ signs, particularly in the $\cos(A \pm B)$ formulae. The following examples illustrate some uses of the formulae.

Example 1 Show that $\sin(x + 90°) + \cos(x - 180°) = 0$.

Using the compound-angle formulae

$$\sin(A + B) = \sin A \cos B + \cos A \sin B$$
$$\cos(A - B) = \cos A \cos B + \sin A \sin B$$

gives

$$\sin(x + 90°) = \sin x \cos 90° + \cos x \sin 90°$$
$$\cos(x - 180°) = \cos x \cos 180° + \sin x \sin 180°$$

Now $\cos 90° = 0 \qquad \sin 90° = 1 \qquad \cos 180° = -1$ and $\sin 180° =$

hence $\sin(x + 90°) + \cos(x - 180°) = \cos x - \cos x = 0$

Example 2 Use the compound-angle formula for $\sin(A + B)$ to express $\sin 2\theta$ in terms of $\sin \theta$ and $\cos \theta$.

We have $\sin(A + B) = \sin A \cos B + \cos A \sin B$

Substituting $A = B = \theta$ gives

$$\sin 2\theta = \sin \theta \cos \theta + \cos \theta \sin \theta$$
$$= 2 \sin \theta \cos \theta$$

Example 3 Simplify the expression $\sin(x + \pi/3) + \sin(x - \pi/3)$.

Using the compound-angle formulae gives

$$\sin(x + \pi/3) = \sin x \cos(\pi/3) + \cos x \sin(\pi/3)$$
$$\sin(x - \pi/3) = \sin x \cos(\pi/3) - \cos x \sin(\pi/3)$$

Adding these equations leaves us with

$$\sin(x + \pi/3) + \sin(x - \pi/3) = 2 \sin x \cos(\pi/3)$$

Now $\cos(\pi/3) = \frac{1}{2}$, and therefore

$$\sin(x + \pi/3) + \sin(x - \pi/3) = \sin x$$

Example 4 Find the value of x between $x = 0°$ and $x = 90°$ for which $3 \cos(x - 14°) = 4 \sin x$.

Using the compound-angle formula

$$\cos(A - B) = \cos A \cos B + \sin A \sin B$$

212

gives $3\cos(x - 14°) = 3(\cos x \cos 14° + \sin x \sin 14°)$

$$= 3(0.9703 \cos x + 0.2419 \sin x)$$

Thus, if $3\cos(x - 14°) = 4 \sin x$

then $2.9109 \cos x + 0.7257 \sin x = 4 \sin x$

giving $3.2743 \sin x = 2.9109 \cos x$

or $\tan x = \dfrac{2.9109}{3.2743} = 0.889$

∴ $x = 41.64°$

Checking this solution in the original equation,

$3\cos(41.64° - 14°) = 2.658$

and $4 \sin 41.64° = 2.658$

D6.2 The expansion of $R \sin(\omega t \pm \alpha)$

In section D5 we looked at graphs of $R \sin(\omega t + \alpha)$ and $R \sin(\omega t - \alpha)$ against values of the angle ωt. You will recall that these curves could also be drawn using projections of a rotating phasor with length R. The angle α is called a *phase angle*, so that $R \sin(\omega t + \pi/2)$, for example, has a *phase lead* of $\pi/2$ rad with respect to the curve $R \sin \omega t$.

We can now expand $R \sin(\omega t \pm \alpha)$ using the compound-angle formulae to give

$$R \sin(\omega t + \alpha) = R \sin \omega t \cos \alpha + R \cos \omega t \sin \alpha$$

and $R \sin(\omega t - \alpha) = R \sin \omega t \cos \alpha - R \cos \omega t \sin \alpha$

Taking the first of these two equations, we can substitute $a = R \cos \alpha$ and $b = R \sin \alpha$ to give

$$R \sin(\omega t + \alpha) = a \sin \omega t + b \cos \omega t$$

Note that a and b are constants, since both R and α have constant values.

This last equation implies that if a sine function and a cosine function with the same frequency (remember that $f = \omega/2\pi$) are added together, the result will be a sine function which also has the same frequency. Many readers will already be aware of this result from previous work.

To express R and α in terms of a and b, we have

$$a = R \cos \alpha \tag{i}$$

and $b = R \sin \alpha$ $\qquad\qquad\qquad\qquad\qquad\qquad\qquad\qquad$ (ii)

Squaring these two equations and adding the results together gives

$$a^2 + b^2 = R^2(\cos^2 \alpha + \sin^2 \alpha)$$

213

But $\cos^2\alpha + \sin^2\alpha = 1$ (this is an *identity* you should know)

$\therefore \quad R = \sqrt{(a^2 + b^2)}$

Dividing equation (ii) by equation (i) gives

$$\frac{b}{a} = \frac{R\sin\alpha}{R\cos\alpha}$$

$\therefore \quad \alpha = \arctan(b/a)$

Example 1   Express $2\sin\omega t + 3\cos\omega t$ as $R\sin(\omega t + \alpha)$ and sketch the three waveforms.

If $a\sin\omega t + b\cos\omega t = R\sin(\omega t + \alpha)$

then $R = \sqrt{(a^2 + b^2)}$ and $\alpha = \arctan(b/a)$

In this example, $a = 2$ and $b = 3$

$\therefore \quad R = \sqrt{(4 + 9)} = 3.61$

and $\alpha = \arctan(3/2) = 56.31°$ or $0.983\,\text{rad}$

Hence $2\sin\omega t + 3\cos\omega t = 3.61\sin(\omega t + 0.983)$

These waveforms are shown in fig. D6.1. Note that the curve $3.61\sin(\omega t + 0.983)$ *leads* the curve $2\sin\omega t$ by $0.983\,\text{rad}$.

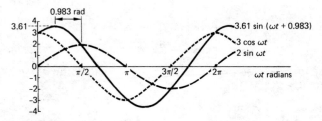

Fig. D6.1 Graph showing $2\sin\omega t + 3\cos\omega t = 3.61\sin(\omega t + 0.983)$

Example 2   Determine the values of k_1 and k_2 if $7\sin(x + \pi/8) = k_1\sin x + k_2\cos x$.

In general, if $R\sin(x + \alpha) = a\sin x + b\cos x$

then $a = R\cos\alpha$ and $b = R\sin\alpha$

hence $k_1 = 7\cos(\pi/8) = 6.47$

and $k_2 = 7\sin(\pi/8) = 2.68$

Example 3   Express $2.5\sin\omega t - 6.1\cos\omega t$ as $R\sin(\omega t + \alpha)$, giving α in radians. Hence find the maximum value of $2.5\sin\omega t - 6.1\cos\omega t$ and

214

determine the value of t at which the maximum first occurs if $\omega = 100\,\text{rad/s}$.

If $\quad a \sin \omega t + b \cos \omega t = R \sin(\omega t + \alpha)$

then $\quad R = \sqrt{(a^2 + b^2)} \quad$ and $\quad \alpha = \arctan(b/a)$

Now, we have $a = 2.5$ and $b = -6.1$, giving

$$R = \sqrt{(6.25 + 37.21)} = 6.59$$

and $\quad \alpha = \arctan\left(\dfrac{-6.1}{2.5}\right) = \arctan(-2.44) = -1.18\,\text{rad}$

hence $\quad 2.5 \sin \omega t - 6.1 \cos \omega t = 6.59 \sin(\omega t - 1.18)$

The maximum value is therefore 6.59, and this occurs when

$$\sin(\omega t - 1.18) = 1$$

$\therefore \qquad \omega t - 1.18 = \pi/2 \quad \text{or} \quad \omega t = 2.75\,\text{rad}$

Substituting $\omega = 100\,\text{rad/s}$,

$$t = 0.0275\,\text{s} \quad \text{or} \quad 27.5\,\text{ms}$$

Exercise D6

1 Write down the compound-angle formulae for $\sin(A \pm B)$ and use them to simplify the expression $\sin(x + 1.4) + \sin(x - 1.4)$.

2 Use the compound-angle formulae to expand the following expressions. Evaluate any constant terms in your expansions correct to three significant figures.

    (a) $\cos(x + \pi/4)$ (b) $\sin(x - 1)$ (c) $\sin(120° + x)$
    (d) $\cos(\sqrt{2} - x)$

3 Use the formula for $\cos(A + B)$ and a trigonometrical identity to show that $\cos 2\theta = 2 \cos^2 \theta - 1$.

4 Find the value of x between $x = 0°$ and $x = 90°$ which satisfies the equation $\sin(x + 20°) = \frac{1}{2} \cos x$.

5 For the triangle in fig. D6.2, show that $\sin(\theta + \phi) = a(e + d)/bc$.

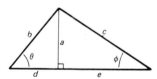

Fig. D6.2

6 Express (a) $4.5 \sin \omega t + 2.8 \cos \omega t$ and
(b) $4.5 \sin \omega t - 2.8 \cos \omega t$ as $R \sin(\omega t + \alpha)$.

7 The single waveform resulting from the addition of the alternating voltages $8 \sin 100t$ volts and $12 \cos 100t$ volts is shown on an

215

oscilloscope screen. Determine the amplitude of the waveform on the screen and its phase angle, measured with respect to 8 sin 100t and expressed in radians.

8 When the mass m in fig. D6.3 is attached to a spring with stiffness k and oscillates in a vertical plane, the displacement x at a time t is given by $x = a \sin \omega t + b \cos \omega t$. Express this as $x = X \sin(\omega t + \phi)$, giving values of X and ϕ if $a = 0.073$ metres and $b = 0.040$ metres.

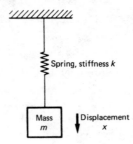

Fig. D6.3

D7 The sum and product formulae

D7.1 Changing sums and differences of sines and cosines into products

Useful formulae for converting sums and differences of sines and cosines into products can be derived from the compound-angle formulae used in section D6.

Starting with the equations

$$\sin(A + B) = \sin A \cos B + \cos A \sin B$$

$$\sin(A - B) = \sin A \cos B - \cos A \sin B$$

adding them together gives

$$\sin(A + B) + \sin(A - B) = 2 \sin A \cos B$$

If we let $A + B = P$ and $A - B = Q$ then

$$A = \frac{P + Q}{2} \quad \text{and} \quad B = \frac{P - Q}{2}$$

The equation becomes

$$\sin P + \sin Q = 2 \sin \left(\frac{P + Q}{2}\right) \cos \left(\frac{P - Q}{2}\right)$$

Formulae for $\sin P - \sin Q$, $\cos P + \cos Q$, and $\cos P - \cos Q$ can be derived in the same way. They may be remembered in the following form:

216

$$\sin A + \sin B = 2 \sin \left(\frac{A + B}{2}\right) \cos \left(\frac{A - B}{2}\right)$$

$$\sin A - \sin B = 2 \cos \left(\frac{A + B}{2}\right) \sin \left(\frac{A - B}{2}\right)$$

$$\cos A + \cos B = 2 \cos \left(\frac{A + B}{2}\right) \cos \left(\frac{A - B}{2}\right)$$

$$\cos A - \cos B = 2 \sin \left(\frac{A + B}{2}\right) \sin \left(\frac{B - A}{2}\right)$$

Note the *reversed* difference in the last of these formulae.

Example 1 Express $\sin 7\theta - \sin 5\theta$ as a product.

Using the formula

$$\sin A - \sin B = 2 \cos \left(\frac{A + B}{2}\right) \sin \left(\frac{A - B}{2}\right)$$

gives $\sin 7\theta - \sin 5\theta = 2 \cos \left(\dfrac{7\theta + 5\theta}{2}\right) \sin \left(\dfrac{7\theta - 5\theta}{2}\right)$

$$= 2 \cos 6\theta \sin \theta$$

Example 2 Show that $\dfrac{\cos 3x - \cos 5x}{\sin 3x + \sin 5x} = \tan x$

Using the formulae

$$\cos A - \cos B = 2 \sin \left(\frac{A + B}{2}\right) \sin \left(\frac{B - A}{2}\right)$$

and $\sin A + \sin B = 2 \sin \left(\dfrac{A + B}{2}\right) \cos \left(\dfrac{A - B}{2}\right)$

we get $\dfrac{\cos 3x - \cos 5x}{\sin 3x + \sin 5x} = \dfrac{2 \sin 4x \sin x}{2 \sin 4x \cos(-x)} = \tan x$

(Note that $\cos(-x) = \cos x$.)

Example 3 Determine the three solutions to the equation

$$\sin 4\theta - \cos 4\theta = \cos 2\theta - \sin 2\theta$$

in the range $0 \leqslant \theta \leqslant \pi/2$.

Rearranging the equation gives

$$\sin 4\theta + \sin 2\theta = \cos 4\theta + \cos 2\theta$$

217

Changing the sums into products, we get

$$2 \sin 3\theta \cos \theta = 2 \cos 3\theta \cos \theta$$

The equation is satisfied if $\cos \theta = 0$. Thus one solution in the range $0 \leqslant \theta \leqslant \pi/2$ is $\theta = \pi/2$. Other solutions are found from

$$\sin 3\theta = \cos 3\theta$$

or $\tan 3\theta = 1$

$\therefore$ $3\theta = \arctan 1 = \pi/4, 5\pi/4, 9\pi/4$, and so on

giving $\theta = \pi/12$ and $\theta = 5\pi/12$ in the range $0 \leqslant \theta \leqslant \pi/2$. The three solutions are therefore $\theta = \pi/12$, $\theta = 5\pi/12$, and $\theta = \pi/2$.

D7.2 Graphs of $\sin A + \sin B$

If we add together two sine waves with different frequencies, the resulting waveform will be periodic but not sinusoidal. An example is shown in fig. D7.1, in which values of $\sin 9\theta + \sin 7\theta$ are plotted against θ. The following table gives some values between $\theta = 0$ and $\theta = \pi/2$:

θ	0	$\pi/16$	$\pi/8$	$3\pi/16$	$\pi/4$	$5\pi/16$	$3\pi/8$	$7\pi/16$	$\pi/2$
$\sin 9\theta + \sin 7\theta$	0.00	1.96	0.00	-1.66	0.00	1.11	0.00	-0.39	0.00

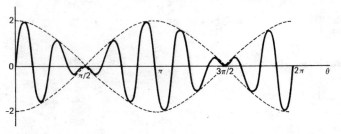

Fig. D7.1 The curve $\sin 9\theta + \sin 7\theta$

The curves shown as broken lines in fig. D7.1 are $2 \cos \theta$ and $-2 \cos \theta$ and we can see that they enclose the curve $\sin 9\theta + \sin 7\theta$. The significance of these cosine curves is made clear when we express $\sin 9\theta + \sin 7\theta$ as a product:

$$\sin 9\theta + \sin 7\theta = 2 \sin 8\theta \cos \theta$$

We can think of the waveform in fig. D7.1 as the sine curve $\sin 8\theta$ with a varying amplitude given by $2 \cos \theta$.

The above example illustrates how *beats* are produced between waves which have different frequencies. With sound waves these beats can be heard, for example when a musical instrument is being tuned.

In radio transmission using *amplitude modulation*, the amplitude of a high-frequency *carrier* wave is made to vary in accordance with modulating waves which have frequencies in the audible range.

D7.3 Changing products into sums and differences

In the previous section we added together two of the compound-angle formulae to give

$$\sin(A + B) + \sin(A - B) = 2 \sin A \cos B$$

Rearranging gives

$$\sin A \cos B = \tfrac{1}{2}[\sin(A + B) + \sin(A - B)]$$

Other formulae like this one for converting products into sums and differences are obtained likewise from the compound-angle formulae and may be remembered as follows:

$$\sin A \cos B = \tfrac{1}{2}[\sin(A + B) + \sin(A - B)]$$
$$\cos A \sin B = \tfrac{1}{2}[\sin(A + B) - \sin(A - B)]$$
$$\cos A \cos B = \tfrac{1}{2}[\cos(A + B) + \cos(A - B)]$$
$$\sin A \sin B = \tfrac{1}{2}[\cos(A - B) - \cos(A + B)]$$

Note that the sum and difference are reversed in the last of these formulae.

Example 1   Express $\sin 3x \cos 2x$ as a sum.

The formula $\sin A \cos B = \tfrac{1}{2}[\sin(A + B) + \sin(A - B)]$

gives $\sin 3x \cos 2x = \tfrac{1}{2} \sin 5x + \tfrac{1}{2} \sin x$

Example 2   Show that $\cos(x + \pi/4) \cos(x - \pi/4) = \tfrac{1}{2} \cos 2x$.

From the formula

$$\cos A \cos B = \tfrac{1}{2}[\cos(A + B) + \cos(A - B)]$$

we get $\cos(x + \pi/4) \cos(x - \pi/4) = \tfrac{1}{2}[\cos 2x + \cos(\pi/2)]$

$$= \tfrac{1}{2} \cos 2x$$

Example 3   Solve the equation $2 \sin 4x \sin 3x = \cos x$, giving values in the range $0 \leqslant x \leqslant \pi/4$.

Using the formula

$$\sin A \sin B = \tfrac{1}{2}[\cos(A - B) - \cos(A + B)]$$

we have $\sin 4x \sin 3x = \tfrac{1}{2}(\cos x - \cos 7x)$

The original equation becomes

$$\cos x - \cos 7x = \cos x$$

∴ $\cos 7x = 0$

or $7x = \arccos 0 = \pi/2, \ 3\pi/2, \ 5\pi/2, \text{ and so on}$

219

Solutions in the range $0 \leqslant x \leqslant \pi/4$ are therefore $x = \pi/14$ and $x = 3\pi/14$.

Exercise D7

1 Express the following as products:

    (a) $\sin 5x + \sin x$ (b) $\sin 6x - \sin 2x$ (c) $\cos 4x + \cos x$
    (d) $\cos 3x - \cos x$ (e) $\sin(3x - y) - \sin(x + y)$

2 Prove the following:

    (a) $\dfrac{\cos\theta - \cos 7\theta}{\sin 7\theta + \sin\theta} = \tan 3\theta$

    (b) $\sin(\theta + \pi/4) - \sin(\theta - \pi/4) = \sqrt{2}\cos\theta$

3 Solve the equation $\sin 5\theta - \sin\theta = \sin 2\theta$ for values of θ in the range $0 \leqslant \theta \leqslant \pi/2$.

4 Find the four solutions to the equation $\cos(3x + \pi) - \cos(7x - \pi) = 0$ in the range $0 \leqslant x \leqslant \pi/2$.

5 Plot values of $\sin 5\theta + \sin 3\theta$ every $\pi/8$ radians between $\theta = 0$ and $\theta = 2\pi$ rad.

6 Express $\sin 14\pi t + \sin 10\pi t$ as a product and sketch the curve defined by your answer between $t = 0$ s and $t = 1$ s.

7 Express the following products as sums or differences:
(a) $2\sin 4x \cos 2x$, (b) $4\cos 3x \sin x$, (c) $\cos 6x \cos x$, (d) $6\sin 5x \sin 2x$.

8 Show that $4\cos(2x - \pi/12)\sin(2x + \pi/12) = 1 + 2\sin 4x$.

9 Solve the equation $4\sin 3\theta \cos 2\theta - 2\sin\theta = 1$, giving values in the range $0 \leqslant \theta \leqslant \pi/4$.

E Statistics and probability

E1 Elementary laws of probability

E1.1 What is probability?

In any problem or experiment, each separate result is called an *outcome*. The particular happening we are looking for will be called the *event*. Probability is the branch of mathematics which enables us to calculate the likelihood of any particular outcome.

We shall define the probability p of the event by

$$p = \frac{\text{number of ways the event can occur}}{\text{total number of possible outcomes}}$$

Two events are *complementary* when together they include every possible outcome without any overlap or duplication. When all possible outcomes are known, the set of outcomes can be referred to as the *sample space*.

Example When a couple have their first child, obviously it must be either male or female. Hence, for one child, the complete set of possible outcomes is $\{M, F\}$.

Assuming equal probability for each possible outcome, the probability of the first child being male is $\frac{1}{2}$ and the probability of it being female is equally $\frac{1}{2}$. Note that the probabilities of the complementary events add together to give 1.

Now consider a family with two children. The sample space is $\{MM, MF, FM, FF\}$. By symmetry, it is obvious that each of these possible outcomes, being equally likely, has a probability of $\frac{1}{4}$ (i.e. 1 in 4).

If we consider the possibility of such a family with two children having at least one boy, we can either add the individual probabilities for MM, MF, FM to get $\frac{1}{4} + \frac{1}{4} + \frac{1}{4} = \frac{3}{4}$, or we can use our basic definition from which

$$p = \frac{3 \text{ (ways the event can occur)}}{4 \text{ (possible outcomes)}}$$

If the probability that a certain event may happen is p, then the probability that the event will not happen is $1 - p$.

A probability of zero implies that there should be no chance at all of the event occurring. Note that negative probabilities are impossible and that p can never be greater than 1, since $p = 1$ implies a certainty. If we spin a coin with a head on both sides, for example,

$$p \text{ (tail)} = \frac{0}{2} = 0 \quad \text{and} \quad p \text{ (head)} = \frac{2}{2} = 1$$

The result will always be a head, never a tail.

E1.2 Expectation
Once we have determined the probability that an event will occur in any one trial, we can use it to predict how many times the event will occur in a number of similar trials. We define *expectation* as the product of the number of trials and the probability that an event will occur in any one trial.

Consider an experiment in which a pack of cards is shuffled and cut eight times. We can determine the expectation of clubs as follows:

$$p \text{ (club) in each trial} = \frac{13}{52} = 0.25$$

$$\therefore \quad \text{expectation in eight trials} = 0.25 \times 8 = 2$$

This does not mean that there definitely will be two clubs when the cards are cut eight times, but that it is our best estimation based on knowledge of the chances that each trial will produce a club. (Note that the probability of the event occurring must be the same in each trial for our definition of expectation to apply.)

Example When 500 injection-moulded components taken at arbitrary intervals from a machine's production were given 100% inspection, 17 were found to be defective. Determine the probability that any single component will be defective and the expectation for defectives in a batch of 3000 components.

The probability that any given component will be defective is found using

$$p \text{ (defective)} = \frac{17}{500} = 0.034$$

In a batch of 3000 components, therefore

$$\text{expectation of defectives} = 0.034 \times 3000$$

$$= 102 \text{ components}$$

E1.3 Dependent and independent events
Two events are independent when the outcome of one event has no effect on the probability of the outcome of the other. Spinning coins,

throwing dice, and cutting a shuffled pack of cards are all examples of independent events. If the outcome of one event can affect the outcome of another, the two events are not independent.

Consider, for example, a bag containing three green beads and two blue beads. The probability of taking out a green bead at random is 3/5 and the probability of taking a blue bead is 2/5. If a bead is taken out and not replaced, the probability of a second bead being green may be 3/4 *or* 2/4 depending on whether the first bead taken was blue or green. These events are therefore not independent.

E1.4 Addition law for probabilities

When two events are *mutually exclusive*, the probability of one or the other occurring is calculated by *adding* their individual probabilities. We write

$$p(A \text{ or } B) = p(A) + p(B)$$

Mutually exclusive events

We say events are mutually exclusive if any one outcome prevents the possibility of another. For example, if a single card is taken from a pack, it may be a six or it could be a nine; but not both. Taking a six and taking a nine are mutually exclusive events. However, the single card could be a six and also a red card (e.g. the six of hearts), so taking a six and taking a red card are not mutually exclusive events.

In fig. E1.1, S represents the sample space and A and B are subsets of possible outcomes which do not overlap. The probability of an event being in S is 1; the probability of it being in A is $p(A)$; the probability of it being in B is $p(B)$. The event cannot be in both A and B, and so the probability of the event being in A or B is given by

$$p(A \text{ or } B) = p(A) + p(B)$$

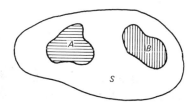

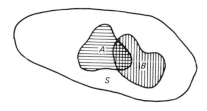

Fig. E1.1 Events which are mutually exclusive

Fig. E1.2 Events which are not mutually exclusive

Figure E1.2 shows the case of two events which are not mutually exclusive, when subsets A and B overlap. It is clearly possible for an event to be in A, or to be in B, or to be in both A *and* B. We can define these probabilities as $p(A)$, $p(B)$, and $p(AB)$ respectively. This

223

duplication means that simple addition of probabilities will not be correct, since it implies that the area shared by A and B will be counted twice. The probability of an event being in either A or B or both becomes

$$p(A \text{ or } B) = p(A) + p(B) - p(AB)$$

Example 1 What is the probability that a single card taken from a pack will be a six or a nine?

As there are four sixes and four nines in a pack,

$$p(A) = p(B) = \frac{4}{52} = \frac{1}{13}$$

The events are clearly mutually exclusive and so the probability that the card is a six or a nine is given by

$$p = p(A) + p(B) = \frac{2}{13} = 0.154$$

Example 2 What is the probability that a single card taken from a pack will be a six or a red card?

As in example 1, $p(A) = 1/13$ and, since half of the cards are red, $p(B) = \frac{1}{2}$. This time the events are not mutually exclusive, since the card taken can be both red and a six. In this case, therefore,

$$p = p(A) + p(B) - p(AB)$$

There are two red sixes in the pack, and so

$$p(AB) = \frac{2}{52} = \frac{1}{26}$$

$$\therefore \quad p = \frac{1}{13} + \frac{1}{2} - \frac{1}{26} = 0.538$$

E1.5 Multiplication law for probabilities
The probability that two or more independent events which are not mutually exclusive will occur together is determined by *multiplying* their individual probabilities. We write

$$p(A \text{ and } B) = p(A) \times p(B)$$

For example, the probability of throwing a 3 with a die is $1/6$. To determine the probability of throwing two threes one after the other, or at once with identical dice, we multiply probabilities as follows:

$$p\,(3 \text{ and } 3) = \frac{1}{6} \times \frac{1}{6} = \frac{1}{36} \quad \text{or} \quad 0.028$$

224

Example   A man enters two raffles by buying three of the 100 tickets sold in the first raffle and one of 50 sold in the second. What is the probability that he will win both?

These events are not mutually exclusive, since the man may win both raffles. They are also independent, since a win in the first will not affect his chances of winning the second. The probabilities of winning the individual raffles are

$$p(1) = \frac{3}{100} \quad \text{and} \quad p(2) = \frac{1}{50}$$

therefore his chance of winning both is given by

$$p \text{ (1 and 2)} = \frac{3}{100} \times \frac{1}{50} = \frac{3}{5000} \quad \text{or} \quad 0.0006$$

E1.6 Practical probability problems

When solving probability problems involving more than one event, care must be taken in deciding whether to add or multiply probabilities. The multiplication law may be applied to events which are not completely independent provided we can determine how the outcome of one event will affect another. Sometimes we may have to use a combination of addition and multiplication laws to solve a problem. The following examples will illustrate some of these points.

Example 1   The probability that there will be no defectives in a batch of transistors is 0.73, and that for one defective per batch is 0.11. What is the probability that a batch will contain (a) not more than one defective? (b) more than one defective?

a) The probability of having no defectives $p(0) = 0.73$, and $p(1) = 0.11$. These are clearly mutually exclusive events, since there cannot be both 0 defectives and 1 defective in a batch. Using the addition law,

$$p(0) + p(1) = 0.73 + 0.11 = 0.84$$

This is the probability that a batch will contain not more than one defective.

b) The probability that there will be more than one defective in a batch is given by the addition law:

$$p \text{ (more than 1)} = p(2) + p(3) + p(4) + \ldots + p(N)$$

where N is the batch size. Even if we knew these probabilities, it would be tedious to add them up for a large batch. We can instead use the fact that the probabilities of complementary events add together to give 1, so that

$$p(0) + p(1) + p(2) + \ldots + p(N) = 1$$

225

We have seen in part (a) of the question that $p(0) + p(1) = 0.84$, and so the sum of all the remaining probabilities is

$$p(2) + p(3) + \ldots + p(N) = 1 - 0.84 = 0.16$$

i.e. the probability that there will be more than one defective per batch is 0.16.

Example 2 Two dice are thrown together. What is the probability that the total score is 4?

There are three ways of scoring a total of 4: these are 3 and 1, 1 and 3, or 2 and 2. Consider the first combination, with 3 from the first die and 1 from the second. These events are clearly independent, since throwing the 3 will not affect the chances of obtaining a 1 with the second die. The probability of obtaining this result is found using the multiplication law. Both $p(3)$ and $p(1)$ are 1/6, and so

$$p \text{ (3 and 1)} = \frac{1}{6} \times \frac{1}{6} = \frac{1}{36}$$

Similarly,

$$p \text{ (1 and 3)} = p \text{ (2 and 2)} = \frac{1}{36}$$

Since each of the three combinations is mutually exclusive, we obtain the total probability by addition, as follows:

$$p \text{ (score of 4)} = p \text{ (3 and 1)} + p \text{ (1 and 3)} + p \text{ (2 and 2)}$$

$$= \frac{1}{36} + \frac{1}{36} + \frac{1}{36}$$

$$= \frac{3}{36} \quad \text{or} \quad 0.083$$

Example 3 A bag contains three green beads and two blue beads. If two beads are taken at random, what is the probability that they will both be green if (a) the first bead taken is replaced before taking a second? (b) the first bead is not replaced?

a) When taking the first bead, the probability that it is green is 3/5. Since the bead is replaced, the two events are independent and the probability of choosing the second green bead is also 3/5. Using the multiplication law, therefore, the probability of choosing two green beads is

$$p \text{ (two green beads)} = \frac{3}{5} \times \frac{3}{5} = \frac{9}{25} \quad \text{or} \quad 0.36$$

b) As in part (a), when taking the first bead,

$$p \text{ (green)} = \frac{3}{5}$$

However, by not replacing this green bead we affect the probability of taking a second green bead. There are now only four beads in the bag of which two are green, and so

$$p \text{ (second green)} = \frac{2}{4}$$

To find the probability of taking two green beads in this way we may still multiply the individual probabilities. Although the events are not completely independent (since leaving the first green bead out of the bag affects the probability of a second), the second probability is identifiable and the first event has no further effect on the second. We say the events are *conditionally independent*, and so

$$p \text{ (two green beads)} = \frac{3}{5} \times \frac{2}{4} = \frac{3}{10} \quad \text{or} \quad 0.3$$

Example 4 A card is taken from a shuffled pack followed by a second without replacing the first. Calculate the probability that the first card is an ace and the second a red card.

These events are not independent, since the ace we draw first could be a red card and thus affect the probability that the second is red. If we consider all the possible outcomes in turn and define their probabilities, we can arrive at an overall probability.

i) The first card taken is a red ace and

$$p \text{ (red ace)} = \frac{2}{52}$$

The second card is one of the 25 remaining red cards,

$$\therefore \quad p \text{ (red card)} = \frac{25}{51}$$

From the multiplication law,

$$p \text{ (red ace and red card)} = \frac{2}{52} \times \frac{25}{51} = \frac{50}{2652}$$

ii) The ace taken first is black, and

$$p \text{ (black ace)} = \frac{2}{52}$$

227

The second card is red,

$$\therefore \quad p\,(\text{red card}) = \frac{26}{51}$$

$$\therefore \quad p\,(\text{black ace and red card}) = \frac{2}{52} \times \frac{26}{51} = \frac{52}{2652}$$

The combinations of cards described in (i) and (ii) are the only successful outcomes possible. They are mutually exclusive and so the total probability of taking an ace followed by a red card can be found by addition:

$$p\,(\text{ace and red card}) = \frac{50 + 52}{2652} = 0.038$$

Exercise E1
1   Define probability and state the range of possible numerical values.
2   If Manchester United play Everton at football, which of the following pairs of events is mutually exclusive?

a) Manchester win and Everton win
b) Everton score three goals and Manchester win.

3   If the probability that an integrated circuit will be damaged during soldering operations is 0.0012, what is the expectation of damaged components on 1000 printed circuit boards each containing 20 integrated circuits?
4   If the probability that a refrigerator fails because of a faulty thermostat is 0.57, what is the total probability of other causes of failure?
5   A box contains 100 discs numbered 1 to 100, from which two are taken at random. Which of the following events are completely independent?

a) Taking an even numbered disc followed by a disc between 1 and 50 if the first is replaced.
b) Taking an even numbered disc followed by an odd one if the first is replaced.
c) Taking an even numbered disc followed by a disc between 1 and 50 if the first is not replaced.
d) Taking an even numbered disc and then, having replaced it, taking a second disc with a smaller number.

6   State the addition law for probabilities when events are mutually exclusive and use it to determine the probability of throwing either a 5 or an even number with a single die.
7   State the addition law for probabilities when events are not mutually exclusive and use it to find the probability of throwing either a score of 8 or a throw including at least one 6 with a pair of dice.

8 The probability that a resistor taken from a batch will have a value greater than $508\,\Omega$ is 0.03, while the probability that it will be less than $446\,\Omega$ is 0.12. Determine the probability that the resistance will lie between these two values.

9 State the multiplication law for probabilities and hence find the probability of throwing two sixes with a pair of dice.

10 A man travels by bus to a railway station with a probability of 0.85 that he will arrive in time for his train. If the probability that his train is cancelled is 0.06, what is the probability that he will arrive at his final destination on time, assuming no further delays?

11 Five discs numbered 1 to 5 are placed in a bag and two are taken at random without replacement. What is the probability that the discs have numbers which differ by one?

12 In a box of ten capacitors, three are defective. One capacitor is taken out at random, replaced, and then another is taken. What is the probability that both are defective?

13 What would be the probability of taking two defective capacitors in question 12 if the first was not replaced before taking the second?

14 A box contains five steel nuts, four brass nuts, three steel washers, and two brass washers. If one item is taken at random and then a second without replacement, what is the probability that the first item was a nut and the second made of brass?

E2 The binomial distribution

In this section and in the two which follow we will be dealing with *probability distributions* and some of their practical applications. Before looking at the first of these distributions, we consider how to calculate the number of permutations and combinations of a given number of objects. This work will help us to simplify probability calculations later on.

E2.1 Permutations and combinations

Permutations
Arrangements of different objects into *different* orders are called *permutations*. There are six permutations of the three letters TEC, taking all three letters each time, and these are TEC   TCE   ECT   ETC   CTE   CET. If the letters are taken two at a time, there are again six permutations: TE   ET   TC   CT   EC   CE.

We denote the number of permutations of n objects taken r at a time as $_nP_r$ and it can be shown that,

$$_nP_r = \frac{n!}{(n-r)!}$$

where $n!$ is *factorial n*, a quick way of writing
$n(n-1)(n-2)(n-3)\ldots \times 3 \times 2 \times 1$. For example,
$4! = 4 \times 3 \times 2 \times 1 = 24$. (Your calculator may have a key marked '$x!$'
with which factorials of a defined range of whole numbers can be evaluated.)
Note that $0! = 1$.

In the two examples above, the permutations of all three letters and
of two letters in TEC are given by,

$$_3P_3 = \frac{3!}{(3-3)!} = \frac{3 \times 2 \times 1}{1} = 6$$

$$_3P_2 = \frac{3!}{(3-2)!} = \frac{3 \times 2 \times 1}{1} = 6$$

Example 1   Evaluate $_6P_3$.

$$_6P_3 = \frac{6!}{(6-3)!} = \frac{6!}{3!} = \frac{6 \times 5 \times 4 \times 3 \times 2 \times 1}{3 \times 2 \times 1} = 120$$

Example 2   How many different seating arrangements are there for
three people in a car with five seats?

The total number of permutations is given by

$$_5P_3 = \frac{5!}{(5-3)!} = \frac{5!}{2!} = 60$$

Combinations

When the *order* of r objects selected from a total of n objects is ignored,
the possible selections are called *combinations*. We saw earlier that there
are six permutations of two letters taken from the three letters TEC
and that these are TE   ET   TC   CT   EC   CE. If the order of the
letters in a pair is ignored, we can see that there are only three
combinations of letters (i.e. T with E, T with C, and E with C). Thus
TE and ET are *two* permutations but only *one* combination.

The number of combinations of n objects taken r at a time is given
by

$$_nC_r = \frac{n!}{(n-r)!\, r!}$$

We can see from this that $_nC_r = {}_nP_r/r!$, i.e. there are $r!$ permutations for
every combination.

The notation $\binom{n}{r}$ is now usually used instead of $_nC_r$ and we will use
this from now on. Some calculators will evaluate $_nP_r$ and $\binom{n}{r}$ directly
from values of n and r.

Example 3   Evaluate $\binom{7}{4}$.

$$\binom{7}{4} = \frac{7!}{(7-4)!\,4!} = \frac{7 \times 6 \times 5 \times 4 \times 3 \times 2 \times 1}{(3 \times 2 \times 1)(4 \times 3 \times 2 \times 1)} = 35$$

Example 4 Find the number of ways of selecting a five-a-side football team from eight players.

A team of five players is the same team regardless of the order of selection, so the required answer is the number of combinations of eight players taken five at a time:

$$\binom{8}{5} = \frac{8!}{(8-5)!\,5!} = 56$$

E2.2 Probabilities from binomial expansions

Consider a machine making components automatically. Suppose the probability that a component taken at random will be defective is p, and let $q = 1 - p$ be the probability that the component is not defective. If a sample of two components is taken and tested, there are three possibilities for the number of defectives in the sample. We can calculate the probabilities associated with each of the three cases as follows.

 i) *No defective* The probability that there will be no defective is given by $q \times q = q^2$. (Since these are independent events, we multiply the probabilities.)

 ii) *One defective* This can happen in two ways: either the first of the two components is defective and the second not defective, or the first is not defective and the second is defective. The probabilities in these cases are given by pq and qp respectively. The total probability of there being one defective is $2qp$. (Note that the two possible occurrences of one defective are mutually exclusive events and we add their probabilities.)

iii) *Two defectives* The probability that both components will be defective is $p \times p = p^2$.

These results are brought together in the table below:

Sample of two components		
Defectives 0 1 2		
Probability q^2 $2qp$ p^2		

We recognise that the probabilities in the table are given by the terms in the expansion

$$(q + p)^2 = q^2 + 2qp + p^2$$

Repeating the analysis with a sample of three components, the probabilities of having 0, 1, 2, and 3 defectives are summarised in the table below. (You may find it useful to check these results.)

231

Sample of three components				
Defectives	0	1	2	3
Probability	q^3	$3q^2p$	$3qp^2$	p^3

This time the probabilities are given by the terms of the expansion

$$(q + p)^3 = q^3 + 3q^2p + 3qp^2 + p^3$$

In the general case, with a sample of n components, the probabilities of $0, 1, 2, 3, \dots, n$ defectives are given by the terms of the *binomial expansion* of $(q + p)^n$.

The binomial theorem is discussed in section B5.1 and the expansion of $(q + p)^n$ is given by

$$(q + p)^n = \binom{n}{0}q^n + \binom{n}{1}pq^{n-1} + \binom{n}{2}p^2q^{n-2} + \dots + \binom{n}{r}p^rq^{n-r} + \dots + \binom{n}{n}p^n$$

(Note that n is a whole number, so the expansion has $n + 1$ terms.)

The general term $\binom{n}{r}p^rq^{n-r}$ of the binomial expansion gives the probability for r defectives in a sample of n in our example. This is the reason for the name 'binomial distribution'.

The binomial coefficients $\binom{n}{r}$ are of course combinations and can be evaluated using a calculator, from

$$\binom{n}{r} = \frac{n!}{(n - r)!\, r!}$$

It is useful to remember that $\binom{n}{0} = 1$, $\binom{n}{1} = n$, and $\binom{n}{n} = 1$.

Table E2.1 gives the coefficients for $n = 0$ to $n = 10$ and can be used to write down expansions directly. For example,

$$(q + p)^7 = q^7 + 7pq^6 + 21p^2q^5 + 35p^3q^4 + 35p^4q^3 + 21p^5q^2 + 7p^6q + p$$

Example 1   A machine produces components of which 18% are defective. Calculate the probability that a sample of five components taken at random will contain two defectives.

The probability that a sample of n components contains r defectives is given by

$$P(r) = \binom{n}{r}p^rq^{n-r}$$

Now if 18% of all components are defective, $p = 0.18$ and $q = 1 - p = 0.82$. Therefore, with $n = 5$ and $r = 2$,

$$P(2) = \binom{5}{2}(0.18)^2(0.82)^3 = (10)(0.0324)(0.5514)$$

$$= 0.179$$

Table E2.1 Binomial coefficients

n	$r =$ 0	1	2	3	4	5	6	7	8	9	10
			$\binom{n}{r}$								
1	1	1									
2	1	2	1								
3	1	3	3	1							
4	1	4	6	4	1						
5	1	5	10	10	5	1					
6	1	6	15	20	15	6	1				
7	1	7	21	35	35	21	7	1			
8	1	8	28	56	70	56	28	8	1		
9	1	9	36	84	126	126	84	36	9	1	
10	1	10	45	120	210	252	210	120	45	10	1

(note that $\binom{5}{2} = 10$ from the above table or by evaluating $5!/[(5-2)!2!]$
i.e. the probability of two defective components in a sample of five is
0.179, or 17.9%.

Example 2 If an average of 20% of candidates fail a driving test,
determine the probability that in a random sample of seven candidates
there will be (a) two failures, (b) fewer than two failures, (c) more than
two failures.

If 20% of candidates fail the test, then the probability that an
individual in the sample will fail the test is $p = 0.20$.

a) The probability that r candidates will fail in a sample of n is given
by

$$P(r) = \binom{n}{r}p^r q^{n-r}$$

where $q = 1 - p = 0.80$

With $n = 7$ and $r = 2$,

$$P(2) = \binom{7}{2}(0.20)^2(0.80)^5$$

$$= (21)(0.040)(0.3277)$$

$$= 0.275$$

i.e. the probability of two failures is 0.275, or 27.5%.

b) The probability of fewer than two failures is given by

$$P(<2) = P(0) + P(1)$$

(Note that the events are mutually exclusive and we add the probabilities of no failure and one failure.)

Now $P(0) = \binom{7}{0}p^0 q^7 = (0.80)^7 = 0.210$

$P(1) = \binom{7}{1}pq^6 = (7)(0.20)(0.80)^6 = 0.367$

hence $P(0) + P(1) = 0.210 + 0.376 = 0.577$

i.e. the probability of fewer than two failures is 57.7%.

c) The probability of more than two failures is given by $P(3) + P(4) + P(5) + P(6) + P(7)$. It is easier in this case to evaluate $1 - [P(0) + P(1) + P(2)]$, which gives the same answer.

We have already seen that

$$P(0) = 0.210 \qquad P(1) = 0.367 \quad \text{and} \quad P(2) = 0.275$$

thus $P(0) + P(1) + P(2) = 0.852$

and $1 - [P(0) + P(1) + P(2)] = 0.148$

i.e. the probability of more than two failures is 14.8%.

E2.3 Bar-chart representation of binomial distributions

In the previous section we saw that the probabilities of an event happening exactly $0, 1, 2, ..., n$ times in n independent trials are given by the terms of the expansion of $(q + p)^n$, where p is the probability of the event happening in any individual trial, and $q = 1 - p$. If we plot values of these probabilities against the number of times an event happens, the shape of the resulting diagram of the *binomial distribution* depends on the values of n and p.

Consider a machine producing components of which 35% are defective. The following table gives values of probabilities of the different numbers of defective components in a sample of three (the probabilities are given by $\binom{3}{r}(0.35)^r(0.65)^{3-r}$ for $r = 0$ to $r = 3$):

Number of defectives	0	1	2	3
Probability	0.2746	0.4436	0.2389	0.0429

(Note that the total probability is one.)

Since there cannot be numbers of defectives between, say, 0 and 1 or between 1 and 2, we are dealing with a *discrete* probability distribution. The best way to present this information on a diagram is with a bar chart. Figure E2.1 shows a bar chart drawn using probabilities from the above table for each number of defectives. This diagram of the probability distribution is clearly not symmetrical (we say it is *positively skew*).

234

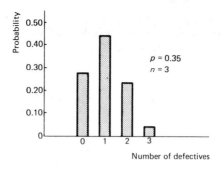

Fig. E2.1 Bar chart showing the binomial probability distribution for a sample of three

If n becomes large or if the value of p approaches 0.5, the distribution tends to be symmetrical. In general, the outline of a binomial-distribution diagram will be reasonably symmetrical and bell-shaped (approximating to the *normal curve*) when the value of np is greater than about 5. If we were to take a sample of twenty components instead of six from a large batch produced by the machine discussed earlier, the binomial probability-distribution diagram is much less skew, as we can see in fig. E2.2.

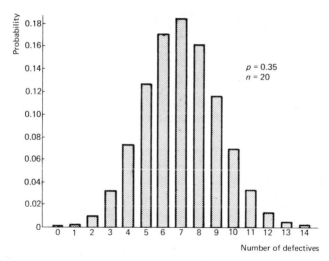

Fig. E2.2 Bar chart showing the binomial probability distribution for a sample of twenty

It can be shown that the mean value of the binomial distribution is $\mu = np$ and the standard deviation is $\sigma = \sqrt{(npq)}$.

Example If it is known that one quarter of the population of a large city owns a car, what is the expected value and the standard deviation of the number of people owning cars in a sample of twelve people chosen at random?

We are dealing with a binomial distribution with $n = 12$, $p = \frac{1}{4}$, and $q = \frac{3}{4}$,

$\therefore$ the mean (expected) value is $\mu = np = 12 \times \frac{1}{4} = 3$

and the standard deviation is $\sigma = \sqrt{(npq)} = 1.50$

It is often useful to compare observed distributions from collected data with expected distributions from probability models such as the binomial distribution. Consider as an example the results of a survey of 2500 families with five children. The following distribution of the occurrence of 0, 1, 2, 3, 4, and 5 boys was indicated by the survey:

Number of boys in family	0	1	2	3	4	5
Observed number of families	93	371	722	742	455	117

We will compare observed frequencies from this table with expected frequencies from the application of the binomial distribution model.

The total number of boys in the 2500 families is given from the table as

$$\text{total number of boys} = (0 \times 93) + (1 \times 371) + (2 \times 722) + (3 \times 742)$$
$$+ (4 \times 455) + (5 \times 117)$$
$$= 6446$$

The total number of children is $5 \times 2500 = 12\,500$. The proportion of boys is therefore

$$p = \frac{6446}{12\,500} = 0.5157$$

hence the proportion of girls is

$$q = 1 - p = 1 - 0.5157$$
$$= 0.4843$$

We can deduce from the results of the survey that our best estimate for the probability of any child in a family being a boy is 0.5157. It follows that the probability that a family with five children has r boys is given by

$$P(r) = \binom{5}{r}(0.5157)^r (0.4843)^{5-r}$$

236

If we assume that the families are independent, the expected frequencies of families with r boys are given by

$$2500 \times \binom{5}{r}(0.5157)^r(0.4843)^{5-r}$$

These expected frequencies for $r = 0, 1, 2, 3, 4,$ and 5, together with the observed values from the survey, are shown in the table below. (You may like to confirm the values of expected frequency.)

Number of boys in family	0	1	2	3	4	5
Observed frequency	93	371	722	742	455	117
Expected frequency	67	355	755	804	428	91

The bar chart in fig. E2.3 shows the difference between the distribution of the observed frequencies and the distribution of calculated expected frequencies. Statistical methods of deciding how closely the two distributions are related are beyond the scope of this book, but we can see from the bar chart that the distributions are generally similar in shape.

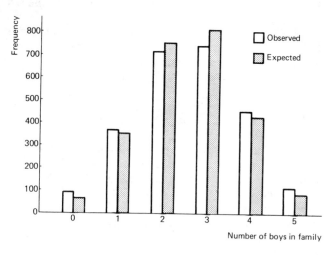

Fig. E2.3 Bar chart comparing observed and expected distribution of boys

Exercise E2

1 Evaluate (a) $_5P_4$, (b) $_7P_2$, (c) $_{12}P_{12}$.
2 How many permutations of the four letters UNIT are there, taken (a) three at a time, (b) two at a time?
3 Evaluate (a) $\binom{6}{2}$, (b) $\binom{11}{9}$, (c) $\binom{13}{5}$.
4 How many sets of six screws can be selected from a box of nine?
5 Twelve programmers wish to use a computer at the same time. If the maximum number of simultaneous users is eight, find the number

of possible groups of eight programmers. If the number of computer inputs is reduced by one, how many different groups of seven programmers are there?

6 State the general term containing p^r in the binomial expansion of $(q + p)^n$. A spot-welding machine fails to operate correctly on an average of one in every twenty welds. Calculate the probability that in a sequence of fourteen welds there will be (a) no failures, (b) one failure.

7 If it is known that 15.0% of the transistors produced in a factory are defective, write down the probabilities, correct to four decimal places, that a sample of four transistors will contain 0, 1, 2, 3, and 4 defectives and show that the sum of these probabilities is one.

8 If an average of one photograph in five taken in rapid succession is of acceptable quality, determine the probabilities, expressed as percentages, that the number of acceptable photographs in any sample of six will be (a) one, (b) more than two.

9 If 90% of the screws in a box have the correct thread for a particular hole, what is the probability that in a sample of eight screws there will be (a) one screw, (b) more than one screw with the wrong thread?

10 A sample of five items is taken at random from a machine's daily output. If 22.0% of all output is known to be defective, write down the probabilities, correct to four decimal places, of 0, 1, 2, 3, 4, and 5 defectives in the sample. Draw a bar chart showing the distribution of these probabilities.

11 Describe the conditions for which the binomial distribution obtained from the expansion of $(q + p)^n$ tends to be symmetrical.

Eight coins are thrown into the air and the number of heads is counted. Draw a bar chart showing the binomial probability distribution of the number of heads between 0 and 8.

12 State the mean value and the standard deviation of the binomial distribution obtained from the expansion of $(q + p)^n$.

Sixty dice are thrown in an experiment and the results are recorded. What is the value and the standard deviation of the number of sixes expected. Determine the probability that there will be ten sixes thrown.

13 In a test on a type of seed, four seeds were planted in each of 1200 pots. At the end of three weeks, the number of shoots in each pot was counted and the following distribution was produced:

Number of shoots in a pot	0	1	2	3	4
Observed number of pots	8	81	304	475	332

From the results in the table, (a) determine the observed proportion of seeds which have produced shoots. Give your answer correct to three significant figures. (b) Assume a binomial probability distribution to find the expected frequencies of pots with 0, 1, 2, 3, and 4 shoots, using the proportion in (a) as a probability. Compare the observed and expected frequencies on a bar chart.

E3 The Poisson distribution

E3.1 Defining the Poisson distribution

If the probability p that an event will happen in any trial is small and the number of trials n is large, it can be shown that the probability of exactly r successes, $\binom{n}{r} p^r q^{n-r}$, approaches the value of $e^{-np}(np)^r/r!$. (The value of e is approximately 2.718.)

Now $\mu = np$ is the arithmetic mean of the distribution, and so

$$P(r) = \frac{e^{-\mu} \mu^r}{r!}$$

The distribution defined in this way is known as the *Poisson probability distribution*. There are many important applications suited to its use, including inspection in industry, biological experimentation, and traffic control.

We have seen that the standard deviation of the binomial distribution is $\sigma = \sqrt{(npq)}$, where $q = 1 - p$, so the *variance* is given by $\sigma^2 = npq$. When the value of p is very small, q approaches unity and the variance is very nearly np, so that mean = variance = μ. We can think of the Poisson distribution as the limit of the binomial distribution as $n \to \infty$ and $np = \mu$ is a finite constant (so that $p \to 0$). We shall see later that the Poisson distribution is also useful as a distribution in its own right.

An advantage of working with the Poisson distribution is that calculations of probabilities when n is large are simpler than those associated with the binomial distribution. Values of e^x can easily be obtained using tables or a calculator.

The probabilities of $0, 1, 2, ..., n$ events happening in n trials are given by putting $r = 0, 1, 2, ..., n$ into the formula

$$P(r) = \frac{e^{-\mu} \mu^r}{r!}$$

Thus $P(0) = e^{-\mu}$, $P(1) = e^{-\mu}\mu$, $P(2) = \dfrac{e^{-\mu}\mu^2}{2!}$, $P(3) = \dfrac{e^{-\mu}\mu^3}{3!}$, ...

Adding these probabilities together gives

$$P(0) + P(1) + P(2) + P(3) + ... = e^{-\mu}\left(1 + \mu + \frac{\mu^2}{2!} + \frac{\mu^3}{3!} + ...\right)$$

The expression enclosed by brackets on the r.h.s. is in fact the expansion of e^μ as a series. This is not surprising, since $e^{-\mu} \times e^\mu = 1$; i.e. the sum of all probabilities is unity, as we would expect.

Example If there is a 0.30% chance that a particular car engine will fail to start at any attempt, what is the probability that there will be

239

(a) two failures, (b) more than two failures in 200 attempts to start the engine at random intervals?

a) Using the Poisson distribution, we have $p = 0.003$, $n = 200$, and $\mu = np = 0.6$;

hence $P(2) = e^{-\mu}\mu^2/2! = e^{-0.6}(0.6)^2/2 = 0.0988$

i.e. the probability that the engine will fail to start twice in 200 attempts is 0.0988 or 9.88%.

b) The probability of more than two failures is given by

$$P(>2) = 1 - [P(0) + P(1) + P(2)]$$

where $P(0) = e^{-\mu} = e^{-0.6} = 0.5488$

and $P(1) = e^{-\mu}\mu = e^{-0.6}(0.6) = 0.3293$

From (a) we have $P(2) = 0.0988$, giving

$$P(>2) = 1 - (0.9769) = 0.0231$$

i.e. the probability of more than two failures is 2.31%.

Note that the above example could also have been completed using the binomial distribution with $p = 0.003$ and $n = 200$. You may like to show that the two probabilities obtained using this method are (a) 0.0988 and (b) 0.0229 and are therefore very close to those we get using the Poisson distribution.

It is useful to compare the probabilities from a binomial distribution with those from a Poisson distribution for the same values of n and p. The table below gives probabilities from both distributions for three cases.

Probability	$n = 500, \ p = 0.001$		$n = 500, \ p = 0.005$		$n = 5, \ p = 0.1$	
	Binomial	Poisson	Binomial	Poisson	Binomial	Poisson
$P(0)$	0.6064	0.6065	0.0816	0.0821	0.5905	0.6065
$P(1)$	0.3035	0.3035	0.2050	0.2052	0.3280	0.3033
$P(2)$	0.0758	0.0758	0.2570	0.2565	0.0729	0.0758
$P(3)$	0.0126	0.0126	0.2144	0.2138	0.0081	0.0126
$P(4)$	0.0016	0.0016	0.1338	0.1336	0.0005	0.0016
$P(5)$	0.0002	0.0002	0.0667	0.0668	0.0000	0.0002

Consider the first section of the table, with $n = 500$ and $p = 0.001$. With one exception, the binomial and Poisson probabilities agree to all four decimal places. With $p = 0.005$ keeping n the same at 500 in the second section of the table, the agreement is reduced, although the values for the two distributions are still the same to within 1%. In the third section of the table, with $n = 5$ and $p = 0.1$, the differences are much greater and we could not use the Poisson distribution as an approximation to the binomial distribution without the introduction of large errors. It is clear from these examples that, as n decreases and p increases, the agreement between the distributions is steadily reduced.

E3.2 Applications of the Poisson distribution

We have seen that the Poisson distribution can be regarded as a limiting case of the binomial distribution, and that there are occasions when either probability distribution can be applied to give results which agree reasonably well. The first of the following examples is of this type. In the second example, the Poisson distribution is used in its own right to solve a problem which is not suitable for the binomial probability model.

Example 1   A haulage company delivers goods using 150 lorries. If the probability that any lorry is broken down at any given time is 0.01, what percentage of the time will there be (a) two lorries, (b) more than two lorries broken down?

a) Using the Poisson model, $n = 150$, $p = 0.01$, and $\mu = np = 1.5$. The probability that r lorries will be broken down at any time is given by

$$P(r) = e^{-\mu}\mu^r/r!$$

hence $P(2) = e^{-1.5}(1.5)^2/2! = 0.2510$

i.e. we estimate that 25.10% of the time there will be two lorries broken down.

Using the binomial model with $n = 150$ and $p = 0.01$,

$$P(2) = \binom{150}{2}(0.01)^2(0.99)^{148} = 0.2525 \quad \text{or} \quad 25.25\%$$

These results are in close agreement, but the calculations involved using the Poisson model are easier.

b) To find what percentage of the time there will be more than two lorries broken down,

$$P(>2) = 1 - [P(0) + P(1) + P(2)]$$

From the Poisson distribution,

$$P(0) = e^{-1.5} = 0.2231$$

$$P(1) = e^{-1.5}(1.5) = 0.3347$$

$\therefore \quad P(>2) = 1 - (0.2231 + 0.3347 + 0.2510)$

$$= 0.1912 \quad \text{or} \quad 19.12\%$$

241

i.e. for 19.12% of the time there are likely to be more than two lorries broken down. (Note that the binomial model gives 19.05%.)

The problem of finding $P(>c)$ is so common that charts have been produced giving $P(>c)$ for a range of values of μ and c.

Example 2　The results of an experiment with a radioactive substance show that the average number of particles emitted in any six-second interval is 3.100. Assuming that this average remains constant over a long period, what is the probability that there will be five particles emitted in any of the six-second intervals?

The Poisson model can be used here but, since we do not know how many particles are *not* emitted in any interval, the binomial model cannot be used.

The probability that there will be five particles emitted in any six-second interval is given by

$$P(5) = e^{-\mu}\mu^5/5!$$

Substituting $\mu = 3.100$ gives

$$P(5) = e^{-3.100}(3.100)^5/5! = 0.1075$$

The above example illustrates the usefulness of the Poisson probability model whenever discrete events occur independently and at random intervals of time or distance (i.e. *continuous* variables).

Example 3　The following table gives the results of a biological laboratory experiment in which the numbers of a particular type of cell in each of the 400 squares of a counting chamber were recorded.

Number of cells	0	1	2	3	4	5	6	7	8	9	10	11	12
Observed number of squares (total 400)	2	13	33	57	77	73	58	42	26	11	5	2	1

Fit a Poisson distribution to the data and calculate the theoretical expected frequencies. Show the observed and expected frequencies on a bar chart.

From the table of observations the total number of cells in the 400 squares is 1956. The average number of cells per square is given by $1956/400 = 4.89$.

Using the Poisson model with $\mu = 4.89$, the probability that any square will contain r cells is

$$P(r) = e^{-\mu}\mu^r/r! = e^{-4.89}(4.89)^r/r!$$

In a counting chamber with 400 squares, therefore, the expected frequency of squares containing r cells is

$$400 \times e^{-4.89}(4.89)^r/r!$$

These expected frequencies, calculated for $r = 0, 1, 2, ..., 12$, are given (rounded to the nearest integer) in the following table, with the observed frequencies for comparison.

Number of cells	0	1	2	3	4	5	6	7	8	9	10	11	12
Observed frequency	2	13	33	57	77	73	58	42	26	11	5	2	1
Expected frequency	3	15	36	59	72	70	57	40	24	13	6	3	1

The bar chart in fig. E3.1 shows the close relationship between the distributions of observed and expected frequency.

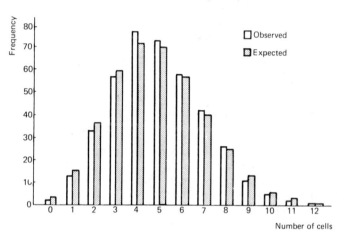

Fig. E3.1 Observed and expected frequency distribution of cells

Exercise E3

1 Given that the probability of r events in a Poisson distribution is $P(r) = e^{-\mu}\mu^r/r!$, calculate $P(0)$, $P(1)$, and $P(5)$ correct to four decimal places if $\mu = 0.58$.

2 State the conditions for which the Poisson distribution approximates to the binomial distribution. A machine produces a large number of components automatically. The probability that any component taken at random will be defective is 0.025. Compare the probabilities given by the Poisson and binomial probability models that there will be three defectives in a sample of 150 components.

3 If 99 % of the output from a paint-spraying machine is of acceptable quality, calculate the probability that there will be more than three rejects in a batch of 120 sprayed components.

243

4 A football team has scored an average of 1.25 goals over a large number of games. What is the probability that the team will score two goals in its next game? Explain why the binomial probability model cannot be used to answer this question.

5 The number of calls per minute to a telephone switchboard between 5 p.m. and 6 p.m. every day was recorded over a number of weeks. It was found that the average number of calls was 3.0 per minute. Calculate the probability that there will be more than eight calls in any minute between 5 p.m. and 6 p.m.

6 Tests on a new drug show that 0.2% of all people suffer from an adverse side-effect. Calculate the probability that in a sample of 800 people (a) one person, (b) more than one person will react adversely.

7 A hire-car company has eleven cars which are available for hire by the day. The daily demand for cars has a Poisson distribution with mean 6.55. Show that, on any day, (a) the probability that demand will exceed the supply by one car is 0.019, (b) there is a 10.8% chance that at least eight cars will remain unused.

8 Fifty identical aluminium test-pieces were anodised and then individually checked for flaws. The table below gives the results of these tests.

Number of flaws on one test-piece	0	1	2	3	4	5	6	7
Observed number of test-pieces	4	10	14	9	7	3	2	1

Find the average number of flaws for a single test-piece and use this value to determine expected frequencies (to the nearest whole number) based on a Poisson model. Compare the distributions of observed and expected frequencies on a bar chart.

9 During a traffic survey, the numbers of vehicles passing an observation point every minute were recorded over a period of two hours. Use the following table of results to determine the average number of vehicles per minute, and draw a bar chart to compare the observed results with those found using a Poisson model based on the calculated average.

Vehicles per minute	0	1	2	3	4	5	6
Observed frequency (total 120)	20	34	29	20	11	4	2

E4 The normal distribution

The binomial and Poisson models describe discrete probability distributions. We now look at the widely used normal (or Gaussian) probability distribution associated with continuous variables such as mass, length, time, and temperature.

E4.1 The normal probability curve

There are many common frequency distributions which, when shown on a diagram, have a familiar 'bell-shaped' outline. If we boarded any bus full of adults and measured their heights, it is most likely that there would be a large number of people with heights of approximately 1.7 m and relatively few at 1.5 m and 1.9 m. The frequencies of heights could be shown in a histogram using class intervals of, say, 0.02 m. While the histogram from this small sample might not be perfectly symmetrical, we can be sure that most of its area would be concentrated in the central region, tailing off quite rapidly at each end. If the number in our sample was greatly increased, the outline of the histogram would approach a smooth curve which could be approximated by a *normal probability curve* like the one shown in fig. E4.1.

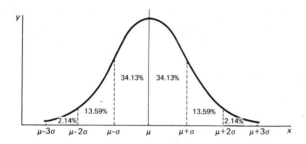

Fig. E4.1 Normal-probability curve

The equation of the normal curve is

$$y = \frac{1}{\sigma\sqrt{(2\pi)}}\, e^{-(x-\mu)^2/2\sigma^2}$$

where μ and σ are the mean and standard deviation of the distribution. The precise shape of the normal curve for a particular distribution depends on the values of μ and σ for that distribution. It must be stressed that, although many distributions conform closely to the widely used normal probability model, we are usually dealing with approximations, as cases of exactly normal distributions are rare.

The total area below the normal curve is unity. Areas below the curve between various ordinates are used, as we shall see, in probability calculations. Percentage areas between ordinates at one, two, and three standard deviations on either side of the mean are shown in fig. E4.1 and are summarised as follows:

68.26 % of the total area lies below the curve between $\mu - \sigma$ and $\mu + \sigma$
95.44 % „ „ „ „ „ „ „ „ „ $\mu - 2\sigma$ and $\mu + 2\sigma$
99.72 % „ „ „ „ „ „ „ „ „ $\mu - 3\sigma$ and $\mu + 3\sigma$

245

The standard normal distribution

We can conveniently deal with all distributions which conform exactly or approximately to the normal distribution but which have different values of μ and σ by relating them to the *standard normal distribution* which has a mean and a standard deviation of 0 and 1 respectively. The equation defining the standard normal function is

$$y = \frac{1}{\sqrt{(2\pi)}} \, e^{-(z^2/2)}$$

where $z = (x - \mu)/\sigma$ is the *standardised normal variate*. We can see from this expression that z is a measure of the number of standard deviations between x and the mean.

Example If the heights of all the adults in a village are considered to be normally distributed with mean 1.71 m and standard deviation 0.08 m, express a height of 1.85 m in terms of the standardised normal variate z.

The standardised normal variate is related to the normal variate x by

$$z = (x - \mu)/\sigma$$

thus a height of $x = 1.85$ m becomes

$$z = \frac{1.85 - 1.71}{0.08} = 1.75$$

(Note that values of z are always dimensionless.)

E4.2 Areas under the normal curve

The normal probability curve is symmetrical about the mean and encloses one unit of area. The area shown shaded under the normal curve in fig. E4.2 gives the proportion of items in the distribution having a value between $x = a$ and $x = b$. This is equal to the probability that a value of x selected at random will lie between a and b.

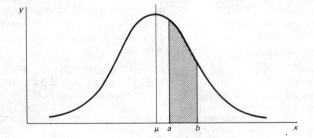

Fig. E4.2

246

Table E4.1 Areas under the standard normal curve (to four decimal places)

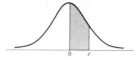

z	0.00	0.01	0.02	0.03	0.04	0.05	0.06	0.07	0.08	0.09
0.0	0.0000	0.0040	0.0080	0.0120	0.0160	0.0199	0.0239	0.0279	0.0319	0.0359
0.1	0.0398	0.0438	0.0478	0.0517	0.0557	0.0596	0.0636	0.0657	0.0714	0.0753
0.2	0.0793	0.0832	0.0871	0.0910	0.0948	0.0987	0.1026	0.1064	0.1103	0.1141
0.3	0.1179	0.1217	0.1255	0.1293	0.1331	0.1368	0.1406	0.1443	0.1480	0.1517
0.4	0.1554	0.1591	0.1628	0.1664	0.1700	0.1736	0.1772	0.1808	0.1844	0.1879
0.5	0.1915	0.1950	0.1985	0.2019	0.2054	0.2088	0.2123	0.2157	0.2190	0.2224
0.6	0.2257	0.2291	0.2324	0.2357	0.2389	0.2422	0.2454	0.2486	0.2517	0.2549
0.7	0.2580	0.2611	0.2642	0.2673	0.2704	0.2734	0.2764	0.2794	0.2823	0.2852
0.8	0.2881	0.2910	0.2939	0.2967	0.2995	0.3023	0.3051	0.3078	0.3106	0.3133
0.9	0.3159	0.3186	0.3212	0.3238	0.3264	0.3289	0.3315	0.3340	0.3365	0.3389
1.0	0.3413	0.3438	0.3461	0.3485	0.3508	0.3531	0.3554	0.3577	0.3599	0.3621
1.1	0.3643	0.3665	0.3686	0.3708	0.3729	0.3749	0.3770	0.3790	0.3810	0.3830
1.2	0.3849	0.3869	0.3888	0.3907	0.3925	0.3944	0.3962	0.3980	0.3997	0.4015
1.3	0.4032	0.4049	0.4066	0.4082	0.4099	0.4115	0.4131	0.4147	0.4162	0.4177
1.4	0.4192	0.4207	0.4222	0.4236	0.4251	0.4265	0.4279	0.4292	0.4306	0.4319
1.5	0.4332	0.4345	0.4357	0.4370	0.4382	0.4394	0.4406	0.4418	0.4429	0.4441
1.6	0.4452	0.4463	0.4474	0.4484	0.4495	0.4505	0.4515	0.4525	0.4535	0.4545
1.7	0.4554	0.4564	0.4573	0.4582	0.4591	0.4599	0.4608	0.4616	0.4625	0.4633
1.8	0.4641	0.4649	0.4656	0.4664	0.4671	0.4678	0.4686	0.4693	0.4699	0.4706
1.9	0.4713	0.4719	0.4726	0.4732	0.4738	0.4744	0.4750	0.4756	0.4761	0.4767
2.0	0.4772	0.4778	0.4783	0.4788	0.4793	0.4798	0.4803	0.4808	0.4812	0.4817
2.1	0.4821	0.4826	0.4830	0.4834	0.4838	0.4842	0.4846	0.4850	0.4854	0.4857
2.2	0.4861	0.4864	0.4868	0.4871	0.4875	0.4878	0.4881	0.4884	0.4887	0.4890
2.3	0.4893	0.4896	0.4898	0.4901	0.4904	0.4906	0.4909	0.4911	0.4913	0.4916
2.4	0.4918	0.4920	0.4922	0.4925	0.4927	0.4929	0.4931	0.4932	0.4934	0.4936
2.5	0.4938	0.4940	0.4941	0.4943	0.4945	0.4946	0.4948	0.4949	0.4951	0.4952
2.6	0.4953	0.4955	0.4956	0.4957	0.4959	0.4960	0.4961	0.4962	0.4963	0.4964
2.7	0.4965	0.4966	0.4967	0.4968	0.4969	0.4970	0.4971	0.4972	0.4973	0.4974
2.8	0.4974	0.4975	0.4976	0.4977	0.4977	0.4978	0.4979	0.4979	0.4980	0.4981
2.9	0.4981	0.4982	0.4983	0.4983	0.4984	0.4984	0.4985	0.4985	0.4986	0.4986
3.0	0.4986	0.4987	0.4987	0.4988	0.4988	0.4989	0.4989	0.4989	0.4990	0.4990
3.1	0.4990	0.4991	0.4991	0.4991	0.4992	0.4992	0.4992	0.4992	0.4993	0.4993
3.2	0.4993	0.4993	0.4994	0.4994	0.4994	0.4994	0.4994	0.4995	0.4995	0.4995
3.3	0.4995	0.4995	0.4996	0.4996	0.4996	0.4996	0.4996	0.4996	0.4996	0.4997
3.4	0.4997	0.4997	0.4997	0.4997	0.4997	0.4997	0.4997	0.4997	0.4997	0.4998
3.5	0.4998	0.4998	0.4998	0.4998	0.4998	0.4998	0.4998	0.4998	0.4998	0.4998
3.6	0.4998	0.4998	0.4999	0.4999	0.4999	0.4999	0.4999	0.4999	0.4999	0.4999
3.7	0.4999	0.4999	0.4999	0.4999	0.4999	0.4999	0.4999	0.4999	0.4999	0.4999
3.8	0.4999	0.4999	0.4999	0.4999	0.4999	0.4999	0.4999	0.4999	0.4999	0.4999
3.9	0.5000	0.5000	0.5000	0.5000	0.5000	0.5000	0.5000	0.5000	0.5000	0.5000

By relating individual normal distributions to the standardised model, we can use the same set of standard tables to find areas (and hence probabilities) for distributions of screw lengths, light-bulb life times, amplifier gains, ball-bearing masses, and many more continuous variables. Areas under the standard normal curve between ordinates at 0 and z on the standardised variate scale are given in Table E4.1. Note that the total area on each side of the mean is 0.5000.

The following examples show how the table can be used to solve various types of probability problem involving normal or approximately normal distributions. It is always advisable to draw a diagram relating required probabilities to areas under the normal curv

Example 1 The mean mass of hens' eggs from a farm is 58 g with standard deviation 8 g. If the distribution is taken to be normal, find the probability that the mass of any egg taken at random will be greater than 58 g and less than 70 g.

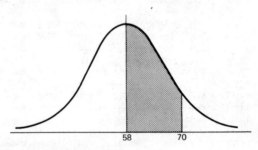

Fig. E4.3 Distribution of the mass of hens' eggs

A sketch is drawn (see fig. E4.3) showing the relevant area under the normal curve. This area represents the required probability.

We relate the mass of 70 g to the standardised normal distribution, giving

$$z = \frac{70 - \mu}{\sigma} = \frac{70 - 58}{8} = 1.50$$

Table E4.1 gives the area between ordinates at 0 and $z = 1.5$ as 0.433 The probability that any egg will have a mass between 58 g and 70 g i therefore 0.4332.

Example 2 The diameter of a type of copper fitting is normally distributed with mean 22.00 mm and standard deviation 0.15 mm. Estimate the number with diameter greater than 22.36 mm in a box o 250 fittings.

The sketch in fig. E4.4 shows the area defining the required probabili

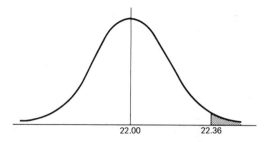

Fig. E4.4 Distribution of the diameter of copper fittings

Standardising the variable,

$$z = \frac{x - \mu}{\sigma} = \frac{22.36 - 22.00}{0.15} = 2.40$$

The area required lies to the *right* of $z = 2.40$, but Table E4.1 gives areas to the *left* of any ordinate. The area under each half of the curve is 0.5000, and we find the required area by subtraction. From the table at $z = 2.40$, we have an area of 0.4918,

$\therefore$ area required $= 0.5000 - 0.4918 = 0.0082$

The probability that any fitting has a diameter greater than 22.36 mm is 0.0082. In a box of 250 fittings, the number expected with diameter greater than 22.36 mm is therefore $250 \times 0.0082 = 2$ (to the nearest integer).

Example 3   The nickel–cadmium batteries from a factory have a life which is normally distributed with mean 33.37 hours and standard deviation 4.26 hours. One hundred batteries are taken at random and tested until they are completely discharged. If all the batteries are connected at the same time, determine how many are expected to become discharged in the first 26 hours of testing.

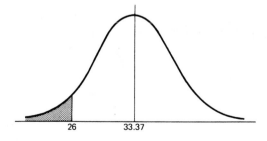

Fig. E4.5 Distribution of the life of batteries

The required area is shown shaded in fig. E4.5.

We have $\mu = 33.37$ hours and $\sigma = 4.26$ hours

$$\therefore \quad z = \frac{26 - 33.37}{4.26} = -1.73$$

The probability that any battery will be discharged in the first 26 hour of testing is given by the area under the standard normal curve to the left of $z = -1.73$ (see fig. E4.6). This area cannot be read directly from the table of normal probabilities, but the symmetry of the curve enable us to find its value.

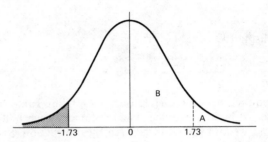

Fig. E4.6 Standard normal distribution

We determine area B directly from the table, for $z = 1.73$:

area B = 0.4582

Now area A + area B = 0.5000

$\therefore$ area A = 0.0418

From the symmetry of the curve, the required area is clearly equal to area A, and the probability that any battery will be discharged in the first 26 hours of testing is 0.0418. In the sample of 100 batteries we expect four (i.e. 4.18 to the nearest battery) to be discharged in this time.

Example 4 A machine produces screws with mean length 15.00 mm and standard deviation 1.29 mm. Assuming the lengths to be normally distributed, find (a) the proportion of screws between 14 mm and 17 mm in length, (b) the value of x if 60% of all screws have lengths between $(15.00 - x)$ mm and $(15.00 + x)$ mm.

a) We require the shaded area in fig. E4.7.

Standardising,

let $z_1 = \dfrac{17 - 15}{1.29} = 1.55$ and $z_2 = \dfrac{14 - 15}{1.29} = -0.78$

250

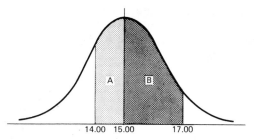

Fig. E4.7 Distribution of screw lengths

From the normal probability table at $z = 1.55$, the proportion related to area B is 0.4394.

From the table at $z = 0.78$, the area is 0.2823. From the symmetry of the curve, the area related to A is also 0.2823 (i.e. the area to the left of $z = 0.78$ is identical to the area to the right of $z = -0.78$ which is the area we want). The proportion of screws with lengths between 14.00 mm and 17.00 mm is therefore $0.4394 + 0.2823 = 0.7217$, or 72.17%.

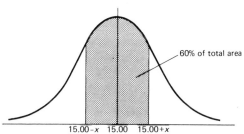

Fig. E4.8

b) The shaded area in fig. E4.8 corresponds to 60% of all screws. Consider the point $(15.00 + x)$. Standardising gives

$$z = \frac{(15.00 + x) - 15.00}{1.29} = \frac{x}{1.29}$$

From symmetry, the area between $z = 0$ and $z = x/1.29$ is 0.3000 (i.e. half of the total specified area of 0.6000). From the table of normal probabilities, the nearest value of z for an area of 0.3000 is $z = 0.84$ (area in table 0.2995);

hence $\quad 0.84 = \dfrac{x}{1.29}$

and $\quad\quad x = 1.08$ mm

i.e. we estimate that 60% of the screws have lengths between 13.92 mm and 16.08.

E4.3 Using normal probability graph paper

If we take a normal distribution and on ordinary graph paper plot a graph of cumulative frequencies expressed as percentages against values of the variate, we obtain an S-shaped curve called an *ogive*, like the one shown in fig. E4.9.

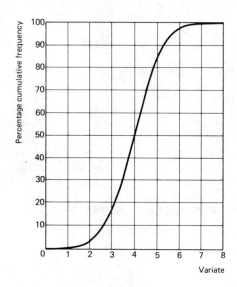

Fig. E4.9 The ogive (cumulative-frequency curve for a normal distribution)

When trying to decide whether a given set of data conforms to a normal distribution, it is difficult to see if the cumulative-frequency curve drawn for the distribution is a true ogive. It is much easier to work with straight lines, and *normal-probability paper* is used to reduce the ogive to a straight line. This is achieved by choosing a scale for the percentage-cumulative-frequency axis such that plotting the same points which gave the curve in fig. E4.9 produces the straight line shown in fig. E4.10 on normal-probability paper.

The linear scale along the horizontal axis of the probability paper can be used for values of the variate with any given set of data. The straightness of the line indicates to what extent the data conforms to a normal distribution.

The following examples show how normal-probability paper may be used to test for a normal distribution and how values of mean and of standard deviation can be found.

Example 1 The following table gives the distribution of examination marks for 1000 students. Use probability graph paper to test the normality of the distribution.

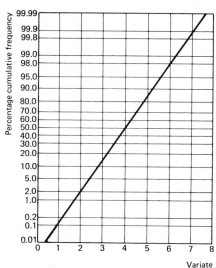

Fig. E4.10 Normal-probability paper

Variate

Examination marks	0–9	10–19	20–29	30–39	40–49	50–59	60–69	70–79	80–89	90–99
Frequency (total 1000)	3	12	44	113	199	241	207	119	49	13

To prepare the data for plotting on normal-probability paper we require the value of percentage cumulative frequency for each of the ten classes of marks. The cumulative frequency for any class is obtained by simply adding the frequency in that class to all the frequencies occurring earlier in the table. There are 3 students with marks below 9.5, and $3 + 12 = 15$ students with marks below 19.5. (Note that we always use *upper class boundaries* (e.g. 9.5 and 19.5) when defining cumulative frequencies for grouped data – see *Mathematics for level-2 technicians*, page 223.) The cumulative frequencies for each class are then expressed as a percentage of the total of 1000 students. The completed table of percentage cumulative frequencies is shown below:

Examination marks (upper class boundary)	9.5	19.5	29.5	39.5	49.5	59.5	69.5	79.5	89.5	99.5
Cumulative frequency	3	15	59	172	371	612	819	938	987	1000
Percentage cumulative frequency	0.3	1.5	5.9	17.2	37.1	61.2	81.9	93.8	98.7	100

When values from this table are used to plot a graph on normal-probability paper, they give the line shown in fig. E4.11. (Note that we

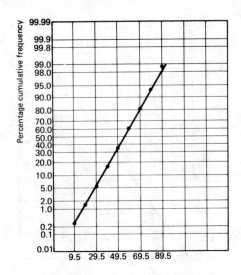

Percentage cumulative frequency

Examination marks (upper class boundaries)

Fig. E4.11

can plot only the first nine points, as the vertical scale does not extend to 100%.) We can see that the line is reasonably straight, and we conclude that the examination marks are normally distributed.

(Examination marks are of course discrete rather than continuous variables. This example illustrates that the normal-probability curve can sometimes be used as a good approximation to a discrete distribution.)

Example 2 Two machines, A and B, fill tubes with toothpaste automatically. Quantities dispensed by each machine in 500 trials are shown in the frequency table below:

Quantity of toothpaste (ml) (upper class boundaries)	121	123	125	127	129	131
Machine A – frequency (total 500)	1	28	159	226	79	7
Machine B – frequency (total 500)	4	41	198	215	37	5

Draw graphs of these frequency distributions on normal-probability paper to show that quantities from one of the machines are normally distributed, and use the graph for this machine to determine the mean and standard deviation of the normal distribution.

Percentage cumulative frequencies for the two machines calculated from the given frequency values are set out in the following table:

254

Upper class boundary (ml)	121	123	125	127	129	131
Machine A						
Cumulative frequency	1	29	188	414	493	500
Percentage cumulative frequency	0.20	5.80	37.6	82.8	98.6	100
Machine B						
Cumulative frequency	4	45	243	458	495	500
Percentage cumulative frequency	0.80	9.00	48.6	91.6	99.0	100

Plotting points from the table on probability paper, we see in fig. E4.12 that a reasonably straight line can be drawn through the points relating to machine A, but that this is not possible for machine B. We conclude that only the quantities dispensed by machine A are normally distributed.

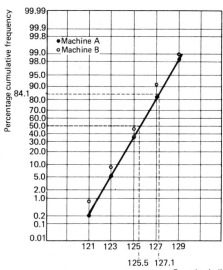

Fig. E4.12

From the graph for machine A, we see that the horizontal line drawn from the percentage-cumulative-frequency axis at 50% cuts the graph at 125.5 ml. The mean of the distribution is therefore 125.5 ml. (Note that the value given by this intersection is in fact the *median*, but, since we have established that the distribution is normal, the mean and median coincide.)

To determine the standard deviation of the distribution, we can use the fact that 34.13% of the area under the normal curve lies between ordinates μ and $\mu + \sigma$ (see fig. E4.1). From this, the *total* area below the normal curve to the left of an ordinate at $\mu + \sigma$ is $34.13\% + 50\% = 84.13\%$.

Consider the horizontal broken line in fig. E4.12, drawn from 84.1%
on the vertical scale to cut the graph relating to machine A at a point
corresponding to 127.1 ml on the variate axis. From this,

$$125.5 + \sigma = 127.1\,\text{ml}$$

$$\therefore \qquad \sigma = 1.6\,\text{ml}$$

i.e. the quantities dispensed by machine A are normally distributed with
mean 125.5 ml and standard deviation 1.6 ml.

Exercise E4

1 A normal distribution has mean μ and standard deviation σ. What
percentage of the total area below the normal curve lies between
ordinates at, (a) $\mu - \sigma$ and $\mu + \sigma$, (b) $\mu - 2\sigma$ and $\mu + \sigma$, (c) $\mu - 3\sigma$ and
μ?

2 The mean and the standard deviation of a large number of resistors
are 470.0 Ω and 2.55 Ω respectively. Assuming a normal distribution,
express resistances of 473.60 Ω and 467.25 Ω in the form of the
standardised normal variate, correct to two decimal places.

3 The mean life of a masonry-drill bit is 20 hours active use. Assuming
a normal distribution and a standard deviation of 3 hours, what is the
probability of a particular drill bit lasting more than 24 hours?

4 The amounts of a solvent in a large number of test-tubes are
normally distributed with mean 20.0 ml and standard deviation 2.4 ml.
Use normal-probability tables to determine the probability that a test-
tube taken at random will contain (a) between 20 ml and 24.8 ml,
(b) more than 23 ml, (c) less than 14.6 ml, (d) between 18 ml and 24 ml.

5 The mean diameter of rivets made on an automatic machine is
12.60 mm, with standard deviation 0.42 mm. Estimate the number of
rivets in a random sample of 200 which will have a diameter between
12.28 mm and 12.86 mm.

6 Times taken for an underground train to complete a regular journey
are found to be normally distributed with mean 122 minutes and
standard deviation 7.5 minutes. What percentage of trains should take
between 128 and 134 minutes?

7 The mean crushing stress of concrete test cubes is 22.5 MPa.
Assuming a normal distribution with standard deviation 2.35 MPa, how
many cubes in a sample of 300 would you expect to be crushed
between 19 MPa and 20 MPa?

8 The switching temperatures of a type of thermostat are found to be
normally distributed with mean 20.3 °C and standard deviation 1.4 °C.
At what temperature can we be 95% sure that any given thermostat
will have switched?

9 By plotting percentage cumulative frequency against values of the
variate on probability paper, show that the distribution given below is
normally distributed.

Variate (upper class boundaries)	1	2	3	4	5	6	7
Frequency (total 1000)	6	61	242	382	242	61	6

10 Determine which of the following distributions of bolt lengths is a normal distribution and estimate the mean and the standard deviation for that distribution using a graph on normal-probability paper.

Bolt length (mm) (upper class boundaries)	96	97	98	99	100
Distribution-A frequency	3	22	48	24	3
Distribution-B frequency	5	17	58	15	5

Revision exercises

Revision exercise A1

1 Convert the following numbers into binary, decimal, or octal form as indicated in brackets: (a) 8_{10} (binary), (b) 46_{10} (binary), (c) 111_2 (decimal), (d) 10010_2 (decimal), (e) 8_{10} (octal), (f) 96_{10} (octal), (g) 35_8 (binary), (h) 40_8 (binary), (i) 100001_2 (octal), (j) 101110010_2 (octal).

2 Add the following pairs of numbers together: (a) $111_2 + 111_2$, (b) $10111_2 + 10000_2$, (c) $11111_2 + 101_2$, (d) $204_8 + 312_8$, (e) $715_8 + 546_8$.

3 Perform each of the following subtractions using the complement method: (a) $1111_2 - 101_2$, (b) $10101_2 - 1010_2$, (c) $110110_2 - 111_2$, (d) $63_8 - 57_8$, (e) $3271_8 - 205_8$.

Revision exercise A2

1 Convert the decimal numbers 97 and 542 into 8421-BCD code.

2 Write down the decimal numbers 42 and 813 in excess-3 BCD code.

3 Describe the following codes, giving one example of each: (a) error-detecting code using even parity, (b) Gray code.

4 The 'two out of five' BCD code shown below uses five digits with weightings 7,4,2,1, and 0. Complete the table for decimal numbers 5 to 9, and describe briefly how this code may be used as an error-detecting code.

Decimal	7	4	2	1	0
0	1	1	0	0	0
1	0	0	0	1	1
2	0	0	1	0	1
3	0	0	1	1	0
4	0	1	0	0	1

Revision exercise A3

1 Evaluate the following using a calculator or tables, giving your answer correct to four significant figures: (a) $2.3\,e^{1.8}$, (b) $0.75\,e^{-0.12}$, (c) $5.5(1 - e^{-1/2})$, (d) $\ln 6.514$, (e) $\ln 422.6$, (f) $\ln(5.708 \times 10^{-7})$.

2 Solve the following equations to find the value of the unknown variable correct to four significant figures: (a) $81 + e^{-t} = 203$, (b) $e^{-4/25v} = 416.3$, (c) $\ln(463/0.8x) = 5$, (d) $\ln(5 - 2e^{3t}) = 0$.

Revision exercise A4

1 Write down the roots of the quadratic equation $2x^2 - 3x + 4 = 0$ in the form $a + jb$ and show both roots on the same Argand diagram.

2 Express each of the following in the form $a + jb$: (a) $(1.8 - j2.2) + (3.6 + j0.9)$, (b) $(-3.4 + j0.7) - (2.4 - j1.3)$, (c) $j(4 - j7)(2 + j9)$, (d) $(-1.3 + j2.1)/(3.4 - j1.6)$.

3 Show the complex numbers $6 + j$, $2 + j4$, and $-3 + j7$ on the same Argand diagram and demonstrate graphically that $(6 + j) + (2 + j4) - (-3 + j7) = 11 - j2$.

Revision exercise A5

1 Determine the modulus r and argument θ of each of the following complex numbers, giving θ in degrees in the range $-180° \leqslant \theta \leqslant 180°$: (a) $2 + j3$, (b) $5.6 + j11.4$, (c) $-4.1 + j9.5$, (d) $7.4 - j2.2$, (e) $-107 - j153$.

2 Express the following complex numbers in rectangular (Cartesian) form: (a) $9\,\underline{/76°}$, (b) $11.7\,\underline{/23°\ 17'}$, (c) $35.6\,\underline{/104.8°}$, (d) $18.5\,\underline{/-36.8°}$, (e) $204.1\,\underline{/0.83}$ rad.

3 Simplify the following, giving your answer in polar form: (a) $(2.7\,\underline{/72°})(3.1\,\underline{/19°})$, (b) $(11.4\,\underline{/84°})/(3.7\,\underline{/17°})$.

4 A circuit has an impedance given by $Z = j\omega LR/(R + j\omega L)$. Express Z as a complex number in polar form if $\omega = 300$ rad/s, $R = 100$ ohms, and $L = 1.5$ henrys.

5 Express the square roots of the following complex numbers in Cartesian form: (a) $18\,\underline{/32°}$, (b) $112 + j78$.

Revision exercise B1

1 Draw a graph of $\log x$ against $\log y$ using values of x and y from the following table. Show that $y = ax^n$, and determine a and n from your graph.

x	3.00	6.00	10.00	15.00	21.00	28.00
y	16.32	26.88	38.84	52.00	66.26	81.51

2 The following results are from an experiment to relate the quantity of a concrete hardener used to the time required for the concrete to set:

Hardener H (litres/m³)	38.0	28.0	22.0	14.0	9.0
Time T (hours)	1.1	1.5	2.1	3.6	6.3

Draw a graph of $\log T$ against $\log H$ to show that $T = kH^n$. Determine values of k and n from your graph.

3 The illumination at a point on the floor of a room is kept at a constant level by increasing the intensity I of a lamp as the height of the lamp h is increased. Use the following table of values to show that $I = ah^n$, by drawing a graph of I against h on log–log graph paper. Determine values of a and n from your graph.

Height h (metres)	2.00	2.75	3.50	4.25	5.00
Intensity I (candela)	880	1664	2695	3974	5500

Revision exercise B2

1 The voltage v across a component in a circuit was measured at intervals of 10 seconds after disconnecting the supply to give the following results:

Time t (s)	10.0	20.0	30.0	40.0	50.0	60.0
Voltage v (V)	36.8	13.5	4.90	1.83	0.67	0.25

Plot values of v against t on log–linear graph paper to show that $v = a\,e^{bt}$. Obtain values of a and b from your graph.

2 The following results were obtained in an experiment to determine the amount m of a salt which would dissolve in a fixed volume of water as the temperature θ was increased:

Mass m (g)	28.0	29.7	31.6	33.5	35.6	37.8
Temperature θ (°C)	15.0	25.0	35.0	45.0	55.0	65.0

If mass and temperature are related by an equation $m = a\,e^{k\theta}$, draw a graph of m against θ on log–linear graph paper to determine the values of a and k.

Revision exercise B3

1 Carry out the following matrix operations where possible:

(a) $\begin{pmatrix} 5 & 8 \\ 1 & 9 \end{pmatrix} + \begin{pmatrix} 7 & 3 \\ 2 & 5 \end{pmatrix}$ (b) $\begin{pmatrix} 3.6 \\ 8.4 \end{pmatrix} - \begin{pmatrix} -2 \\ 6 \end{pmatrix}$

(c) $\begin{pmatrix} -2 & 8 \\ -4 & 3.6 \end{pmatrix} \times \begin{pmatrix} 2.1 & -1 \\ 4 & 0.4 \end{pmatrix}$ (d) $\begin{pmatrix} 0 & 3 \\ -2 & 15 \end{pmatrix} \times \begin{pmatrix} 1 & 0 \\ 6 & 3 \end{pmatrix}$

(e) $\begin{pmatrix} -7 & 4 \\ 3 & -2 \end{pmatrix} \times \begin{pmatrix} x \\ y \end{pmatrix}$ (f) $\begin{pmatrix} 4 \\ 6 \end{pmatrix} \times \begin{pmatrix} -2 & 1 \\ 0 & 7 \end{pmatrix}$

2 Evaluate the following determinants:

(a) $\begin{vmatrix} 7 & -3 \\ 2 & 4 \end{vmatrix}$ (b) $\begin{vmatrix} \frac{1}{2} & \frac{3}{4} \\ -\frac{1}{3} & -\frac{1}{4} \end{vmatrix}$ (c) $\begin{vmatrix} 0 & -1.8 \\ 2.2 & 6.6 \end{vmatrix}$ (d) $\begin{vmatrix} 4 & 8 \\ 4 & 8 \end{vmatrix}$

Revision exercise B4

1 Find the inverse, where possible, of the following matrices:

(a) $\begin{pmatrix} -8 & -9 \\ 4 & 2 \end{pmatrix}$ (b) $\begin{pmatrix} 2 & 7 \\ 8 & 0 \\ 3 & 9 \end{pmatrix}$ (c) $\begin{pmatrix} a & -a \\ -a & 2a \end{pmatrix}$

(d) $\begin{pmatrix} -2.7 & 4.2 \\ -0.9 & 1.4 \end{pmatrix}$

2 Solve the following simultaneous equations using matrices:

(a) $4x + 2y = 10$ (b) $1.6x - 0.6y = 7.8$
    $2x + 3y = 11$ $1.4x + 1.0y = -0.8$

3 A mass of 20 kg is connected to a mass of 8 kg by a light string which passes over a smoothly running pulley. The tension F in the string and the acceleration a of the masses when they are released are given by the equations

$$20a = 196.2 - F$$
$$8a = F - 78.48$$

Use a determinant method to find F and a.

Revision exercise B5

1 Write down the first four terms of the binomial expansions of the following expressions: (a) $(a - 2b)^7$, (b) $(2 + t^2)^5$, (c) $\sqrt{(9 - 2x)}$.

2 What is the term containing z^4 in the binomial expansion of $(2/3 - x/3)^9$? For what values of z is the expansion convergent?

3 The rate at which energy is radiated from a body which has area A at absolute temperature T is given by evaluating the expression kAT^4, where k is a constant. If an error of $+2\%$ is made in measuring A, and -3% in measuring T, estimate the error in the calculated radiation rate.

Revision exercise B6

1 Draw Karnaugh maps to reduce the following expressions to their minimum forms: (a) $\overline{A}.\overline{B}.\overline{C} + A.\overline{B} + \overline{A}.\overline{B}.C$, (b) $\overline{A}.\overline{C}.\overline{D} + \overline{A}.B.D + A.B.\overline{C}.\overline{D} + \overline{A}.B.C + A.\overline{B}.\overline{C}.\overline{D}$.

2 Draw a truth table for the expression $A.B.C + A.B.C + A.B$. Simplify the expression using the laws of Boolean algebra, and check your answer using a second truth table.

Revision exercise B7

1 Draw a truth table for the logic diagram in fig. RQ1.

2 Replace the AND, OR, and NOT functions in the following expressions with NAND functions: (a) $A.\overline{B}$, (b) $\overline{A}.(B + C)$.

3 How many NOR gates would you need to implement the expression

$\overline{\overline{A + B + C}}$?

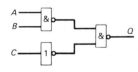

Fig. RQ1

Revision exercise C1

1 Differentiate the following functions with respect to x: (a) $7.4x^{3.5}$, (b) $11/\sqrt{x}$, (c) $(2x - 3)^2$.

2 Find the gradient of the curve $y = x^3 - 2x^2 + 4x - 7$ at the point where $x = 2.5$.

3 The velocity v of a vehicle is given in metres per second by the equation $v = 0.6\,t - 0.02\,t^2$. Calculate the acceleration a when $t = 1.8$ s, if $a = dv/dt$.

Revision exercise C2

1 Differentiate the following functions with respect to x:
(a) $\frac{1}{4} \cos x + 2\,e^x$, (b) $3 \tan x + \frac{1}{2} \ln x$.

2 If $z = 2 \sin t - t^3$, calculate the value of dz/dt when $t = 0.68$.

3 Determine the slope of the graph of $v = (\ln t - \sqrt{t})/4$ when $t = 0.32$.

Revision exercise C3

Differentiate the following functions with respect to x, using a substitution where necessary: (a) $6\,e^{x/2}$, (b) $(2x^3 - x)^5$, (c) $e^{\sin x}$, (d) $\ln (x^2 + 1)$.

2 Use the product rule or the quotient rule to differentiate the following with respect to x: (a) $x^2 \sin 4x$, (b) $e^{2x} \ln x$, (c) $(x^2 - 2)^2 \tan 4x$, (d) $(\cos 2x)/x$, (e) $(4 - 3x)/(4 + 3x)$, (f) $(\ln 4x)/\sin 3x$.

Revision exercise C4

1 Find the value of d^2z/dt^2 at $t = 0.80$, if $z = e^{2t} + t^2$.

2 The bending moment M(kN m) at a point x metres from the end of a beam is given by $M = EI(d^2y/dx^2)$, where E and I are constants and y, the deflection of the beam at that point, is given by $y = (4x^3 - x^4/12 - 16x)/EI$. Find the value of M when $x = 3.7$ m.

3 If $y = x\,e^{-2x}$, show that $d^2y/dx^2 = 4y(1 - 1/x)$.

Revision exercise C5

1 Find the co-ordinates of the maximum and minimum points on the curve $y = (8x^3/3) + 5x^2 - 3x + 1$ and sketch the curve.

2 A rectangular window frame is to be designed to fit exactly into an area of 2.50 m². If the dimensions of the frame are x metres by y metres, the piece of glass used will measure $(x - 0.120)$ metres by $(y - 0.150)$ metres. Find the dimensions of the glass for maximum area.

3 A shaft is subjected to a torque T (N m) given by the equation $T = 35\theta - 140 \sin 2\theta + 200$. Find the minimum torque in the range $0 \leqslant \theta \leqslant \pi/2$ and the value of θ at which this minimum occurs.

Revision exercise C6

1 Evaluate the following definite integrals: (a) $\int_3^4 (2x^2 - x)dx$,

(b) $\int_1^3 (v^{0.8} + 3v - 1)dv$, (c) $\int_{-2}^5 (x^2 + 1)^2 dx$.

2 Sketch the curve $y = 3x - x^2$ and integrate to find the numerical sum of the three areas enclosed by the curve and the x-axis between $x = -1$ and $x = 5$.

Revision exercise C7

1 Evaluate the following definite integrals: (a) $\int_{\frac{1}{3}}^{\frac{1}{2}} (x - 2 \sin 3x)dx$,

(b) $\int_{-1}^2 (2 - e^{x/2})dx$, (c) $\int_{0.75}^{1.40} (x^2 + 3/x)dx$.

2 Using the mid-ordinate rule with four strips, the area enclosed by the curve $y = e^{2x} + 4$ and the x-axis between $x = 0.20$ and 1.00 was estimated to be 6.129 sq. units. Show using integration that the error in this answer is approximately $-\frac{1}{3}\%$.

3 Find the mean value of $x + 1/x$ between $x = 2.50$ and $x = 3.80$.

4 Determine the r.m.s. value of $2 + \sin x$ between $x = 0$ and $x = 2\pi$. (Note that $\sin^2 x = (1 - \cos 2x)/2$.)

Revision exercise C8

1 Find the volume of the solid of revolution formed when the area enclosed by the curve $xy^2 = 9$ and the x-axis between $x = 2$ and $x = 5$ is rotated through one complete revolution about the x-axis.

2 The quantity of an antibiotic in a capsule is given by the volume generated when the area enclosed by the ellipse $(x/a)^2 + (y/b)^2 = 1$ is rotated through one revolution about the x-axis. Find an expression for the volume, using integration between the limits $x = -a$ and $x = a$, and determine the value of a if $b = 3.00$ mm and the capacity of the capsule is 0.20 ml.

3 Find the co-ordinates of the centroid of the solid of revolution formed by rotating about the y-axis the area enclosed by the curve $y = x^2 + 2$ and the y-axis between $y = 3$ and $y = 11$.

Revision exercise C9

1 A curve passes through the point (2, 15) and has a gradient given by $4x + 3$ for all values of x. Find the equation of the curve.

2 The rate of change of current in a circuit is given by the equation $di/dt = 30 \cos 200t$. Find the current flowing when $t = 5$ ms, if $i = 0.2$ A when $t = 0$ s.

3 The number N of people in a new town after t years can be estimated using the differential equation $dN/dt = kN$. If the population

rose from 21 000 after 4 years to 27 000 after 7 years, determine the population after 9 years. Give your answer correct to the nearest thousand people.

Revision exercise D1

1 Using integration, locate the centroid of the area enclosed by the curve $y = 8 - x^2$ and the x-axis between $x = 1$ and $x = 2$.
2 Determine the position of the centroid of the cross-sectional areas in fig. RQ2 with reference to the axes defined. (All dimensions are in mm.)

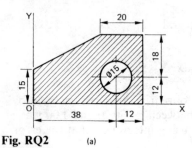 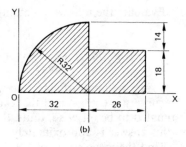

Fig. RQ2   (a)   (b)

Revision exercise D2

1 Determine the second moment of the area enclosed by the curve $y = x^3 + 2$ and the x-axis between $x = 1$ and $x = 2$, about the y-axis.
2 Find the second moment of area for the cross-sectional areas in fig. RQ3 about the base. (All dimensions are in cm.)
3 A torque T is applied to one end of a steel shaft with a radius r. The maximum shear stress is given by $\tau = Tr/J$, where J is the polar second moment of area of the shaft. Find the diameter of the shaft if $\tau = 11.0$ MPa when $T = 300$ N m.

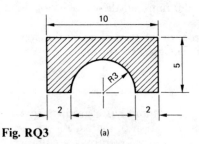 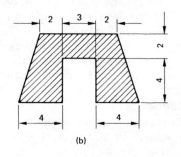

Fig. RQ3   (a)   (b)

Revision exercise D3

1 The polar second moment of area of a solid steel shaft is 1.029×10^5 mm^4. Determine the diameter of the shaft and calculate the percentage reduction in polar second moment of area when the shaft is replaced with a steel tube which has the same outside diameter and a bore of 18 mm. Calculate I_{XX} for the tube section.

2 Using a tabular method, find I_{XX} and I_{YY} for the cross-sectional areas in fig. RQ4. (All dimensions are in cm.)

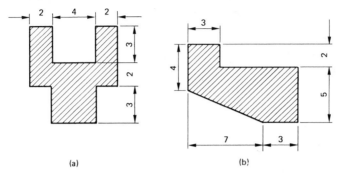

(a)   (b)

Fig. RQ4

Revision exercise D4

1 Solve the following triangles ABC:

  (a) $c = 5.30$, $A = 58°$, $B = 63°$ (b) $a = 3.06$, $c = 6.25$, $B = 90°$
  (c) $b = 20.0$, $c = 8.50$, $A = 38°$ (d) $a = 4.00$, $c = 2.60$, $C = 30°$

2 The base ABCD in fig. RQ5 is a square of side 80 mm. If side BEC is perpendicular to the base and if $BE = EC = 100$ mm, find (a) the angle between line AE and plane ABCD, (b) the angle between sides ABE and ABCD, (c) the angle between sides AED and ABCD.

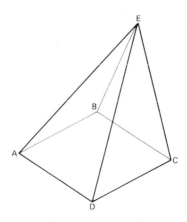

Fig. RQ5

265

Revision exercise D5
1 The instantaneous displacement of a vibrating mass is given by the equation $x = 0.28 \sin 9t$ metres. State the amplitude, periodic time, and frequency of the vibration.
2 Draw the curves $2 \sin t$, $\sin^2 t$, and $\sin (2t + \pi/2)$ on the same axes for values of t between $t = 0$ s and $t = 7$ s. Is there a point in this range at which all three curves cross?

Revision exercise D6
1 Express $3.6 \sin 4x + 5.4 \cos 4x$ as $R \sin (4x + \alpha)$, giving α in radians. Find the value of x in the range $0 \leqslant x \leqslant \pi/2$ for which this function is a maximum.
2 Determine the values of a and b if $13 \sin (\theta + 38°) = a \sin \theta + b \cos \theta$.
3 Find the value of x in the range $0° \leqslant x \leqslant 90°$ for which $5 \cos (x + 40°) = 3 \sin x$.

Revision exercise D7
1 Express $\cos 5x - \cos 11x$ as a product.
2 Find the values of x between $x = 0°$ and $x = 90°$ for which $\sin 3x + \sin x = \sqrt{3} \sin 2x$.
3 Express $2 \cos 7x \sin 5x$ as a sum or difference of two sine terms.
4 Solve the equation $2 \sin 4x \cos x = \sin 5x$, giving values in the range $0° \leqslant x \leqslant 90°$.

Revision exercise E1
1 Faults discovered in washing machines during inspection are classified as mechanical or electrical. Of all the machines tested over a long period, 12% have mechanical faults while 8% have electrical faults. If these figures include 5% which have both types of fault, determine the expectation for machines with one or more faults in a weekly output of 2200 units.
2 Integers from 0 to 9 can be displayed using the random-number key on a calculator. If this key is pressed twice and the displayed digits are written down in order, what is the probability that the outcome is (a) the number 33, (b) over 95?
3 Sugar has been added to four of the twelve cups of coffee on a tray. If two cups are taken at random, calculate the probability, correct to three decimal places, that there is sugar in (a) both, (b) one, (c) neither of the cups.

Revision exercise E2
1 If 11% of the welds in a pipeline fail X-ray inspection, assume a binomial distribution to calculate the probability that there will be two failures in a section containing seven welds.
2 An average of one in every five cars in a large car park is blue. Assume a binomial distribution to determine the probability that there will be 0,1,2,3, and 4 blue cars in a sample of four cars. Give your

answers correct to four decimal places and show the distribution on a bar chart.

3 Two parts of a turbine-case assembly are fastened together using nine rivets. It is known that 4.5% of all riveting operations are defective, and engineers are considering whether to use an additional rivet. Use the binomial distribution to find the probability of having less than eight sound rivets per assembly if (a) nine, (b) ten rivets are used.

Revision exercise E3

1 Fifteen out of a total of 240 employees travel to a factory by bicycle. Calculate the probability that there will be three of the cyclists in a random sample of 20 employees, using (a) the binomial model, (b) the Poisson model.

2 Records made over a period of several years show that an insurance company receives an average of three claims per week. Determine the probability that there will be more than three claims in any one week.

3 The number of errors on each of 120 pages of typing was counted, giving the following results:

Errors per age	0	1	2	3	4	5	6	7	8
Number of pages (total 120)	4	18	26	28	23	12	6	2	1

Determine the average number of errors per page, and use the Poisson probability model to calculate the probability that any given page will contain more than two errors.

Revision exercise E4

1 During tests in which a large number of ball-point pens were used continuously, the lifetimes of the pens were found to be normally distributed with mean 48.6 hours and standard deviation 6.2 hours. How many pens from a box of 50 would you expect to carry on writing after 56.0 hours of continuous use?

2 Ceramic capacitors with a mean value 392 pF have a standard deviation 5 pF. Assuming a normal distribution, estimate the number of rejects in a batch of 750 capacitors, if only values between 385 pF and 400 pF are selected for use.

3 Measurements of indicated power from 250 diesel engines gave the results in the following table:

Power (kW) (upper class boundary)	32.0	33.0	34.0	35.0	36.0	37.0	38.0
Observed number of engines	4	22	57	82	59	21	5

By plotting values of upper class boundary against percentage cumulative frequency on normal probability paper, show that these results suggest a normal distribution. From your graph, estimate the mean power and the standard deviation.

Answers to numerical exercises

Exercise A1

2 (a) 111, (b) 1011, (c) 10110, (d) 100111, (e) 111000, (f) 1000000

3 (a) 5, (b) 13, (c) 29, (d) 78, (e) 42, (f) 149

4 (a) 111, (b) 10011, (c) 1000111, (d) 100000, (e) 1110100, (f) 1001101

5 (a) 6, (b) 13, (c) 35, (d) 63, (e) 125, (f) 205, (g) 777

6 (a) 110010, (b) 101011, (c) 101001100, (d) 10010111, (e) 11110001, (f) 100000001011

7 (a) $13_8, 11_{10}$; (b) $32_8, 26_{10}$; (c) $35_8, 29_{10}$; (d) $156_8, 110_{10}$; (e) $265_8, 110_{10}$

8 (a) 100_2, (b) 100_2, (c) 1010_2, (d) 11101_2, (e) 631_8, (f) 31_8, (g) 154_8

9 (a) 10_2, (b) 11_2, (c) 101_2, (d) 126_8, (e) 677_8, (f) 6_8

10 (a) 11_2, (b) 1001_2, (c) 10010_2, (d) 431_8, (e) 356_8, (f) 363_8

11 See answers to Q8.

Exercise A2

2 1001, 00010101, 011000101000

4 (a) 00100110, 01011001
(b) 010100000100, 100000110111

(c) 0011000101111000, 0110010010101011

6 0, 1, 1, 0, 1, 0

Exercise A3

1 (a) 44.49, (b) 1.169, (c) 9.640, (d) 21.70, (e) 3.672, (f) 0.04971

2 (a) 1.1575, (b) 2.0855, (c) 0.9643, (d) 1.0250, (e) 4.4397, (f) 4.7724, (g) -2.6971 or $\bar{3}.3029$,

(h) -5.5468 or $\bar{6}.4532$,
(i) 11.7150,
(j) -7.1581 or $\bar{8}.8419$

3 (a) 0.2216, (b) 4.712, (c) 0.5197, (d) 4.343

Exercise A4

1 (a) Imaginary, (b) real, (c) real, (d) real, (e) complex

2 2.25

4 (a) $7 + j15$, (b) $6 + j7$, (c) 2, (d) $-11 + j6$, (e) j5, (f) $5 - j$, (g) $6.76 + j5.39$

6 (a) $3 + j5$, (b) $3 + j11$, (c) $-11 - j8$, (d) 12, (e) $18 - j4$, (f) $-4.32 + j1.26$

8 (a) $-11 + j41$, (b) $54 + j3$, (c) $49 - j43$, (d) $-22 - j46$, (e) 80, (f) $32.04 + j6.79$

9 (a) $1.85 - j0.769$, (b) $-0.034 - j1.59$, (c) $1.46 + j0.692$, (d) $16.62 + j24.92$

10 $20 + j10$

Exercise A5

1. (a) $9.43\angle 32.01°$,
   (b) $5.77\angle 27.90°$,
   (c) $12.53\angle 118.6°$,
   (d) $4.42\angle -127.6°$ or $4.42\angle 232.4°$,
   (e) $15.56\angle -30.52°$ or $15.56\angle 329.5°$

2. (a) $6.71\angle 2.68\,\text{rad}$,
   (b) $30.55\angle -2.45\,\text{rad}$,
   (c) $2.72\angle -0.942\,\text{rad}$,
   (d) $3\angle \pi/2$, (e) $5\angle -\pi/2$

3. (a) $4.53 + j5.60$,
   (b) $-0.102 + j0.239$
   (c) $11.1 + j12.6$,
   (d) $-3.27 - j4.04$,

(e) $3.32 - j1.74$

4. (a) $30\angle 53°$, (b) $1.53\angle -8°$,
   (c) $165\angle (5\pi/12)$,
   (d) $24.35\angle 1.29\,\text{rad}$

5. (a) $2.67\angle 43°$, (b) $1.76\angle 41°$,
   (c) $2.5\angle (3\pi/4)$, (d) $0.78\angle 58.3°$

6. $9.49\angle 32.5°\ \Omega$, $26.34\angle -32.5°$ A

7. (a) $4\angle 41°$ and $4\angle -139°$,
   (b) $2.39\angle 81°$ and $2.39\angle -99°$,
   (c) $3.69\angle -13.8°$ and $3.69\angle 166.2°$,
   (d) $4.71\angle 15.6°$ and $4.71\angle -164.4°$,
   (e) $2.78\angle 75°$ and $2.78\angle -105°$

8. 0.97, $-14.04°$ or $-0.245\,\text{rad}$

Exercise B1

2. 0.43
3. 108.6 mA
4. 0.90, 2.30

5. 2121
7. 0.348, -0.149, 0.17 m/min

Exercise B2

1. Slope = 43.8
2. (1.61, 7.25)
3. 129, 0.008
4. 0.65, 1.40

5. 7.31 °C, 502 Ω
6. 1.15, 2.60
7. 4.76 V, 105 μF

Exercise B3

2. $\begin{pmatrix} 4 & 5 & 4 \\ 5 & 5 & 6 \\ 2 & 2 & 6 \\ 3 & 2 & 4 \end{pmatrix}$

3. (a) $\begin{pmatrix} 8 & 7 \\ 8 & 7 \end{pmatrix}$,

   (b) $\begin{pmatrix} 6 & -12 \\ 0 & 11 \end{pmatrix}$,

   (c) $\begin{pmatrix} -5 \\ 3 \\ 10 \end{pmatrix}$,

   (d) impossible,

   (e) $\begin{pmatrix} 9.1 & -5.2 \\ -0.5 & 3.7 \end{pmatrix}$,

   (f) $(-7 \quad 14 \quad 16\ )$,

(g) impossible,

(h) $\begin{pmatrix} a + 2c & 5b \\ c - a & -d \end{pmatrix}$

4. (a) $\begin{pmatrix} 8 & 2 \\ 1 & -3 \end{pmatrix}$,

   (b) $\begin{pmatrix} 19.3 & 2.9 \\ 4.3 & 12.6 \end{pmatrix}$,

   (c) impossible,

   (d) $\begin{pmatrix} -4.7 \\ 10.7 \end{pmatrix}$,

   (e) $\begin{pmatrix} -4x & y - x \\ 3(y - x) & 2y \end{pmatrix}$

5 (a) $\begin{pmatrix} 3 & 10 \\ 13 & 2 \end{pmatrix}$,

(b) $\begin{pmatrix} 1 & 2 \\ -3 & 16 \end{pmatrix}$,

(c) $\begin{pmatrix} 50 & -34 \\ 77 & -43 \end{pmatrix}$,

(d) $\begin{pmatrix} 22 & 42 \\ -19 & -15 \end{pmatrix}$,

6 (a) $\begin{pmatrix} 18 & 6 \\ 47 & 24 \end{pmatrix}$,

(b) $\begin{pmatrix} 20 \\ 17 \end{pmatrix}$,

(c) $\begin{pmatrix} 28 & 10 \\ -29 & -25 \end{pmatrix}$,

(d) impossible,

(e) $\begin{pmatrix} 67.8 \\ 66.3 \end{pmatrix}$,

(f) $\begin{pmatrix} 15.4 & 19.2 \\ 33.0 & -49.8 \end{pmatrix}$,

(g) $\begin{pmatrix} 0 & 0 \\ 0 & 0 \end{pmatrix}$,

(h) $\begin{pmatrix} 2x^2 \\ x^3 \end{pmatrix}$

8 (a) -13, (b) 26, (c) 34, (d) $5x^3$, (e) 55.51, (f) 28, (g) -0.50, (h) 10.34

Exercise B4

1 (a) $\begin{pmatrix} 8 & -5 \\ -3 & 2 \end{pmatrix}$,

(b) $\begin{pmatrix} 1.00 & 0.667 \\ 3.00 & 2.33 \end{pmatrix}$,

(c) $\begin{pmatrix} -0.25 & 0 \\ -2.0 & 1.0 \end{pmatrix}$,

(d) $\begin{pmatrix} 43.6 & -31.8 \\ -20.9 & 15.5 \end{pmatrix}$,

(e) impossible,

(f) $\begin{pmatrix} -2/x & -1/x \\ 3/x & 1/x \end{pmatrix}$,

(g) $\begin{pmatrix} -0.754 & 0.230 \\ -0.525 & 0.377 \end{pmatrix}$,

(h) impossible

2 $\begin{pmatrix} -0.250 & -0.250 \\ -0.250 & -0.583 \end{pmatrix}$

3 (a) $x = 5.5$, $y = 5.0$;
(b) $r = 14.16, s = -4.89$;
(c) $x = -76.90$, $y = 63.67$;
(d) impossible (parallel lines)

4 $I_1 = 0.766\,\text{A}$, $I_2 = 0.409\,\text{A}$

5 $F = 80.0\,\text{N}$, $R = 94.1\,\text{N}$

6 (a) $x = 1.09$, $y = -0.147$;
(b) $s = -0.788$, $t = 1.05$;
(c) impossible; (d) $r = 2.90$, $t = -0.623$

7 $m = 3$, $c = 4$

8 -4.68

Exercise B5

1 $a^6 + 6a^5x + 15a^4x^2 + 20a^3x^3 + 15a^2x^4 + 6ax^5 + x^6$

2 (a) $x^3 + 6x^2y + 12xy^2 + 8y^3$
(b) $16x^4 - 96x^3y + 216x^2y^2 - 216xy^3 + 81y^4$
(c) $m^5 + 10m^3 + 40m + 80/m + 80/m^3 + 32/m^5$

3 $35a^3x^4$

4 $30.7x^3$

5 $-956.8/s^3$

6 $1 - 2z + 3z^2 - 4z^3 + 5z^4$, $|z| < 1$

7 (a) $1 - 6x + 24x^2 - 80x^3, |x| < \frac{1}{2}$

   (b) $1 + \frac{t}{2} + \frac{3t^2}{8} + \frac{5t^3}{16}, |t| < 1$

   (c) $1 + \frac{s}{12} - \frac{s^2}{144} + \frac{5s^3}{5184}, |s| < 4$

   (d) $\frac{1}{32}\left(1 + \frac{15x}{2}\right.$

   $\left. + \frac{135x^2}{4} + \frac{945x^3}{8}\right), |x| < \frac{2}{3}$

   (e) $2\left(1 + \frac{z}{8} - \frac{z^2}{128} + \frac{z^3}{1024}\right),$
        $|z| < 4$

8   3%
9   -5.2%
10 -3.8%
11 -8.9%
12 $+7.3\%$

Exercise B6

1   Fig. X1 (a)–(e)

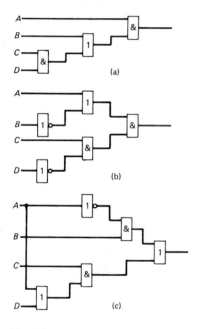

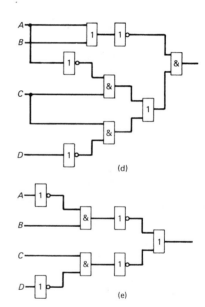

Fig. X1

2   (a)

A	B	Q
0	0	1
0	1	0
1	0	0
1	1	1

(b)

A	B	C	Q
0	0	0	0
0	0	1	0
0	1	0	1
0	1	1	0
1	0	0	1
1	0	1	1
1	1	0	0
1	1	1	0

271

(c)

A	B	C	Q
0	0	0	1
0	0	1	1
0	1	0	0
0	1	1	0
1	0	0	0
1	0	1	1
1	1	0	0
1	1	1	1

(d)

A	B	C	D	Q
0	0	0	0	0
0	0	0	1	0
0	0	1	0	0
0	0	1	1	0
0	1	0	0	0
0	1	0	1	1
0	1	1	0	0
0	1	1	1	1
1	0	0	0	1
1	0	0	1	0
1	0	1	0	1
1	0	1	1	1
1	1	0	0	1
1	1	0	1	0
1	1	1	0	0
1	1	1	1	0

3 (a) $B.(A+C)$
  (b) A
  (c) $A.\bar{B}.C$
  (d) $\bar{A}.B.\bar{C}$
  (e) $A.\bar{B}.C.\bar{D}$
4 (a) $B.\bar{C}, \bar{A}.B.C$
  (b) $\bar{A}, A.\bar{C}$
  (c) $A.\bar{B}, C.\bar{D}, \bar{A}.\bar{B}.D$
5 $B.\bar{D}$
6 Fig. X2
7 (a) Fig. X3, $B.\bar{C}$
  (b) Fig. X4, $\bar{A}$
  (c) Fig. X5, $\bar{A}.D$
  (d) Fig. X6, $B.\bar{A} + A.\bar{B}.\bar{D}$

AB \ CD	00	01	11	10
00		1		
01		1	1	
11	1	1	1	
10	1			

Fig. X2

C \ AB	00	01	11	10
0		1	1	
1				

Fig. X3

C \ AB	00	01	11	10
0	1	1		
1	1	1		

Fig. X4

CD \ AB	00	01	11	10
00				
01	1	1		
11	1	1		
10				

Fig. X5

CD \ AB	00	01	11	10
00		1		1
01		1		
11		1		
10		1		1

Fig. X6

272

Exercise B7

1

A	B	C	Q
0	0	0	0
0	0	1	0
0	1	0	1
0	1	1	1
1	0	0	1
1	0	1	1
1	1	0	1
1	1	1	1

2 Fig. X7
3 (a) $\overline{A + \bar{B}}$; fig. X8
   (b) $\overline{\bar{A} + \bar{\bar{B}} + C}$, fig. X9
4 (a) $\overline{A \cdot \bar{B}}$, fig. X10
   (b) $\overline{\overline{A \cdot \bar{B}} \cdot \overline{\bar{C} \cdot D}}$, fig. X11

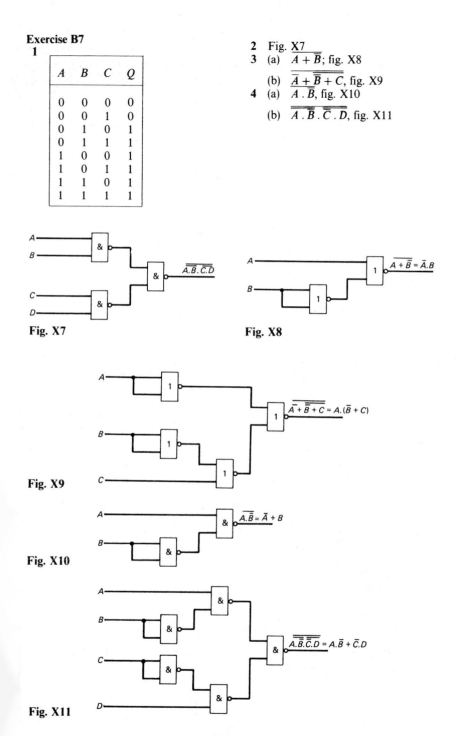

Fig. X7

Fig. X8

Fig. X9

Fig. X10

Fig. X11

273

Exercise C1

1 (a) $8x$, (b) $18x^2$, (c) $1/\sqrt{x}$,
  (d) $-20/x^5$, (e) $5.4x^{0.5}$ or $5.4\sqrt{x}$,
  (f) $-6x^{-2.5}$ or $-6/x^{2.5}$,
  (g) $\frac{3}{2}x^{-1/4}$ or $3/2\sqrt[4]{x}$, (h) $7.2/\sqrt[3]{(x^7)}$
2 (a) $15t^2$, (b) $3/2\sqrt{v}$, (c) $-7.6z^{0.9}$,
  (d) $-6.3/u^{1.7}$, (e) $1.4/r^{0.6}$,
  (f) $1.1/\sqrt{(y^3)}$

3 (a) $12x$, (b) $9x+4$, (c) $2x+10$,
  (d) $3x^2-12x+9$
4 (a) $10x^4$, (b) $1/t^2-4/t^3$,
  (c) $-1/\sqrt{v}-1/2\sqrt{(v^3)}$,
  (d) $0.98/z^{0.3}$
5 24

Exercise C2

1 (a) $3e^x+5$, (b) $3/2\sqrt{x}-4\cos x$,
  (c) $1+(\sqrt{3}/2)\sin x$, (d) $8/x$,
  (e) $3.6x^{0.8}-\sec^2 x$
2 5.70

3 1.04
4 21.1
5 0.47

Exercise C3

1 (a) $3(5x^4-2x)^2(20x^3-2)$,
  (b) $3.2\,e^{0.8x}$, (c) $6x\cos(3x^2+4)$,
  (d) $\dfrac{2\sin(1/x)}{x^2}$, (e) $\dfrac{3x}{\sqrt{[(8-x^2)^3]}}$,
  (f) $3/x$, (g) $\sec^2 x\,e^{\tan x}$,
  (h) $6\sin x\cos x$
2 (a) $7\,e^{7x}$, (b) $4\cos 4x$,
  (c) $-4\omega\sin\omega t$, (d) $5/z$,
  (e) $\frac{3}{4}\cos(\theta/4)$, (f) $-\frac{3}{2}\,e^{-t/4}$
3 (a) $x^2(3\cos x-x\sin x)$,
  (b) $3(1+\ln x)$,
  (c) $e^{2x}[2\cos(x/2)-\frac{1}{2}\sin(x/2)]$,
  (d) $(x-4)^2[2(x-4)\cos 2x$
      $+3\sin 2x]$,
  (e) $\cos^2 x-\sin^2 x$,
  (f) $x^3(1+4\ln 2x)$

4 (a) $\dfrac{x(x+2)}{(x+1)^2}$,
  (b) $\dfrac{2\,e^{5t}(3\cos t+\sin t)}{\cos^2 t}$,
  (c) $\dfrac{1-\frac{1}{2}\ln 2s}{\sqrt{(s^3)}}$,
  (d) $\dfrac{2(\cos 2\theta-2\sin 2\theta)}{e^{4\theta}}$,
  (e) $\dfrac{2(z-z^2+2)}{(1-2z)^2}$,
  (f) $\dfrac{\sin x\cos x-x}{\sin^2 x}$ or $\cot x-$
      $x\,\mathrm{cosec}^2$
6 1.18
7 5.38
8 21.2

Exercise C4

1 (a) $60x^3-2$,
  (b) $1/x^2-1/4\sqrt{(x^3)}$,
  (c) $-32\sin 4x$, (d) $3(2-1/e^x)$
2 (a) $-50\cos 5t$, (b) $4(1+3s^2)$,
  (c) $(\cos^2\theta-\sin\theta)\,e^{\sin\theta}$,
  (d) $-(2n^2+6n+9)/(n^2+3n)^2$
3 (a) 5.41, (b) -4.87, (c) -0.625

5 6, increasing
6 (a) $168\,\mathrm{m/s}$, $46\,\mathrm{m/s^2}$,
  (b) $t=\frac{2}{3}\mathrm{s}$ and $t=4\,\mathrm{s}$
7 $123.3\,\mathrm{m}$
8 (a) $1.24\,\mathrm{rad/s}$, (b) $0.319\,\mathrm{rad/s^2}$,
  (c) $9.42\,\mathrm{s}$
9 $18.0\,\mathrm{m/s}$

Exercise C5

2 (a) $(0.25, 4.63)$;
  (b) $(-0.25, -3.25)$; (c) $(\pi/4, 2)$;
  (d) $(1, -3.67)$ and $(3, -5)$;
  (e) $(-3, -6)$ and $(3, 6)$
3 Maximum
4 -3.2
5 $(1, 9)$ maximum;
  $(-3, -23)$ minimum

6 $(0.33, 6)$ minimum;
  $(-0.33, -6)$ maximum
7 $(0.67, -9.48)$ minimum;
  $(-2, 0)$ maximum
10 $20.3\,\mathrm{m}$
11 $0.39\,\mathrm{m}$
12 $69.3\,\mathrm{N}$
13 Height $0.86\,\mathrm{m}$, radius $0.43\,\mathrm{m}$

Exercise C6
(Arbitrary constants and units of area have been omitted.)

1 (a) $2x^2$, (b) $2x^4$, (c) $0.5x^2 + 2x$,
 (d) $2x^3 - 2x^2 + 3x$
2 $3x^3 + 3x^2 - 10x + 4$
3 122.5
4 (a) $3x^3 - x^4$, (b) $2x^2 - 8x$,
 (c) $0.6x^3 - 1.1x^2$
5 (a) $4\pi r^3/3$, (b) $4t - 3.6t^3$

6 (a) 1.0, (b) 56.0, (c) 21.3,
 (d) -7.33, (e) 1.95, (f) 23.3
7 4.5
8 20.8
9 4.67
10 -27.0
11 8.0, 5.33
12 15.0

Exercise C7

1 (a) $\dfrac{x^{1.8}}{0.9} + 3\sin 2x + C$,

 (b) $\dfrac{e^{-2.1x}}{0.7} - 12\cos\dfrac{x}{3} + x + C$,

 (c) $\ln x - \dfrac{1}{x} + C$

2 $s = t - \sin 2t - \pi/2$
3 (a) 7.50, (b) 1.70, (c) 9.76,
 (d) 3.41, (e) 1.67, (f) -7.35

4 3.82 sq. units
5 9.67 N m
6 (a) 12.5, (b) 5.04, (c) -0.783,
 (d) 0.493
7 3.96 m/s
8 3.06
9 10.49
10 2.12 V

Exercise C8
(Units of length and volume have been omitted.)

1 (a) 100.5, (b) 527.8, (c) 4.26,
 (d) 14.4, (e) 35.6, (f) 7.35
2 132.6, 102.1

3 2.24
4 (1.39, 0)
5 (0.375, 0)

Exercise C9

2 $y = 2x^3 - 4x + C$
3 $y = x^2 - x + 3$
4 $z = t^3/3 + 5t - 6$
5 $r = 2\sin\theta + 1$
6 $x = kt^2/2 + t + 1$; 1
7 14.4 m

8 $y = 1.24\,e^{3x}$
9 $z = 5\,e^{kt}$; 1.10
10 0.61, 1.03 A
11 10.3 s
12 45.5 minutes

Exercise D1

1 (3, 2)
2 $(\frac{4}{3}, 2)$
3 (3.71, 1.86)
4 (2.25, 5.40)
5 (1.71, 2.12)

6 $\bar{x} = 3.50$ cm, $\bar{y} = 2.15$ cm
7 $\bar{x} = 3.40$ cm, $\bar{y} = 3.40$ cm
8 $\bar{x} = 7.79$ cm, $\bar{y} = 5.95$ cm
9 $\bar{x} = 3.33$ cm, $\bar{y} = 2.98$ cm

Exercise D2

1 (a) 34.67, (b) 32.50, (c) 8.00,
 (d) 14.67, (e) 58.13
2 22.67 cm^4
3 185.0 cm^4

4 118.0 cm^4
5 163.3 cm^4
6 41.1 mm

Exercise D3
1. $5.75 \times 10^4\,\text{mm}^4$
2. $2450\,\text{mm}^4$
3. $1624\,\text{cm}^4$
4. $206.1\,\text{cm}^4$
5. $3264\,\text{cm}^4$, $4686\,\text{cm}^4$, $7950\,\text{cm}^4$
6. $1564\,\text{cm}^4$
7. $6759\,\text{cm}^4$, $1491\,\text{cm}^4$
8. $194.3\,\text{cm}^4$
9. $34.9\,\text{cm}^4$
10. $517.0\,\text{mm}^4$
11. $178.3\,\text{cm}^4$
12. $54.3\,\text{cm}^4$

Exercise D4
1. (a) $b = 1.58$, $c = 2.63$, $A = 53°$
   (b) $b = 14.8$, $A = 35.8°$, $B = 94.2°$
   (c) $b = 2.39$, $A = 57.2°$, $C = 74.8°$
   (d) $a = 12.1$, $B = 95.4°$, $C = 29.6°$
   (e) $c = 1.38$ or 5.42, $B = 65.1°$ or $114.9°$, $C = 62.9°$ or $13.1°$
2. $18.75°$
3. $29.85°$
4. $12.51°$, $54.32°$, $32.79°$
5. (a) $55.5°$, (b) $108.7°$
6. $18.03\,\text{mm}$, $28.71°$
7. (a) $59.0°$, (b) $32.0°$, (c) $120.7°$
8. 164
9. $342\,\text{km/h}$, 072

Exercise D5
4. (a) 2, $2.09\,\text{s}$, $0.477\,\text{Hz}$;
   (b) 240, $0.02\,\text{s}$, $50\,\text{Hz}$;
   (c) 3, $12.6\,\text{s}$, $0.08\,\text{Hz}$;
   (d) 0.5, $3.14\,\text{s}$, $0.318\,\text{Hz}$
5. $4.76\,\text{Hz}$
6. $6\,\text{A}$, $25\,\text{Hz}$, $40\,\text{ms}$
8. (a) $1.57\,\text{s}$, $0.637\,\text{Hz}$;
   (b) $1.0\,\text{s}$, $1.0\,\text{Hz}$
9. 10
12. (a) $120\,\text{V}$, $60\,\text{Hz}$;
    (b) $52.2\,\text{V}$, $118.1\,\text{V}$; (c) $2.97\,\text{ms}$;
    (d) a phase lead of $0.45\,\text{rad}$ or $25°\,47'$

Exercise D6
1. $0.340 \sin x$
2. (a) $0.707(\cos x - \sin x)$,
   (b) $0.540 \sin x - 0.841 \cos x$,
   (c) $0.866 \cos x - 0.500 \sin x$,
   (d) $0.156 \cos x + 0.988 \sin x$
4. $9.54°$ or $9°\,32'$
6. (a) $5.3 \sin(\omega t + 0.557)$,
   (b) $5.3 \sin(\omega t - 0.557)$
7. $14.42\,\text{V}$; lead of $0.983\,\text{rad}$
8. $x = 0.083 \sin(\omega t + 0.501)$ metres

Exercise D7
1. (a) $2 \sin 3x \cos 2x$,
   (b) $2 \cos 4x \sin 2x$,
   (c) $2 \cos 2.5x \cos 1.5x$,
   (d) $-2 \sin 2x \sin x$,
   (e) $2 \cos 2x \sin(x - y)$
3. 0, $\pi/9$, and $\pi/2$
4. 0, $\pi/5$, $2\pi/5$, $\pi/2$
6. $2 \sin 12\pi t \cos 2\pi t$
7. (a) $\sin 6x + \sin 2x$,
   (b) $2 \sin 4x - 2 \sin 2x$,
   (c) $\frac{1}{2} \cos 7x + \frac{1}{2} \cos 5x$,
   (d) $3 \cos 3x - 3 \cos 7x$
9. $\pi/30$, $\pi/6$

Exercise E1
2. (a)
3. 24
4. 0.43
5. (a) and (b)
6. 0.667
7. 0.389
8. 0.85
9. 0.028
10. 0.799
11. 0.4
12. 0.09
13. 0.067
14. 0.275

Exercise E2

1 (a) 120, (b) 42, (c) 1
2 (a) 24, (b) 12
3 (a) 15, (b) 55, (c) 1287
4 84
5 495, 792
6 (a) 0.488, (b) 0.359
7 0.5220, 0.3685, 0.0975, 0.0115,
   0.0005
8 (a) 39.32%, (b) 9.89%
9 (a) 38.26%, (b) 18.69%

10 0.2887, 0.4072, 0.2297, 0.0648,
    0.0091, 0.0005
11 When p approaches $\frac{1}{2}$ or when
    np is large.
12 $\mu = np$, $\sigma = \sqrt{(npq)}$; 10, 2.89,
    0.137
13 (a) 0.717 or 71.7%; (b) expected
    frequencies are 8, 78, 296, 501,
    317

Exercise E3

1 0.5599, 0.3247, 0.0003
2 0.2067 (Poisson),
   0.2084 (binomial)
3 0.034
4 0.224
5 0.0038
6 (a) 0.323, (b) 0.475

8 Average $= 2.54$; expected
   frequencies are 4, 10, 13, 11, 7, 3,
   1, 0
9 Average $= 1.9$; expected
   frequencies are 18, 34, 32, 21,
   10, 4, 1

Exercise E4

1 (a) 68.26%, (b) 81.85%,
   (c) 49.86%
2 1.41, -1.08
3 0.092
4 (a) 47.7%, (b) 10.6%, (c) 1.2%,
   (d) 74.9%

5 102
6 15.7%
7 23
8 22.6 °C
10 A, 97.5 mm, 0.80 mm

Revision exercise A1

1 (a) 1000_2, (b) 101110_2, (c) 7_{10},
   (d) 18_{10}, (e) 10_8, (f) 140_8,
   (g) 11101_2, (h) 100000_2, (i) 41_8,
   (j) 562_8

2 (a) 1110_2, (b) 100111_2, (c) $\overline{1}00100_2$,
   (d) 516_8, (e) 1463_8
3 (a) 1010_2, (b) 1011_2, (c) 101111_2,
   (d) 4_8, (e) 3064_8

Revision exercise A2

1 10010111, 010101000010
2 01110101, 101101000110

4

5	0 1 0 1 0
6	0 1 1 0 0
7	1 0 0 0 1
8	1 0 0 1 0
9	1 0 1 0 0

Revision exercise A3

1 (a) 13.91, (b) 0.6652, (c) 2.164,
   (d) 1.874, (e) 6.046, (f) -14.38

2 (a) $t = -4.804$, (b) $v = -0.02653$,
   (c) $x = 3.900$, (d) $t = 0.2310$

Revision exercise A4

1 $0.75 + j1.20$ and $0.75 - j1.20$

2 (a) $5.4 - j1.3$, (b) $-5.8 + j2.0$
   (c) $-22 + j71$, (d) $-0.55 + j0.36$

Revision exercise A5

1 (a) $3.61\,\underline{/56.31°}$, (b) $12.7\,\underline{/63.84°}$,
   (c) $10.35\,\underline{/113.34°}$,
   (d) $7.72\,\underline{/-16.56°}$,
   (e) $186.7\,\underline{/-124.97°}$

2 (a) $2.18 + j8.73$, (b) $10.75 + j4.62$,
   (c) $-9.09 + j34.42$,

   (d) $14.81 - j11.08$,
   (e) $137.7 + j150.6$

3 (a) $8.37\,\underline{/91°}$, (b) $3.08\,\underline{/67°}$

4 $97.62\,\underline{/12.53°}\ \Omega$

5 (a) $4.08 + j1.17$ and $-4.08 - j1.17$,
   (b) $11.2 + j3.50$ and $-11.2 - j3.50$

Revision exercise B1

1 $7.40, 0.72$

2 $91.5, -1.2$

3 $220, 2.0$

Revision exercise B2

1 $-0.10, 99.3$

2 $25.6, 0.006$

Revision exercise B3

1 (a) $\begin{pmatrix} 12 & 11 \\ 3 & 14 \end{pmatrix}$,

   (b) $\begin{pmatrix} 5.6 \\ 2.4 \end{pmatrix}$,

   (c) $\begin{pmatrix} 27.8 & 5.2 \\ 6.0 & 5.44 \end{pmatrix}$,

   (d) $\begin{pmatrix} 18 & 9 \\ 88 & 45 \end{pmatrix}$,

   (e) $\begin{pmatrix} 4y - 7x \\ 3x - 2y \end{pmatrix}$,

   (f) impossible

2 (a) 34, (b) 0.125, (c) 3.96, (d) 0

Revision exercise B4

1 (a) $\begin{pmatrix} 0.10 & 0.45 \\ -0.20 & -0.40 \end{pmatrix}$,

   (b) impossible,

   (c) $\begin{pmatrix} 2/a & 1/a \\ 1/a & 1/a \end{pmatrix}$,

   (d) impossible

2 (a) $x = 1, y = 3$, (b) $x = 3, y = -$
3 112.1 N, 4.20 m/s^2

Revision exercise B5

1 (a) $a^7 - 14a^6b + 84a^5b^2 - 280a^4b^3$,
   (b) $32 + 80t^2 + 80t^4 + 40t^8$,
   (c) $3 - x/3 - x^2/54 - x^3/486$

2 $448x^4/2187$,
   all values of z
3 -10.2%

Revision exercise B6

1 (a) Fig. X12 (a), $\overline{B}$;
   (b) Fig. X12 (b), $A\,.\,B + \overline{C}\,.\,\overline{D}$

2
A	B	C	Q
0	0	0	0
0	0	1	0
0	1	0	0
0	1	1	0
1	0	0	1
1	0	1	1
1	1	0	1
1	1	1	0

, $A\,.\,(\overline{C} + \overline{B})$

AB \\ C	00	01	11	10
0	1			1
1	1			1

(a)

CD \\ AB	00	01	11	10
00	1	1	1	1
01		1		
11		1		
10		1		

(b)

Fig. X12

Revision exercise B7

1

A B C	Q
0 0 0	0
0 0 1	1
0 1 0	0
0 1 1	1
1 0 0	0
1 0 1	1
1 1 0	1
1 1 1	1

2 (a) $\overline{\overline{A}.\overline{B}}$, (b) $\overline{\overline{A}.\overline{B}.\overline{C}}$

3 Three

Revision exercise C1

1 (a) $25.9x^{2.5}$, (b) $-5.5/\sqrt{(x^3)}$,
   (c) $8x - 12$

2 12.75

3 0.528 m/s^2

Revision exercise C2

1 (a) $2\,e^x - \frac{1}{4}\sin x$,
   (b) $3\sec^2 x + 1/2x$

2 0.168

3 0.560

Revision exercise C3

1 (a) $3\,e^{x/2}$, (b) $4(6x^2 - 1)(2x^3 - x)^4$,
   (c) $\cos x\, e^{\sin x}$,
   (d) $2x/(x^2 + 1)$

2 $2x(2x \cos 4x + \sin 4x)$,
   (b) $e^{2x}(1/x + 2 \ln x)$,

(c) $4(x^2 - 2)[(x^2 - 2)\sec^2 4x + \tan 4x]$,
(d) $-(2x \sin 2x + \cos 2x)/x^2$,
(e) $-24/(4 + 2x)^2$,
(f) $\dfrac{(\sin 3x)/x - 3 \ln 4x \cos 3x}{\sin^2 3x}$

Revision exercise C4

1 21.81

2 75.1 kN m

Revision exercise C5

1 (0.25, 0.604) minimum,
   $(-1.5, 7.75)$ maximum

2 1.294 m by 1.618 m

3 86.4 N m, 0.723 rad

Revision exercise C6

(Units of area have been omitted.)
1 (a) 21.17, (b) 13.46, (c) 727.1

2 15.00

Revision exercise C7
1   (a) −0.244, (b) 1.776, (c) 2.647

3   3.472
4   2.12

Revision exercise C8
1   25.91 cubic units

2   5.3 mm
3   (0, 8.07)

Revision exercise C9
1   $y = 2x^2 + 3x + 1$

2   0.326 A
3   32 000

Revision exercise D1
1   (1.46, 2.90)

2   (a) $\bar{x} = 26.0$ mm, $\bar{y} = 13.4$ mm,
    (b) $\bar{x} = 28.2$ mm, $\bar{y} = 11.9$ mm

Revision exercise D2
1   15.17 (units)^4

2   (a) 384.9 cm^4, (b) 512.0 cm^4
3   51.8 mm

Revision exercise D3
1   32.0 mm, 10.0%, 4.63×10^4 mm^4

2   (a) 173.3 cm^4, 213.3 cm^4,
    (b) 121.0 cm^4, 390.3 cm^4

Revision exercise D4
1   (a) $a = 5.24$, $b = 5.51$, $C = 59°$,
    (b) $b = 6.96$, $A = 26.09°$,
    $C = 63.91°$,
    (c) $a = 14.29°$, $B = 59.48°$,
    $C = 82.52°$,

(d) either $b = 5.13$,
    $A = 50.28°$, $B = 99.72°$,
    or $b = 1.80$, $A = 129.7°$,
    $B = 20.28°$
2   (a) 45.70°, (b) 66.42°, (c) 48.88°

Revision exercise D5
1   0.28 m, 0.698 s, 1.43 Hz

2   No

Revision exercise D6
1   $6.49 \sin(4x + 0.983)$, 0.147 rad

2   10.24, 8.00
3   31.65°

Revision exercise D7
1   $2 \sin 8x \sin 3x$
2   0°, 30°

3   $\sin 12x - \sin 2x$
4   0°, 60°

2   (a) 0.01, (b) 0.04
Revision exercise E1
1   330

3   (a) 0.091, (b) 0.485, (c) 0.424

Revision exercise E2
1   0.142
2   0.4096, 0.4096, 0.1536, 0.0256,
    0.0016

3   (a) 0.059, (b) 0.009

Revision exercise E3
1   (a) 0.0929, (b) 0.0933

2   0.3528
3   0.5842

Revision exercise E4
1   6

2   102
3   34.5 kW, 1.2 kW

Index